G000135784

Microelectronic Systems
Level III

Units in this series

Microelectronic Systems Level I
Microelectronic Systems Level II
Microelectronic Systems Level III
Microprocessor-based Systems Level IV
Microprocessor-based Systems Level V

Microprocessor Appreciation Level III
Microprocessor Principles Level IV

Practical Assignments

An Introduction to Practical Microelectronics
Further Practical Microelectronics

Study Guides

TEC Study Guide for Microelectronic Systems Level I
TEC Study Guide for Microelectronic Systems Level II
BTEC Study Guide for Microelectronic Systems Level III
BTEC Study Guide for Microprocessor-based Systems Level IV
BTEC Study Guide for Microprocessor Appreciation Level III
BTEC Study Guide for Microprocessor Principles Level IV

Microelectronic Systems

Level III

Dr D. J. Woollons

BUSINESS & TECHNICIAN EDUCATION COUNCIL
in association with
HUTCHINSON
London Melbourne Sydney Auckland Johannesburg

Hutchinson & Co. (Publishers) Ltd

An imprint of the Hutchinson Publishing Group

17-21 Conway Street, London W1P 6JD

Hutchinson Publishing Group (Australia) Pty Ltd
16-22 Church Street, Hawthorn, Melbourne, Victoria 3122

Hutchinson Group (NZ) Ltd
32-34 View Road, PO Box 40-086, Glenfield, Auckland 10

Hutchinson Group (SA) (Pty) Ltd
PO Box 337, Bergvlei 2012, South Africa

First published 1982
Reprinted 1983, 1985

Set in Times

Printed and bound in Great Britain by
Anchor Brendon Ltd, Tiptree, Essex

British Library Cataloguing in Publication Data

Woollons, D. J.
Microelectronic Systems.
Level 3
1. Microelectronics
I. Title II. Technician Education Council
621.381'71 TK874

ISBN 0 09 147801 4

Contents

Preface

This book is one of a series on microelectronics/microprocessors published by Hutchinson on behalf of the Business & Technician Education Council. The books in the series are designed for use with units associated with Business & Technician Education Council programmes.

In June 1978 the United Kingdom Prime Minister expressed anxiety about the effects to be expected from the introduction of microprocessors on the pattern of employment in specific industries. From this stemmed an initiative through the Department of Industry and the National Enterprise Board to encourage the use and development of microprocessor technology.

An important aspect of such a development programme was seen as being the education and training of personnel for both the research, development and manufacture of microelectronics material and equipment, and the application of these in other industries. In 1979 a project was established by the Technician Education Council for the development of technician education programme units (a unit is a specification of the objectives to be attained by a student) and associated learning packages, this project being funded by the Department of Industry and managed on their behalf by the National Computing Centre Ltd.

TEC established a committee involving industry, both as producers and users of microelectronics, and educationists. In addition widespread consultations took place. Programme units were developed for technicians and technician engineers concerned with the design, manufacture and servicing aspects incorporating microelectronic devices. Five units were produced:

Microelectronic Systems	Level I
Microelectronic Systems	Level II
Microelectronic Systems	Level III
Microprocessor-based Systems	Level IV
Microprocessor-based Systems	Level V

Units were also produced for those technicians who required a general understanding of the range of applications of microelectronic devices and their potential:

Microprocessor Appreciation	Level III
Microprocessor Principles	Level IV

This phase was then followed by the development of the learning packages, involving three writing teams, the key people in these teams being:

Microelectronic Systems I, II, III — P. Cooke
Microprocessor-based Systems IV — A. Potton
Microprocessor-based Systems V — M. J. Morse
Microprocessor Appreciation III — G. Martin
Microprocessor Principles IV — G. Martin

The project director during the unit specification stage was N. Bonnett, assisted by R. Bertie. Mr Bonnett continued as consultant during the writing stage. The project manager was W. Bolton, assisted by K. Snape.

Self-learning

An an aid to self-learning, questions are included in every chapter. These appear at the end of the chapters with references in the margin of the chapter text (for example, Q1.2), indicating the most appropriate position for self-learning use. Answers to each question are given at the back of the book.

The books in this series have therefore been developed for use in either the classroom teaching situation or for self-learning.

Introduction

This book sets out to fulfil a number of objectives. First, it is intended to introduce the range of hardware facilities currently available within microprocessor large-scale integrated circuits and to discuss the set of support circuits provided to go with the microprocessor. Thus, Chapters 2, 3 and 4 describe the microprocessor itself and consider how memory circuits, input/output facilities and other peripheral chips are interconnected and combined to form a complete microcomputer system.

Secondly, the book introduces a number of important concepts and facilities used in microcomputers. In particular, Chapters 5, 6, 7 and 8 consider subroutines, stacks and interrupt systems. Finally, Chapter 9 covers further interfacing techniques such as polling and serial data transfer between the microcomputer and its peripherals, whilst Chapter 10 introduces the software development facilities appropriate to microcomputers.

The book is written to the objectives specified in the BTEC Unit Microelectronic Systems U79/604.

Whenever possible the topics described are illustrated by examples drawn from real microcomputer systems. As more and more micro-electronic circuits become available, the details of these will inevitably change. However, the underlying principles of the system operation and of the component parts which make it up will, it is thought, remain constant, as they have done for many years.

The book is not intended to be a manual for use in designing micro-computer systems of a particular type. The examples given are based, in the main, on the facilities provided by the Intel 8080, 8085 series of devices, but this should not limit the student to consideration of only this system. Hopefully he will be able, after studying the book, to transfer the general concepts presented to other series of devices and to see their relevance to these.

The ideas introduced in the earlier chapters are drawn together by the practical design developed in outline in Chapter 10. This example is, in a sense therefore, the culmination of the book and a proper under-standing of it should be one major aim of the reader. Overall it is hoped that the material presented herein will give the student a good impression of the true versatility of microcomputer systems and of the ease with which they can be applied to practical problems.

Acknowledgements

I thank my wife, Jan, for her constant help and encouragement during the preparation of this book as well as for her considerable efforts in typing the manuscript.

DAVID WOOLLONS

Chapter 1 The microprocessor-based system

Objectives of this chapter *When you have completed studying this chapter you should be able to:*

1. *Distinguish between a microprocessor and a microcomputer.*
2. *Understand the need for hardware and software in a working microcomputer system.*
3. *Understand the composition of a microcomputer system as a collection of LSI circuits including:*
   - *(a) a CPU chip,*
   - *(b) a clock oscillator,*
   - *(c) some read-only memory,*
   - *(d) some random-access memory,*

   which are interconnected by data, address and control highways and which require power supplies.
4. *Understand the disparity in speed which exists between the CPU and the peripheral devices attached to it.*
5. *Appreciate the need for synchronisation between the microcomputer and its peripherals and the use of peripheral interface circuits and handshaking in achieving this synchronisation.*
6. *Understand the basic principles of the two peripheral communication techniques of:*
   - *(a) software polling and*
   - *(b) interrupt systems.*
7. *Understand the principle of the use of instruction execution time to generate time delays in a real-time application.*
8. *Know the facilities available in a microcomputer's CPU, including*
   - *(a) the processor register set and*
   - *(b) the instruction set.*

1.1 Introduction

The microprocessor or, more accurately, the microcomputer is the end result of a sequence of developments that began with a Professor of Mathematics at Cambridge named Charles Babbage in the early nineteenth century.

Babbage, who was interested in calculating lists containing large amounts of numerical data, such as tables of the times of high tide around the country, spent a large part of his life considering how such calculations could be performed automatically, and fast, by a machine.

In his design for an 'Analytical Engine', which he began in 1833, Babbage proposed several ideas that are fundamental in modern computer systems. In particular he suggested:

1. That the operation of the machine should be controlled by a *stored program*, i.e. by a list of instructions stored in a *memory*. Each instruction would be able to cause the machine to perform some simple step such as an addition, a subtraction or movement of a number from one place to another. A sequence of them performed one after the other, automatically and at high speed (compared to a human being with pencil and paper), would then allow complex calculations to be done.
2. That the instructions which the machine performed should include a number of *conditional test* orders. These are special instructions which control the way in which the computer goes through the program. They can be used by the programmer to make the computer examine the result of a calculation and to cause it to *branch*, that is to *jump* to appropriate sections of program code depending on the result of the examination. Thus the program itself determines which instructions are executed following a test of this type. This is a very powerful feature as will be seen later in the book.

Although Babbage made considerable progress in the theoretical design of his analytical engine he was not able to develop a full working system because of the difficulty of machining the precise mechanical components which he required. The production of large-scale computer systems had to wait for the advances arising from the sophisticated electronic developments during the Second World War, and it was in the era following this that such systems began to appear. The early computers were built with thermionic valves and used large amounts of power.

The reliability of these valve-based computers was poor so the advent of transistors in the late 1950s gave added impetus to computer system design. With increased reliability due to the use of transistor active elements came a corresponding decrease in power consumption and physical size. Thus computers became cheaper, more convenient and more widely applicable.

The trend towards miniaturisation was further continued with the advent of the integrated circuit during the 1960s and with the development of medium and large-scale integration during the 1970s. The latter has resulted in the availability of very complex logical functions on a single circuit chip. At the time of writing it is possible to fabricate approximately 260,000 components on a single chip, including 29,000 transistors.

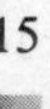

Figure 1.1 LSI chip – approx. 5 mm across *(Courtesy: Open University)*

The techniques that have made this possible are based on the field-effect transistor fabricated using P-MOS, N-MOS or C-MOS processes. N-MOS (N-channel metal oxide semiconductor) is two or three times faster in switching speed than P-MOS and has therefore gained wider acceptance. C-MOS has the advantage of very low power dissipation but is slower than N-MOS. It is, however, well suited to certain applications. MOS systems in general have the advantage that they can be fabricated using relatively fewer steps in the manufacturing process than systems based on bipolar techniques. Moreover the yield of 'good' circuits from a production run is comparatively high.

See note in Preface about questions

Q1.3

Microprocessors and microcomputers

As outlined in the previous section there are two main features which give computer systems their power and flexibility:

1. They are controlled by a program stored in a memory.
2. The set of program instructions available, i.e. the *order code* or *instruction set* of the computer, contains conditional branch orders.

A minimum microcomputer system must, therefore, contain a processor and some memory. The former is needed to provide the arithmetic and logical functions of the device and to perform the major part of the control of the system. The latter is needed to provide storage for the program instructions as well as for the data upon which they operate.

Normally the microcomputer also needs to communicate with external devices attached to it. These *peripheral devices* are used to supply information to the microcomputer system and to act upon values output from it. There are many types of peripheral device, each tailored to a particular application.

To allow the computer to print out results on paper, a *line printer* peripheral device is used. To allow numerical inputs to be typed into the computer a *keyboard* is a suitable peripheral. A keyboard combined with a television-type cathode-ray-tube screen provides a convenient *terminal* to the computer, allowing both input (the keyboard) and output (the display screen) of information.

Applications of the computer in which it forms part of a larger system require other types of peripheral. For example, a microcomputer might be used to control the functions of a washing machine. To be able to do this it requires information about the parameters of the system – the water temperature, the water level in the washing drum, how long the wash cycle has been going on and so on. Thus the peripherals of the microcomputer in this case are thermometers (to sense water temperature), water level detection devices, timers, etc.

Peripheral devices are connected to the computer through special circuits which handle input and output of information. These are discussed in detail in later chapters.

When the processor, the memory and the input/output circuits are combined, the block diagram of a typical microcomputer system becomes as shown in Figure 1.2. The three main units are interconnected by a set of wires known as the *system highway* or *system bus*.

It is appropriate, here, to consider the distinction between the *microprocessor* and the *microcomputer*. One frequently used definition is that the microprocessor is the unit responsible for arithmetic

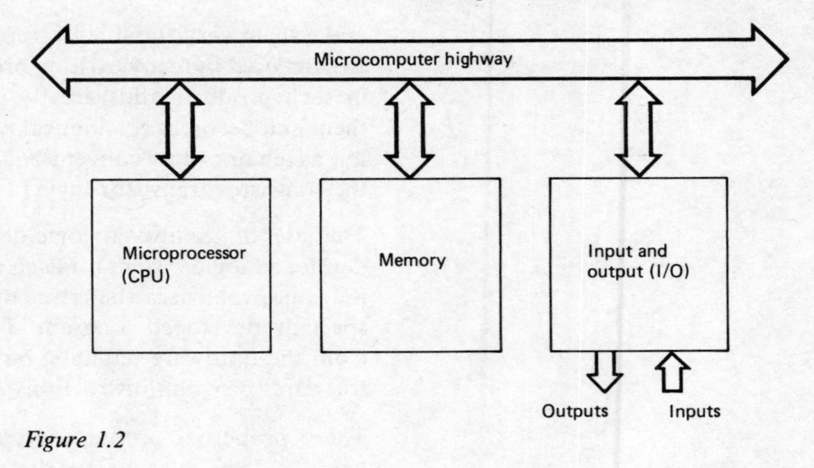

Figure 1.2

functions and system control. The microcomputer is the whole system including the memory and input/output (I/O) circuits.

In practice both microprocessors and microcomputers can be purchased as single-chip integrated circuits. Often, however, the microprocessor occupies a chip on its own and must be combined with other large-scale integrated circuits (memories and I/O circuits) to form a microcomputer.

Microcomputer application areas

The applications of microcomputers are many and diverse. Their unique features are their flexibility, which arises from stored program control, and their low cost.

Because the function that a microcomputer performs is governed by the program within its memory, it is extremely easy to alter it simply by changing that program. Hence simple microcomputers for use in the home may, at one moment, be used to calculate the household finances and at another, after entering a new program into memory, be used to play a game such as 'Space Invaders'.

Between these two quite different applications the *hardware*, i.e. the circuit, of the microcomputer does not alter. The *software*, i.e. the program in the memory, does alter and the effect is to make the computer function in a completely different way.

The low cost of microcomputers is due to several factors. The materials of which they are made are cheap and abundant (ordinary sand is largely composed of silicon). Chips can be made by the million on a production-line process; and world competition to sell integrated circuits is fierce, thus forcing their price down.

Taken together the flexibility and cheapness of microcomputers make them very suitable for replacing the purpose-built specialised circuits used in many existing products. The use of microcomputers in such products adds greatly increased functional capabilities to them and becomes economical when the microcomputer replaces as few as ten or twenty conventional integrated circuits of, for example, the transistor-transistor-logic (TTL) type.

The use of traditional logic-design methods requires a specially developed logic system for each application. Using microcomputers the same problem can be solved by standard hardware controlled by a specially developed program. The design emphasis is thus shifted from the hardware (circuits, busses, interconnecting wires, etc.) to software (program instructions).

These properties produce several advantages for microprocessor-based systems over their earlier random-logic equivalents:

1 The time and expenditure involved in new developments can be substantially reduced.
2 The flexibility of microcomputers allows modification of a product to adjust to market requirements.
3 Greatly increased functional capability allows better, more sophisticated systems. For instance, microcomputer-controlled telephone coin boxes can measure the time of a call and give change to the customer.
4 Microcomputers greatly reduce the number of wired connections used in a system. This in turn gives increased reliability.

Microcomputer application areas include:

1 *Instrumentation* The control and calibration of complex instrument systems.
2 *Industrial control systems* for sequencing the operations of industrial plant, e.g. a chemical production process or a rolling mill. In this type of process a number of operations have to be carried out in time sequence and the positions of mechanical components of the process have to be closely controlled. For example, the roller positions in a steel mill have to be accurately set. The microcomputer, together with the appropriate peripherals as outlined earlier, can be used to do this.
3 *Computer systems* Microcomputers are employed in the design of new general-purpose computers. Multimicroprocessors are important in this respect.
4 *Consumer applications* Control of domestic apparatus, vehicles, electronic programmable games.
5 *Office equipment* Word-processing systems.
6 *Military systems.*
7 *Medical* diagnostic and monitoring instruments.
8 *Intelligent systems* for use as computer terminals.
9 *Educational aids.*

10 *Communication systems* Use in error detection and correction in communication circuits, as well as for controlling telephone switching networks.

Q1.1

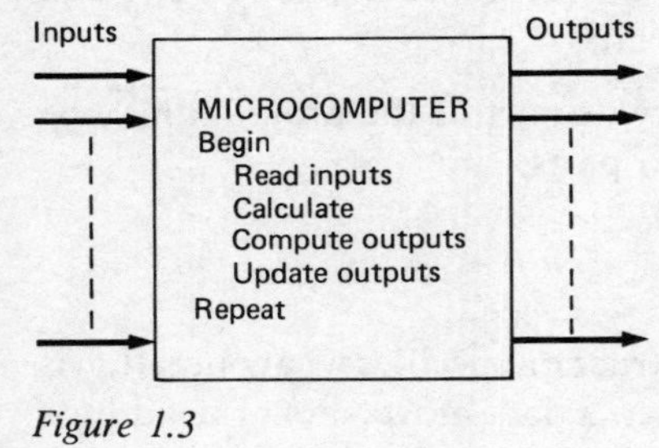

Figure 1.3

1.2 The need for hardware and software

As discussed in the previous sections a microcomputer system consists of interacting hardware and software modules. The operation of such a system can be symbolically represented as shown in Figure 1.3. The microcomputer:

1 Takes in values from the outside world through a number of input lines. These values can be numbers typed on an input keyboard, values of water temperature in a washing machine, etc.
2 Calculates new values to be placed on the output lines. This calculation is the main part of the program.
3 Outputs the new values to the output lines. These can be letters or numbers to be displayed on a TV screen or to be printed, or control signals to increase the power fed to the washing machine heater and so on.

These three steps are repeated over and over again until the microcomputer either encounters an instruction which causes program execution to stop (a HALT instruction, for example) or until some external event interrupts the cycle of operations.

As suggested earlier the program which controls the machine consists of a list of simple instructions held in a memory. The processor refers to these instructions by specifying their *address* in the memory as illustrated in Figure 1.4.

The memory consists of a sequence of *locations* each of which can be used to hold an item of information. This may be either a program instruction or a piece of data, i.e. a number for the program to work on.

All information stored in the memory, whether it be data items or program instructions, is held in binary form. Numbers are represented by a sign bit and magnitude bits and instructions are represented by coded binary patterns. Thus the size of the memory is usually specified in terms of the numbers of bits each location can hold together with the total number of locations.

In microcomputer systems each location can normally hold 8 bits, i.e. one *byte* of data or a part or whole program instruction. As we shall see later, some instructions need to be specified by more than 8 bits and thus 2 or even 3 bytes are required to hold them.

The number of locations in the memory, and hence the total memory size, is governed by the number of binary digits (*bits*) available to specify memory addresses. Each location must have a unique address so that it alone can be accessed by the processor. Thus, for example, an address containing 16 bits allows numbers (addresses) between 0 and 65,535 to be specified giving the possibility of 65,536 locations in the memory. In such a system the *address space* is said to be 65,536 bytes (if each location contains 8 bits).

Instructions stored in the memory as part of the program may be broadly considered to contain two parts:

1 An *operation code* (or *opcode*).
2 An *address*.

The operation code part of the instruction specifies what operation is to be performed (an add, a subtract, a data move, etc). The address part specifies where the *operand* to be used in the instruction is to be found in the memory.

The computer operates by repetitively fetching an instruction from the memory, decoding this instruction and, according to the operation code which it finds, executing the instruction. Unless a branch instruction is reached the processor progresses sequentially through the program executing the instructions one after the other. To do this it uses a register (a place where information can be held) in the processor called the *program counter*.

The program counter is used to keep track of where the processor has reached in the execution of the program. It holds the address of the *next* instruction due to be fetched from memory and executed.

When execution of the current instruction has been completed the processor:

1 Sends the value held in the program counter as an address to the memory.
2 Fetches the instruction held at that address from the memory into the processor chip.
3 Examines the operation code part of the instruction and performs the specified operations.

Steps 1 and 2 above are the *instruction fetch* cycle of the processor and step 3 is the *execution* cycle.

Immediately after the instruction fetch has been performed the contents of the program counter are incremented. They then hold the address of the next instruction to be fetched, during the instruction cycle following the current execution cycle.

Q1.6

The program counter may thus be considered to hold a number which 'points' to the next instruction to be executed. This is shown diagrammatically in Figure 1.4.

It can be seen, then, that the hardware of a microcomputer system is designed simply to execute program instructions. Thus there must

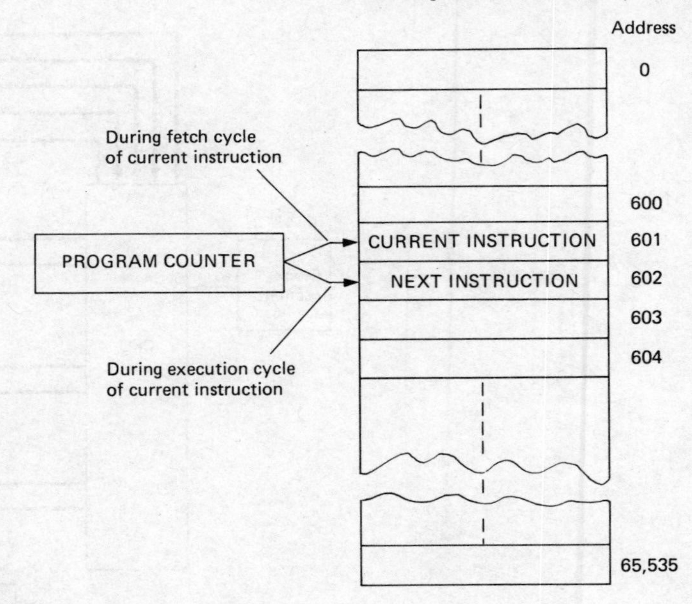

Figure 1.4

be instructions present in the machine before it can perform any function whatsoever; even to read in an application program and put it into the memory requires that a 'loader' program already be present in the memory to make the processor take in the application program instructions from a suitable peripheral. For this reason the system contains a resident *monitor*, i.e. a program permanently stored in the memory, which permits control of basic machine functions such as input and output of programs or data, initiation of application program execution, halting program execution and so on.

Q1.2

1.3 The complete microcomputer system

It has been seen that a microcomputer system consists of a number of modules. It is now convenient to expand this concept and to consider the system components in greater detail. Figure 1.5 is a more detailed illustration of such a microcomputer system.

As discussed in Section 1.1, the microcomputer consists of a number of large-scale integrated circuits interconnected by the system highway or system bus. The microprocessor (MPU – Microprocessor Unit or CPU – Central Processing Unit) is the central chip of the system. This unit contains the circuits for implementing the instruction set of the machine, for controlling the timing and synchronisation of the other units, for sequencing the instruction fetch and execution cycles, for determining the addresses of instruction operands and so on.

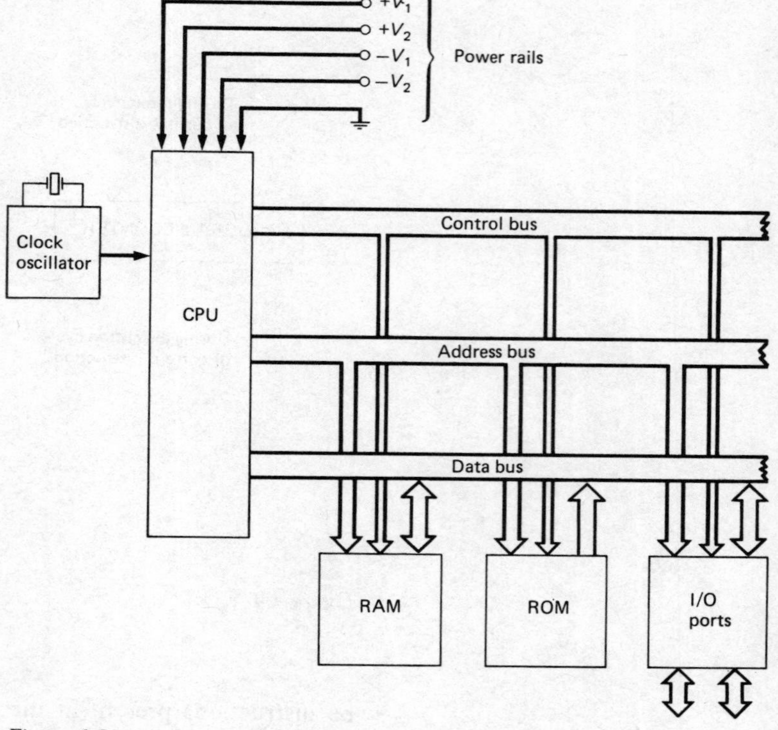

Figure 1.5

The system bus

The system bus is a collection of wires. It may be conveniently subdivided, as in Figure 1.5, into an *address* bus, a *data* bus and a *control* bus.

The address bus is used to send addresses to the memory from the processor or, sometimes, from other chips in the system. Such addresses specify the locations to be accessed in the memory to obtain instructions or items of data or to write information into store. Figure 1.5 shows two types of memory, the *random access memory* (RAM) and the *read only memory* (ROM). The differences between these will be discussed later.

The number of wires required in the address bus is determined by the size of the address space of the microcomputer. For instance if the system has 16 address wires, a 16-bit address can be sent to memory, thus permitting access, as seen earlier, to 65,536 (64K where 1K = 1,024) addressable locations. This address range is very common in second- and third-generation microprocessors (see Section 2.2 for a definition of generations of microcomputers) such as the Intel 8085, the Zilog Z80 and the Motorola MC 6800. Fourth-generation machines such as the Intel 8086, the Zilog Z8000 or the Motorola 6800 have larger address spaces.

Q1.5

It should be noted that addresses are always sent *to* the microcomputer memory. Hence the connections to the RAM and ROM from the address highway in Figure 1.5 are shown as being *unidirectional.*

The data bus is used to transfer the information in a memory reference or a peripheral I/O operation around the system. The *width* of this bus, that is the number of wires within it, depends on the size of the data unit used. Second- and third-generation microcomputers commonly use 1-byte data units so the data bus contains eight wires. More advanced fourth-generation systems operate on 16-bit parallel data and have a data bus which is 2 bytes wide.

The data bus is *bidirectional* in microcomputers. Thus information can pass along it from the processor to memory, or to peripherals, as well as from memory or peripherals to the processor. Moreover, not all data involves the processor. A peripheral unit can often exchange information directly with the memory without processor intervention.

The use of a bidirectional data bus reduces the number of pins on the processor integrated circuit since it is not necessary to allocate separate connections for input and for output. This is a desirable feature as there is a practical and economic limit to the number of connections made to a chip.

The control bus is composed of wires which carry signals generated within the processor and the other units. These signals are used by the system to synchronise the operations of the separate modules. This will be discussed in more detail later.

The clock oscillator

All operations occurring in the microcomputer system must be correctly synchronised. In extracting an item of data from the memory, for example, several steps, as outlined in Section 3.1, must occur in the correct time sequence. Thus the microcomputer contains a *clock oscillator*, sometimes known also as a *clock generator* (Figure 1.5).

The clock oscillator generates the timing signals required to synchronise the operations of the various parts of the system. It produces a train, or sometimes two trains of square wave pulses. These are fed into connections on the processor chip and used within it to time each of the steps involved in executing an instruction. Since most instructions involve several steps, a number of clock periods is required for each of them. This is discussed further in Chapter 3.

The clock oscillator is generally another integrated circuit in the system and usually requires the addition of an external crystal or some other frequency-determining circuit outside the chip. Clock frequencies from 2 to 8 MHz or more can be used, depending on the particular microprocessor system under consideration.

Power supplies

The microcomputer system must contain a power supply to generate the voltages and currents needed by the various integrated circuits. The range of voltages required varies from system to system. For instance the Intel 8080 microprocessor chip needs four voltage supplies of +12, –12, +5 and –5 V, whereas the Zilog Z80 or Intel 8085 devices only need a single +5 V supply. Generally the tendency adopted by manufacturers has been to attempt to reduce the number of different supply rails used.

Memories

As has been seen the microcomputer memory is of two types, RAM and ROM. The read only memory is used for holding the program instructions and for data which does not change such as standard lists or tables. The random access memory is used when information changes or intermediate results must be stored temporarily.

Both types of memory are connected to the address, data and control highways and exchange information with other units via them.

ROM, as implied by its name, can only be *read* by the processor. The data in such a memory is placed there by the manufacturers when the memory is manufactured. RAM can be used by the processor for writing away results which must be remembered.

An intermediate circuit which, in a way, is between RAM and ROM is the PROM – the *programmable read only memory*. In normal use this behaves just like a ROM. However, it is possible for an applications engineer to place data or program instructions in it (once only) by 'blowing' tiny fuses within the PROM chip to write in the pattern he requires. To do this a special piece of equipment, a *prom-programmer*, is used.

Once a PROM has been programmed, its contents are fixed and cannot be altered again. However another type of memory, the EPROM (*erasable programmable read only memory*) can be reprogrammed over and over again. Its contents can be erased, normally by shining ultra-violet light through a quartz window in the top of the integrated circuit package, and new data can then be written into it as for an ordinary PROM. This process can be repeated many times.

There is further discussion of memories in Chapter 2.

I/O chips

The importance of communication between the microprocessor and the outside world has already been mentioned. No matter how powerful the processor of any computer system might be, it is of little use unless data can pass into it from peripheral devices and out from it to affect the external system of which it is a part.

Hence, as discussed in detail in later chapters, there are a number of special integrated circuits on the market which are designed to make connection of peripherals to a microcomputer an easy task. These circuits are commonly known by various names; peripheral interface adaptor (PIA), peripheral interface circuit (PIC) and peripheral input-output (PIO) circuit are the most common.

In essence these circuits all perform the same function. They are designed to have one set of pins which connect directly to the micro-computer highway and another set which provide *ports* to which external equipment can be attached. The ports of the microcomputer allow information to flow in and out of the system just as ports in a country allow goods to be exchanged with the rest of the world.

The facilities provided by peripheral interface circuits vary from chip to chip but, typically, two or three ports, each containing eight input or output lines, are available to the user. Any port may be used either as an input or as an output.

The choice of whether a particular port is to be used as an input or an output is made by the programmer. The peripheral interface circuits are designed to be *software-configured*, i.e. the programmer can choose which ports are to act as inputs and which as outputs and can then set up the PIC by sending control data to it using instructions in his program.

At the beginning of a program, therefore, it is normal for the programmer to *initialise* all the peripheral interface circuits in the microcomputer system to operate in the way he requires. If, later in the program, he wishes to alter a port from input to output or *vice versa* he can do so. No hardware alterations are needed in the PIC.

Serial communication

Peripheral interface circuits, as outlined above, provide input and output of information in *parallel* form. Thus each port sends or receives 8 bits of data at a time.

Although parallel data transmission of this type is often used between microcomputers and their peripheral devices, particularly when speed of transfer is of paramount importance, the cheapest type of link is the *serial* interface.

In a serial interface data is exchanged between devices one bit at a time. When a byte has to be transmitted, the 8 bits within it are sent one after the other in time sequence. This tends to be a slow process, of course, but it minimises the number of wires needed to form the connection.

Because they require less interconnections, serial links are important when a peripheral device is situated at a distance from the computer or when it is necessary to make a connection between them using the public-switched telephone system.

Large-scale integrated circuits for use in serial data transmission have been available for a number of years. They connect to the processor data, address and control highways on one side and provide serial data transfer lines on the other. They are generally known as *UARTs* (*U*niversal *R*eceiver and *T*ransmitter) or USARTs (*U*niversal Synchronous/Asynchronous Receiver and Transmitter). They are considered further in Chapter 9.

Q1.7

1.4 The speed of computers and peripherals

Because the computer is so much concerned with exchanging data with the outside world, many different types of peripheral device have been developed.

One general problem that arises in connection with exchanging information between the processor and these devices is that there is often a large disparity in speed between them. The processor is an extremely fast device whereas peripherals, which often include mechanical operations or require information to be accessed in a serial way (one bit at a time rather than many bits in parallel), are necessarily slow.

In order to gain an idea of the range of speeds in common use it is interesting to consider some typical peripheral devices. Perhaps the slowest device is the *teletype* which can accept and print characters from the computer at a rate of 10 per second. Each character is specified by 11 bits giving a transfer rate of 110 *baud* (1 baud = 1 bit per second). Faster devices which also involve mechanical operations are the paper-tape reader which typically reads 1,000 8-bit characters per second (8,000 baud) and the line printer. The latter may print 1000 lines, each containing 160 8-bit characters, per minute (a transfer rate of approximately 20 Kbaud). Fixed-head disks, at the other end of the scale, have transfer rates of 500,000 words per second. For a wordlength of 16 bits, this gives a data rate of 8 Mbaud.

The microcomputer instruction execution rate is determined by the basic clock frequency of the machine, as discussed in the previous section, and by the number of clock periods required to execute each instruction. This latter parameter is a variable quantity so the execution time varies from instruction to instruction.

For an Intel 8080 processor using a 2.048 MHz clock frequency (0.488 μs clock period) some sample instruction timings are shown in Table 1.1. It can be seen that an instruction, for this microcomputer and this clock frequency, takes between 2 and 10 μs. For higher clock frequencies these times are correspondingly reduced and execution times of less than 1 μs are quite common.

Table 1.1 *Instruction execution times*

Instruction	*Clock cycles used*	*Execution time/μs*
LDA (memory address)	13	6.344
ORA (register)	4	1.952
JMP (address)	10	4.880
MVI B (data)	7	3.416
NOP	4	1.952

1.5 Synchronising with peripherals

It is important that information transfers between the processor and its peripherals should be synchronised in time. The processor instruction set contains two special I/O orders IN and OUT. When IN is encountered whilst the processor is executing a program, it causes data to be taken from a peripheral port into the processor. When OUT is encountered, data is sent from the processor to a peripheral port. These points are described in greater detail in Chapter 2.

Input or output of data from the processor occurs at specific instants of time, namely whenever an IN or an OUT instruction is encountered during program execution. Peripheral devices, on the other hand, also need to produce or take data at specific times, namely when they are ready to do so. In other words the processor and its peripherals work at their own speeds and it is necessary to have some way of interlocking their operation for a brief period whenever data has to be exchanged. *Handshaking* is used for this.

Handshaking

When a peripheral is connected to a microcomputer system, usually via a peripheral interface circuit, two wires are used to carry signals

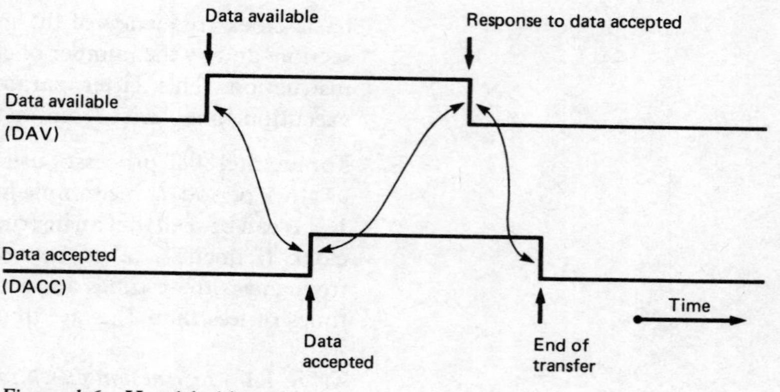

Figure 1.6 Handshaking

synchronising the processor and the external device. These two *control lines* are known by various names. For this explanation we shall call them DAV (data available) and DACC (data accepted).

Figure 1.6 shows the signal patterns on these lines during a peripheral/processor data transfer.

Suppose that the processor is sending data to a peripheral device. When it comes to the OUT instruction in the program, data is sent to the device and control line DAV is set to logical 1. This signal indicates to the peripheral that the data is available for it to take. The peripheral, on detecting that DAV is '1', takes the data and causes DACC to be set to logical 1. This signal tells the processor that the data has been accepted.

The processor responds to the setting of DACC by resetting DAV to logical 0 and the peripheral responds to this by resetting DACC to 0. The transfer is then complete.

It does not have to be the processor which initiates the transfer. It is possible to allow the peripheral device, when it requires to send data to the processor, to set DAV to 1. The processor then responds and the transfer continues as described previously.

In general, then, a handshake-controlled transfer proceeds as follows. The device with data to send (either the peripheral, for an input of information to the microcomputer, or the microcomputer itself for output of data to a peripheral) places the data on the data lines and sets DAV. The receiving device (the computer or the peripheral respectively) takes the data and sets DACC. The sender detects the setting of DACC and responds by resetting DAV whereupon the receiver detects the resetting of DAV and itself resets DACC ready for the next transfer.

Polling of peripherals and interrupts

Although handshaking synchronises the actual transfer of one item of data between processor and peripherals it is not adequate, on its own, to deal with all processor/peripheral communication problems.

These problems are associated with the speed disparity described in Section 1.4. If, for instance, a peripheral device works at a rate of only one thousandth of the processor speed (it is ready to perform an information transfer every millisecond and the processor is ready every microsecond, say) how does the processor know when it can send or take data?

Two important techniques in this respect are:

1 *Polling* of peripheral devices using software.
2 External *interrupts*.

Each of these is considered in detail later in the book. Interrupts are described in Chapter 8 and software polling in Chapter 9. At this juncture it is only necessary to briefly outline what each involves.

Software polling is the process by which the processor examines the state of readiness (to exchange data) of its peripherals. Thus it consists of a list of program instructions which interrogate the peripheral devices in sequence:

'Peripheral 1 have you any data?'
'Peripheral 2 have you any data?'
'Peripheral 3 have you any data?'
And so on.

If, after any of the above requests, the answer from the peripheral is 'yes', a transfer of data is initiated. If it is 'no', then the next request in the sequence is sent out.

Interrupts are signals that a peripheral device generates when it needs to attract the attention of the processor. The effect of such a signal is to cause the processor to jump to a special section of program which deals with the situation causing the interrupt. For example, if a peripheral has data for the processor it can send an interrupt. On receipt of this the processor jumps to a piece of program which takes in the data.

1.6 Processor facilities and instruction sets

In later chapters there are discussions of many aspects of microcomputer systems. All these involve both hardware and software since, as has been seen in Section 1.2, the two are intimately related. Hence it is important at this stage of the book to briefly review the facilities of the microprocessor chip within a microcomputer system.

The following paragraphs are, therefore, included as a necessary precursor to later sections. Most of the topics included here are explained in succeeding chapters. In addition, the complete instruction set of the Intel 8085 microprocessor, which is used as an example throughout the book, is given in Appendix 1.

Processor chip features

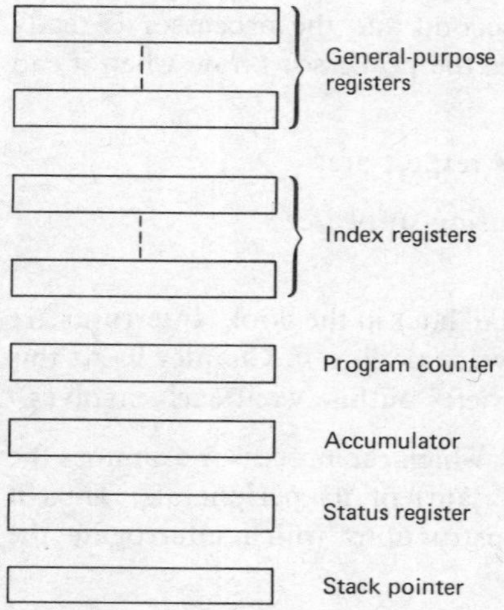

General-purpose registers
Index registers
Program counter
Accumulator
Status register
Stack pointer

Figure 1.7 Processor registers

The microprocessor chip of a microcomputer system contains a number of registers. The idea of a register has already been discussed in Section 1.2 in which a special-purpose register, the program counter, was introduced. It may be recalled that this register is used to hold the address of the next program instruction to be executed.

Other registers on the processor chip fall into a number of categories. The facilities offered by different systems from different manufacturers do, of course, vary, but the register types shown in Figure 1.7 are generally present.

1 *General-purpose registers* These are used for holding the data required in a calculation. Both arithmetic operands or addresses can be stored.

2 *Accumulators* The arithmetic and logical operations carried out in a microcomputer take place in an *accumulator*. This register generally holds one of the operands involved in a two-operand instruction such as an add or a subtract operation, as well as the result obtained when the operation is complete. Instructions that only require a single operand like the logical functions, shift, or rotate, also operate upon data held in the accumulator.

3 *Index registers* Index registers are used in the formation of the address part of an instruction. That is to say the memory address of the operand referenced by an instruction can, in many microcomputers, be built up from several parts, one of which is the index register. This is elaborated in Section 2.2.

In an *index-modified* address the contents of the index register are added to the *offset* address specified in the instruction to produce the full memory address of the operand. This procedure may seem complicated but it produces a number of useful features. By modifying the contents of the index register under program control it is possible for a program to step through a list or an array of data. Some microcomputers also possess the facility to automatically increment the register contents after their use in forming an address (auto-increment address mode) or to decrement the register contents before they are used in an address (auto-decrement mode). Alternatively the register contents may be kept constant whilst the

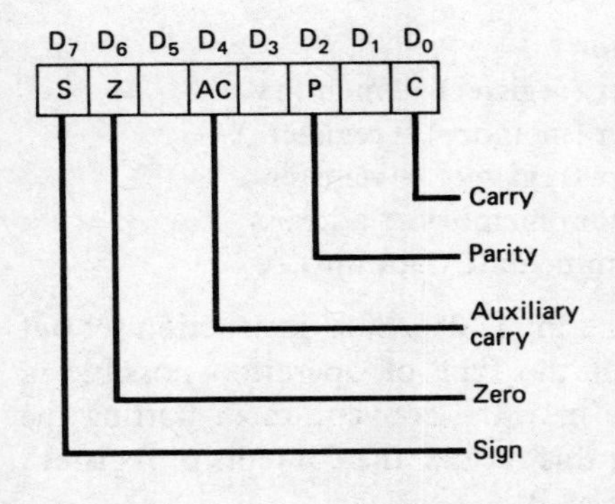

Figure 1.8 Flags in the Zilog Z80

other components of the address, e.g. the offset, are altered. In this situation the register may be considered to be acting as a *pointer* to the *base* address of a block of data.

4 *The program counter* As has been discussed this register holds the address of the instruction following the one currently under execution.

5 *The status register* The status register contains a number of *flag bits* which are used to record the state of the microcomputer. For example in the Intel 8085 microprocessor the status bits used are as shown in Figure 1.8.

The sign bit of the result of any arithmetic operation is placed in Flag D_7. Thus, if the result of an operation is negative, D_7 becomes a 1 and if it is positive D_7 becomes a 0. This bit can be subsequently tested by a conditional branch instruction. For instance, the order JP (jump on positive) is an instruction which tests D_7. If bit D_7 is 0 when tested the jump is performed. Any arithmetic operation producing a result of zero causes flag D_6 to be set to 1. This bit can be tested using the JZ (jump on zero) order. If D_6 is set to 1 when this order is executed the jump specified occurs. The other flag bits are used as follows:

D_4 To record a carry out from bit 3 of the adder. This is useful in performing binary-coded-decimal arithmetic.

D_2 The *parity flag*. All logical instructions affect this flag. If the parity (the number of ones in the result of an operation) is odd, the parity flag is reset to 0. If the number of ones in the result of an operation is even the flag is set to 1.

D_0 Signifies that a carry has arisen from the most significant bit of the adder.

6 *Stack pointer* The stack pointer is used, as will be described in detail later, to implement a last-in-first-out stack in random access memory.

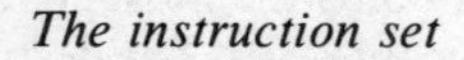

The instruction set

It is convenient to classify the orders making up the instruction set of a microprocessor into groups.

Data transfer orders Movement of data from one place to another is a very common operation in computer programs. Information is stored, mainly, in the computer memory and in the processor registers. Thus the majority of data transfer orders provided in a microprocessor are concerned with exchanging the contents of these registers one with another or with moving information between a register and a location in the memory. Typical examples are:

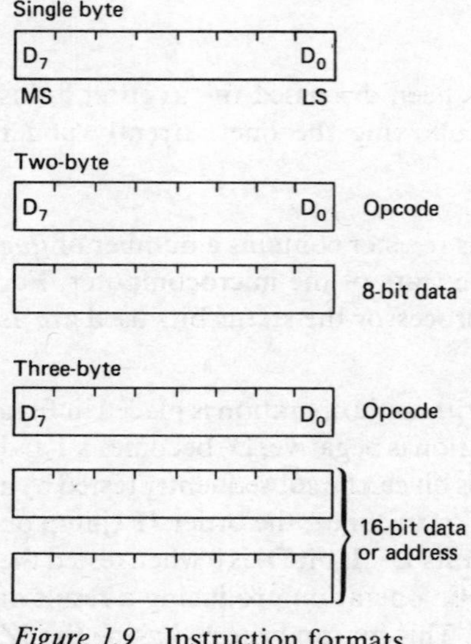

Figure 1.9 Instruction formats

Instruction	*Operation*
MOV M,C	Transfer (register) → memory
MOV D,M	Transfer (memory) → register
MOV C,H	Transfer (register) → register
LDA address	Load from memory at address → A
MVI A,byte	Move immediate data into A

These orders are taken from the Intel 8080/8085 instruction set but are generally representative of the type of operation possible in microcomputer systems. Note here the convention of putting the word 'register' in parentheses; this means 'the contents of register'. Thus, (B) means 'the contents of B'.

The registers used in these examples, designated as C, D and H, are part of the register set of the 8080 and 8085 microprocessors. These devices have six general-purpose registers called B, C, D, E, H and L.

Instructions in the 8080 or 8085 microprocessors can occupy one, two or three bytes of memory as shown in Figure 1.9. The number of bytes needed to store any particular instruction depends on how much information must be specified in that instruction.

When register A, which is the accumulator, is loaded with a data value from the memory, the memory address to be used to get that value is specified in the second and third bytes of the 3-byte 'LDA address' instruction.

The instruction 'MVI A,byte' moves the data specified by 'byte' into the accumulator. For example MVI A,37 places the value +37 in A. To store this instruction requires 2 bytes of memory, the data to be placed in A occupying the second byte.

The memory address to be used in an instruction can be written directly into some instructions, like the 'LDA address' just discussed. Sometimes, however, the memory address is assumed to be the value held in the H and L registers.

Thus a MOV M,C instruction transfers the number held in register C into the memory at a byte whose address is the number in H and L. Register H holds the most significant 8 bits of the address and L the least significant 8 bits. The destination of the data, memory, M, in this case, is written before the source, C, in the instruction.

The instruction 'MOV M,C' and others of the same type occupy a single byte in the memory.

Arithmetic and logical orders

The processor generally has comprehensive facilities for performing arithmetic operations and for manipulating bit patterns. Some examples are given below:

Instruction	*Operation*
ADD E	Add (register) into A
SUB H	Subtract (register) from A
INR B	Increment (register) by 1
DCR L	Decrement (register) by 1
ADI byte	Add immediate data into A
RLC	Rotate (A) left one position
RRC	Rotate (A) right one position
ANI byte	Logically 'and' (A) with immediate data

Program flow control

Instruction	*Operation*
JMP address	Jump unconditionally to 'address'
JZ address	Jump on zero to 'address'
JP address	Jump on positive to 'address'
JPO address	Jump on odd parity to 'address'
CALL address	Call subroutine
RET	Subroutine return
CZ address	Call subroutine on zero
CPE address	Call subroutine on even parity
RZ	Return on zero

The concept of *subroutines*, implied in the instructions listed above, is fully discussed in Chapters 5–7.

The jump orders above are the conditional branch instructions mentioned in the introduction to this chapter. They allow the values of the status register bits to be tested and the flow of control in the program to be determined by the result of the test.

Input-output

Instruction	*Operation*
IN address	Input to A from port 'address'
OUT address	Output from A to port 'address'
EI	Enable interrupts
DI	Disable interrupts

Miscellaneous operations

Instruction	*Operation*
NOP	Perform no operation
HLT	Halt
RST	Restart

The complete instruction set of a modern microcomputer system contains many orders not included in the foregoing list. However the examples given are indicative of the types of operation available to the programmer.

1.7 Assembly language and machine code

The instructions in the previous section have been written as *mnemonics*. This representation has been used here, and is used in the programming examples to follow, because it is easy to read and understand.

In fact the instructions stored in the microcomputer memory when it is running a program are in binary code. Thus the code for the instruction MOV M,C just quoted is:

01110001

This occupies a single byte of memory space. For some purposes it is convenient to write such a single-byte instruction in *hexadecimal code*. Thus 01110001 is written as 71 (hexadecimal), or 71 (hex).

Both binary and hexadecimal machine code are less convenient than assembly language. Of course, a program written in assembly language must be translated into machine code before it can be stored and executed in the microcomputer, but this can easily be done by the microcomputer itself using a program called an *Assembler*.

The assembler takes in input data, namely the assembly language *source* program written by the programmer. It then translates this into machine language and puts it in the microcomputer store.

Assembly language, as has been seen, allows the use of mnemonics to represent the operation code part of an instruction. It also permits the use of *labels* and *names* to represent addresses and data. One assembly language instruction translates (via the assembler) into one machine language instruction.

The concepts involved in assembly language programming can be illustrated with a simple example.

Q1.8

1.8 The use of programs to generate time delays

An interesting programming example, illustrating some of the concepts outlined in this chapter, is provided by considering the use of programs in the generation of time delays. Such delays are often required as sections of longer programs. Indeed, an example of a time delay subroutine in a microcomputer pulse train generator is included in Chapter 7.

Many examples can be quoted of the need for specified precise time intervals. The use of a microcomputer to generate waveforms, for

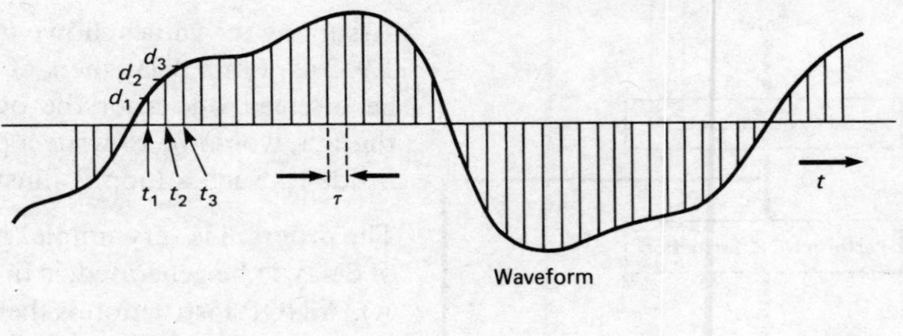

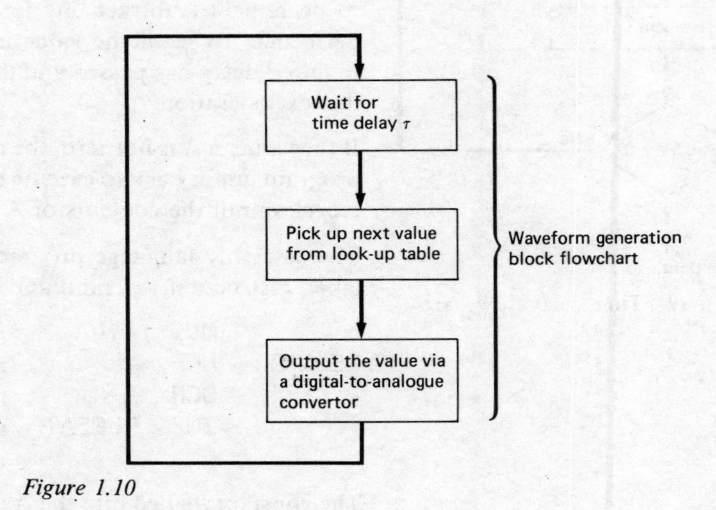

Figure 1.10

instance, requires that values defining the amplitude of the waveform be output at precise intervals. These values can be held as a look-up table in memory if the waveform is repetitive. Figure 1.10 outlines the procedure. The amplitudes of the waveform at instants t_1, t_2, t_3, etc., are specified by the values d_1, d_2, d_3, etc., respectively. These values represent *samples* of the waveform at intervals τ seconds apart. The waveform-generation program simply outputs successive values through a suitable peripheral interface circuit to a digital-to-analogue converter. In order to do this the system must contain a means for measuring τ.

There are two main possibilities. One, as discussed later, is to include a special circuit known as an interval timer in the chip set making up the microcomputer. The other is to use the instruction execution times of the microcomputer itself to produce the required delay.

The microprocessor instruction set contains an instruction, NOP, which does not perform any operation. In other words it does not affect any of the values in the processor registers or in the memory, nor does it perform any other function. It does, however, occupy some processor time to execute this instruction and it is useful, therefore, for causing a time delay.

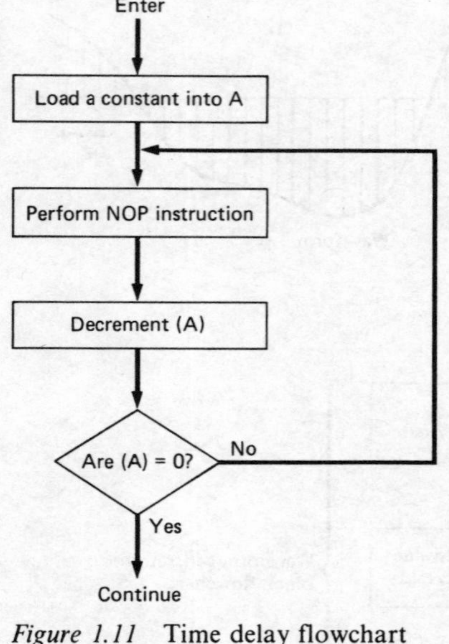

Figure 1.11 Time delay flowchart

Assuming the values shown in Table 1.1, each NOP instruction takes 1.952 μs. For a delay then, of about 19 μs ten NOP instructions could be inserted one after the other in a program. A better solution, though, would be to write a program loop with the NOP instruction inside it. Such a loop is illustrated in Figure 1.11.

The program is very simple. A constant, which determines the length of delay to be generated, is first loaded into the accumulator (register A). A NOP instruction is then performed followed by an instruction to decrement (subtract one from) from register A. Next, a test is performed to see if the value in A has reached zero. If it has the required delay has passed and the program goes on to continue with its next operation.

If the value in A is not zero, the required delay has not expired so the program jumps back to execute the NOP instruction again. This loop recycles until the contents of A become zero.

The assembly language program (consisting of, from left to right, label, instruction, operand and comment) to perform these steps is

```
        MVI  A,0A     ;Put (+10) into A
REPEAT: NOP           ;Delay
        DCR  A        ;Decrement (A)
        JNZ  REPEAT   ;If (A) ≠ 0, go back to
                      ;REPEAT
```

The constant loaded into the A register at the start of the program is 10. If a longer delay were required this could be altered to a larger value. In the instruction this value is specified in hexadecimal code [10 (decimal) = 0A (hex)].

The loop consists of three instructions: NOP, DCR A and JNZ REPEAT. The latter two require, respectively, 2.441 and 4.882 μs. Thus, since the loop is executed ten times, the total time which it occupies is:

$$10\,(1.952 + 2.441 + 4.882) = 92.75\ \mu s$$

The use of the label REPEAT in the program makes the jump instruction simple to write and easy to understand.

For completeness the binary and hexadecimal versions of this program are shown in Table 1.2. It is assumed that the machine code program is in memory between 00AF (hex) and 00B5 (hex). The individual instructions in Table 1.2 are separated by lines to show the number of bytes that each of them occupies.

Q1.9–1.11

Table 1.2

Address (hex)	*Instruction*		*Comment*
	Binary	*Hex*	
00AF	00111110	3E	Move 0A (hex) into A
00B0	00001010	0A	
00B1	00000000	00	NOP
00B2	00111101	3D	Decrement (A)
00B3	11000010	C2	If (A) $\neq 0$
00B4	10110001	B1	jump to 00B1
00B5	00000000	00	

Questions

1.1 Discuss the likely application areas of microcomputer systems. What are the properties of microcomputers which make them uniquely suitable for such applications?

1.2 What are the meanings of the terms *hardware* and *software*? Describe the way in which a computer system is a combination of hardware and software and outline the relationship between the two.

1.3 Write an essay on the history of the development of computer systems. Highlight the fundamental principles underlying these systems and discuss how (if at all) they have changed following the advent of microcomputers. (This question will require further reading.)

1.4 Give brief descriptions of the properties and uses of each of the following:

(a) Read only memory.
(b) Random access memory.
(c) The processor status register.
(d) Assembly language.

1.5 What is the maximum possible address space for a microcomputer with a 24-bit address bus? Express the answer in Kbytes and Mbytes.

1.6 Outline the operations involved when the computer is executing a sequence of instructions in a program. What part does the program counter play in these operations? Describe what happens when a JUMP instruction is encountered in the sequence.

1.7 Describe the modules making up a complete microcomputer system, giving brief reasons why each module is required and explaining its function.

1.8 Write a simple assembly language program to:

(a) Load the C register with immediate data 92 (hex).
(b) Load the D register with immediate data 64 (hex).
(c) Transfer the value in C into A.
(d) Add the value in D into A.
(e) Write the result in A into memory address 3130 (hex).

1.9 A microcomputer possesses a single output port having eight output lines. The least significant one of these lines is connected via logic to a loudspeaker in such a way that a square pulse is applied to the speaker each time that the line goes from 0 to 1. A transition from 1 to 0 does not affect the speaker. Assuming that the duration of this pulse is 100 μs draw a flowchart to show how the computer could be programmed to produce musical notes of varying pitch.

1.10 Using the Intel 8085 instruction set given in Appendix 1, write an assembly language program implementing the flowchart of Question 1.9. Assume that the address of the output port is 32 (hex).

1.11 Write an assembly language program to produce an output sawtooth waveform from a microcomputer system. Assume that the output is to be from port 32, as in Question 1.10. The output waveform is to be as shown in Figure 1.12. Each section of the sawtooth is represented by ten output values, $d_0, d_1, d_2, \ldots, d_9$, which are separated by 2 ms intervals. Assume for simplicity that each instruction in the microcomputer occupies 2 μs.

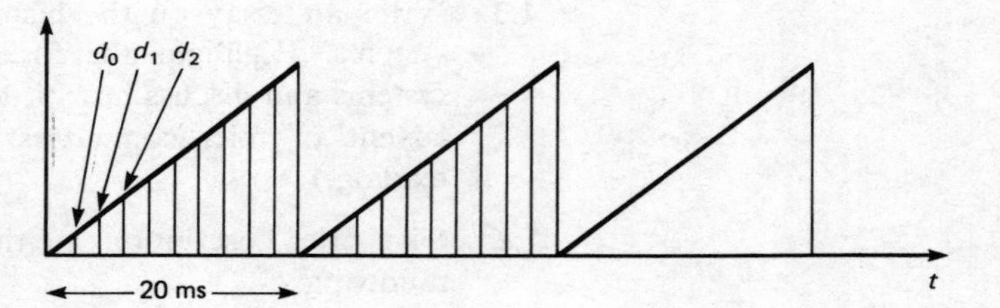

Figure 1.12

Chapter 2 Hardware for microprocessor-based systems

Objectives of this chapter *When you have completed studying this chapter you should be able to:*

1. *Describe the hardware configuration of a microcomputer system.*
2. *Understand the concept of the microcomputer bus and the availability of standard busses.*
3. *Describe the important parameters of a microprocessor, including:*
   - *(a) the instruction set,*
   - *(b) the processor register facilities,*
   - *(c) the address mode and address range,*
   - *(d) the data types that can be manipulated,*

   and have an appreciation of the availability of such properties in practical systems.
4. *Describe the types of memory used in microcomputer systems and the availability and parameters of the various integrated circuits provided by manufacturers.*
5. *Describe the properties and components of a parallel-programmable peripheral interface including:*
   - *(a) the data input register,*
   - *(b) the data output register,*
   - *(c) the status flags and*
   - *(d) the control register.*
6. *Describe the method used to address the components of the PPI and to select individual interface circuits or memory chips within the total system.*
7. *Describe the modes of operation of a practical programmable interface circuit.*
8. *Describe the applications of an interval timer as a peripheral device of the computer and the distinction between this device and the clock oscillator which synchronises the machine operation.*
9. *Describe the facilities available in an interval timer chip.*
10. *Describe the use of an interval timer chip as an event counter and as a real-time clock.*
11. *Appreciate the need for a range of support chips for use in microcomputer systems and, in particular, recognise that uni- and bi-directional bus buffers, drivers and address decoders are important components within the computer.*

2.1 Introduction

Chapter 1 introduced the concept of a microcomputer system as a collection of modules. Each module, for example the processor or the random access memory, is made up of one or more integrated circuits. The processor itself is often a single VLSI (Very Large Scale Integrated) circuit. The memory system normally requires several large-scale integrated circuits. This chapter discusses the hardware aspects of such microcomputer systems and illustrates the facilities and chips available for use within them.

Figure 2.1 is a block diagram of a typical microcomputer system. As has been seen, the modules making up the complete machine are interconnected using data, address and control busses. These busses forming, as they do, a central feature of the microcomputer, are an important influence on the determination of the physical characteristics of the machine.

The system modules can be conveniently classified as:

1 The processor module.
2 Memory modules.
3 Parallel input/output modules.
4 Serial input/output modules.
5 Miscellaneous and support modules. For example the microprocessor unit may require a *clock generator* to supply the system timing pulses. Backing stores such as floppy disk systems require a *controller* to interface them to the microcomputer bus. Very often a *timer/event counter* chip is needed, especially in real-time applications of the microcomputer. Support circuits such as bus drivers, data selectors and multiplexers, addressable latches and so on are also used in assembling a complete system.

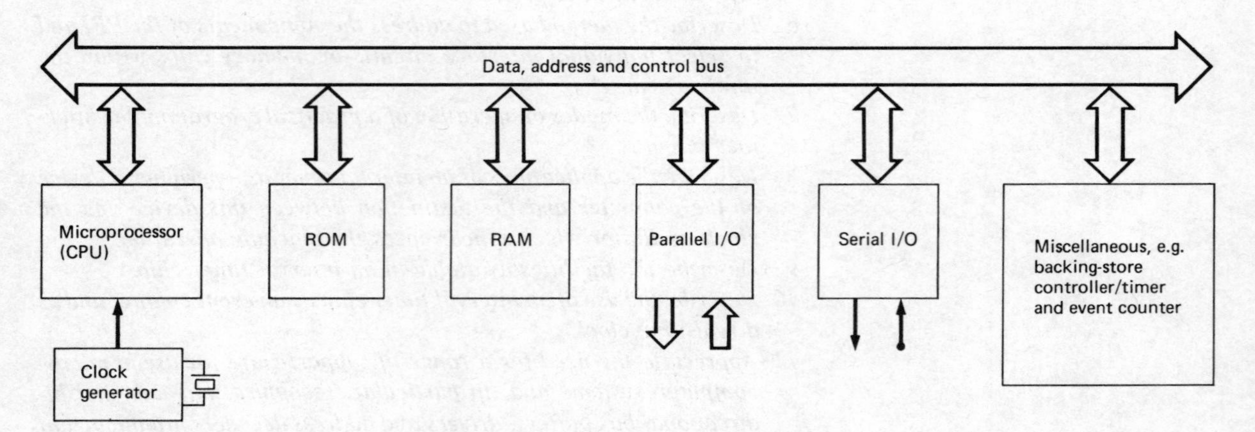

Figure 2.1 A microcomputer system

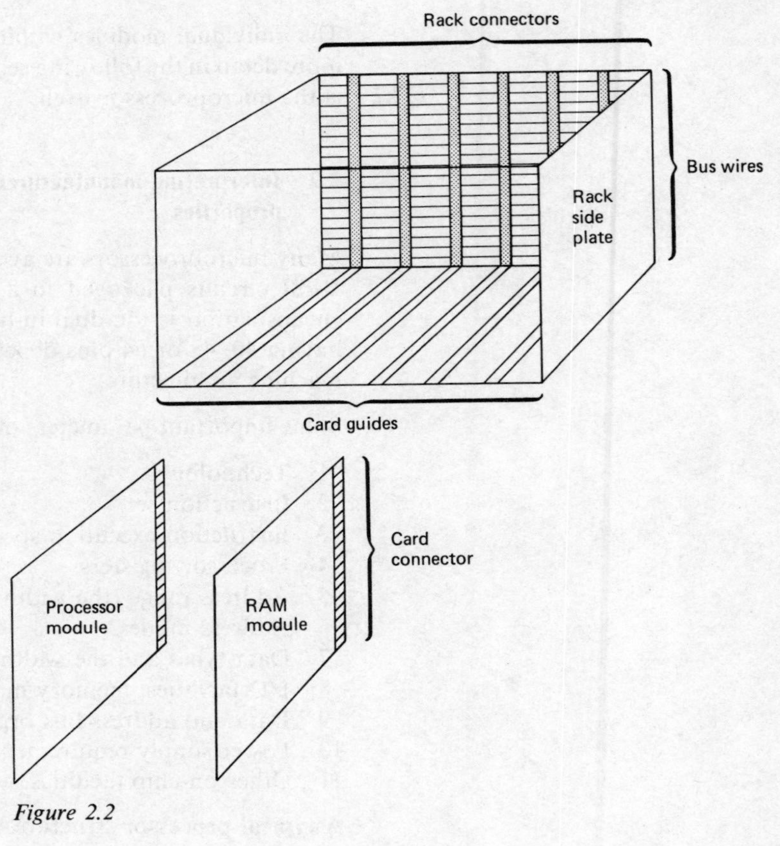

Figure 2.2

Hardware configuration and standard busses

The modules making up the microcomputer are constructed on printed circuit cards. These cards then plug into a rack system which carries the wires forming the data, address and control busses on connectors at its rear. This is shown in Figure 2.2. The cards are fitted with male connectors and the rack with female connectors.

The definition of the position and function of each of the bus wires on the rack is clearly most important. A standard specification is desirable since this allows independent manufacturers to develop modules on cards and to be certain that these cards will plug together in a system without modification.

A common standard for use within microcomputers is the so-called S100 bus. This was originated in 1976 by MITS, producers of the ALTAIR microcomputer, as a standard for use in hobbyist microcomputer systems, but has since been modified and redefined as the 'IEEE S100' standard. It has gained widespread acceptance and many modules compatible with it are commercially available.

The individual modules within the microcomputer are examined in more detail in the following sections. The main module in any system is the microprocessor itself.

Q2.2

2.2 Interpreting manufacturers' data – processor facilities and properties

Many microprocessors are available on the market. They consist of VLSI circuits packaged in a variety of ways. The most popular encapsulation is the dual-in-line (DIL) plastic or ceramic package having 40, 48 or 64 pins depending on the facilities offered and the machine architecture.

Some important parameters of the microprocessor are listed below:

1 Technology.
2 Instruction set.
3 Instruction execution speed (clock rate).
4 Processor registers.
5 Address range (the width of the address bus).
6 Address modes.
7 Data types and the width of the data bus.
8 I/O facilities; memory-mapped I/O.
9 Data and address bus organisation.
10 Power supply requirements; power consumption.
11 Other on-chip facilities.

A typical processor structure layout is shown in Figure 2.3.

The main components of the processor are the internal registers, the arithmetic logic unit and status register, the instruction register and control circuits and the data and address bus buffers and control circuits.

Instruction set and data types

Chapter 1 has already outlined the instruction set of a representative microprocessor and Appendix 1 contains the complete Intel 8085 list of orders. The scope of the instructions available in various systems varies a good deal. It is dependent, amongst other things, on the *generation* of the system under discussion.

In this book the generations of microprocessors are taken to be:

First generation – early microprocessors such as the Intel 4004/4040 range.
Second generation – Intel 8080, Motorola MC6800, etc, i.e. early 8-bit machines.
Third generation – Intel 8085, Zilog Z80, etc.
Fourth generation – Motorola MC68000, Zilog Z8000, Intel 8086, etc.

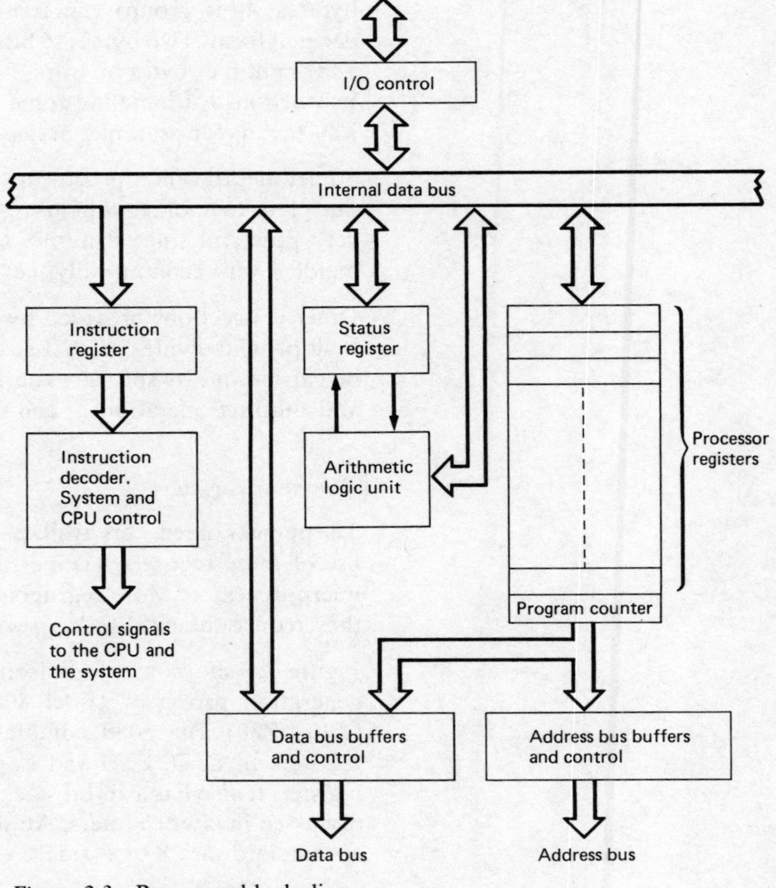

Figure 2.3 Processor block diagram

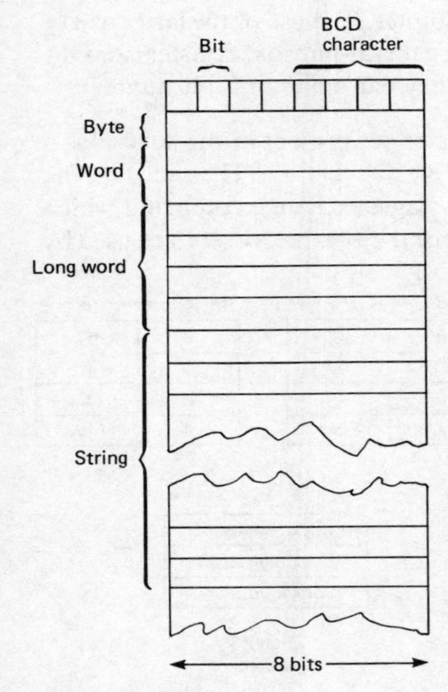

Figure 2.4 Data types

Of course, there are other microprocessors, not mentioned in these examples, in each classification.

Second- and third-generation machines all have good instructions for moving and manipulating data. They also have an adequate range of conditional branch orders and I/O instructions. They are organised to handle data as 8-bit bytes and contain an 8-wire data bus. Sometimes these microprocessors can perform arithmetic on 16-bit operands. The Zilog Z80 microprocessor, for example, can do addition and subtraction of 16-bit values.

Fourth-generation machines are more flexible. In particular they can operate on a range of data-types including bits, characters, bytes, words, long words and strings. These are shown in Figure 2.4. The data busses of these machines generally contain 16 wires.

Information is held in memory as bytes, i.e. as 8-bit groups. Half a byte (a 4-bit group) can represent a *character* in binary-coded-decimal form. Two bytes (16 bits) form a *word*, four bytes a *long word* and multiple bytes a *string*. The microprocessor may contain instructions for handling some or all of these data types. The Zilog Z8000 can, for example, manipulate them all.

Sometimes the microprocessor can move a whole string of data from one place to another with just one instruction. Such an instruction is very powerful since it allows large amounts of information to be handled very economically, i.e. employing only short programs.

Other instructions provided by fourth-generation machines include multiply and divide orders. In earlier systems these operations had to be carried out by software routines written using the processor add and subtract operations. Such routines are necessarily slow.

Processor registers

The number of registers available in the processor chip and the ease of use of these registers has increased with succeeding generations of microprocessor. More registers make for easier programming since they reduce the need to keep writing results into the memory.

Figure 2.5 shows a comparison between the registers in a second-generation processor (Intel 8080) and a third-generation device (Zilog Z80) The 8080 contains (Chapter 1) six general-purpose registers B, C, D, E, H and L, plus an accumulator (A) and a flag register. It also has a 16-bit stack pointer. The use of the latter will be discussed in later chapters. All the general-purpose registers and the accumulator are 8 bits wide, i.e. they can hold an 8-bit number.

The Z80 contains the normal register set present in the 8080 plus a complete alternative group, A′, B′, C′, D′, E′, H′ and L′. The machine instruction set includes a single exchange command which allows either the normal register set or the alternative set to be used by

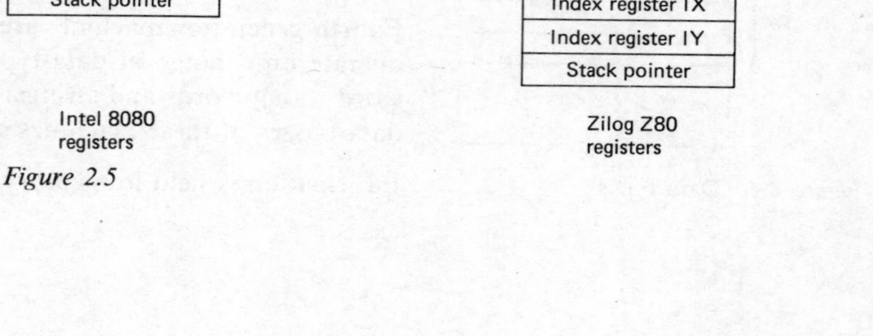

Intel 8080 registers:

8 bits	8 bits
B	C
D	E
H	L
A	Flags

16
Stack pointer

Zilog Z80 registers:

8	8	8	8
B′	C′	B	C
D′	E′	D	E
H′	L′	H	L
A′	Flags′	A	Flags

16
Index register IX
Index register IY
Stack pointer

Intel 8080 registers

Zilog Z80 registers

Figure 2.5

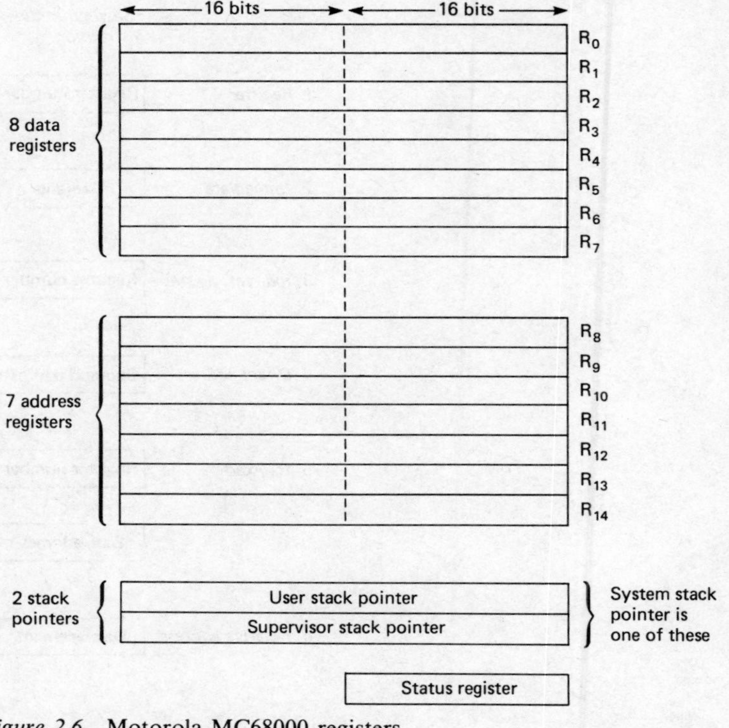

Figure 2.6 Motorola MC68000 registers

the programmer. This arrangement effectively doubles the amount of working space available on the processor chip and is very useful in, for example, interrupt handling, as will be described later.

The register set of a fourth-generation microprocessor, the Motorola MC68000, is shown in Figure 2.6.

The processor possesses 17 registers, each 32 bits wide, plus a program counter (also 32 bits) and a status register. The first eight of the registers (R_0–R_7 in Figure 2.6) can be used to hold operands and the remainder (R_8–R_{14}) are employed in forming addresses. This allows very flexible and convenient programming.

Q2.3

Address modes

Each instruction which refers to one or two operands must contain addresses. For instance, the instruction:

ADD (address of operand 1)(address of operand 2)

forms the sum of operands 1 and 2. The quantities 'address of operand 1' and 'address of operand 2' may be the numbers of registers, if operands 1 and 2 are held in registers, or may be memory addresses.

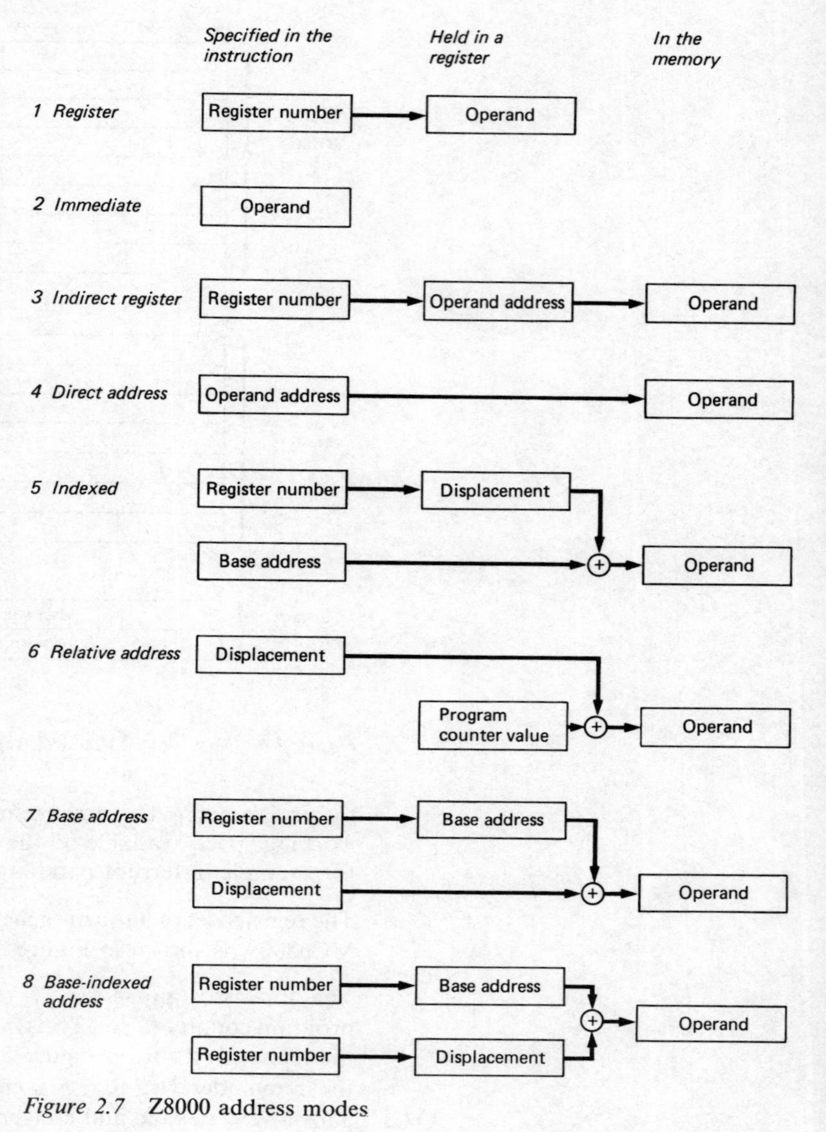

Figure 2.7 Z8000 address modes

The various ways in which addresses can be specified form the *address modes* of the microprocessor.

In general an instruction address can be made up of a number of parts. It has been seen in Chapter 1, for example, that index registers can supply one part of such a compound address. Figure 2.7 shows the address modes of the Zilog Z8000 microprocessor. The diagram is organised to show, for each address mode, what is held in the instruction and what is held in registers. For instance, in *register* mode the operand for the instruction is held in a register in the processor. In this case the address part of the instruction simply specifies the number of the register to be used.

In *immediate* mode the value of the operand itself is held in the instruction.

Indirect mode illustrates the use of a register to hold the address of the operand. The register number is written into the instruction and the contents of that register are used as the operand address.

In *direct* mode the address of the operand is held in the instruction.

The last four modes all use compound addresses made up from two or more parts. For instance in *indexed* mode the base address, held in the instruction, is added to a displacement, held in a register, to form the address of the operand. Modes 6, 7 and 8 are similar.

The availability of these modes allows flexible address construction and helps in programming extraction of information from lists and arrays of data.

Q2.4, 2.5

Address range

Using the address modes of the machine as described allows addresses of a certain size to be produced. For instance, if the registers in the processor are 16 bits wide, as in the Zilog Z8000 or Intel 8086, the address formed is also of 16 bits. The address range is thus 64 Kbytes. To enable the processor to access memory sizes greater than 64 Kbytes thus requires a further step since for this to occur address sizes of greater than 16 bits are needed. Thus the size of the addresses produced by the processor must be *expanded* to 20 or more bits.

As an example of address expansion in a fourth-generation microprocessor, the 8086 system is shown in Figure 2.8. The 8086, as has been mentioned, has an address highway containing 20 wires, giving a range of 1 Mbyte. As well as the general-purpose registers, the processor contains four *segment registers*. Each of these registers contains 20 bits and can thus hold a number representing an address in the range 0 to 1 Mbyte. In practice, the least significant four bits of a segment register are always zero so the address in it is a multiple of 16. Thus a segment register can point to addresses within a 1 Mbyte range, as long as such addresses are a multiple of 16.

The segment registers are used as shown in Figure 2.9.

The 16-bit address formed in the instruction, using any of the range of address modes available, is automatically added to the contents of the relevant segment register by the processor hardware to produce a 20-bit operand address. The segment register used, i.e. the 'relevant' register in the previous sentence, depends on the type of address being

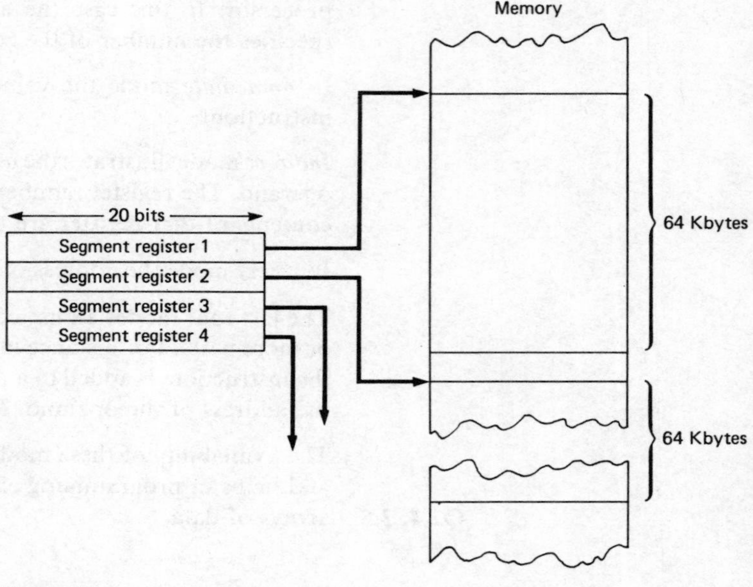

Figure 2.8

formed. For example:

1 All addresses used in fetching program instructions from memory are added to the *code* segment register.
2 All addresses used in program data references employ the *data* segment register.
3 All stack references (see later) use the *stack* segment register, and so on.

Address and data busses

As mentioned at the start of this section, microprocessors are available in 40-, 48- and 64-pin packages. One important parameter determining the number of pins required on a processor integrated circuit is the organisation of the data and address highways. Sometimes these are completely separate, i.e. separate pins are allocated for each bit of both highways, but sometimes shared pins are used. For example, the Motorola MC68000 processor uses a 64-pin package having 23 pins dedicated to the address bus and another 16 pins for the data highway and the Zilog Z80 has a 40-pin package with 8 pins for data and another 16 for addresses. The Intel 8086, on the other hand, uses a 40-pin package with 16 pins shared between the data bus and the least significant 16 bits of the address bus plus a further 4 pins for the most significant address bus connections. The Zilog Z8000 also uses shared address and data connections on the processor chip.

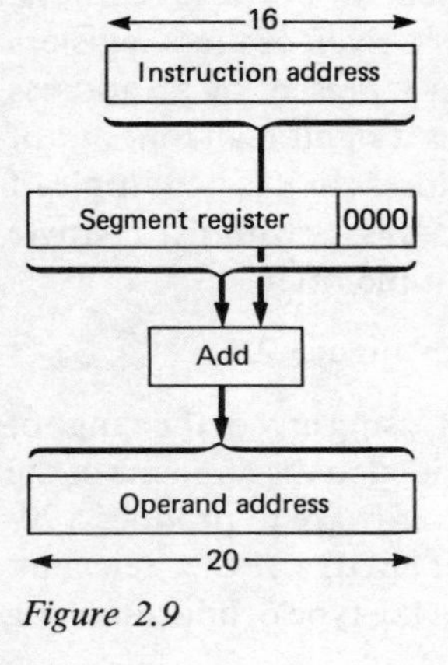

Figure 2.9

The memories and peripheral control circuits in a microcomputer system require separate address and data I/O lines. Thus the address information and data output from the processor on a *shared* highway must be divided and placed on separate highways. This is achieved by special circuits which are also part of the microcomputer system.

The address information and data information on a shared bus are separated by the *time* at which they are placed on the bus. In other words the bus is *time-multiplexed.* To write data into the memory the processor must, for example, first place the address to receive that data on the bus. This address must be stored somewhere, perhaps within the memory chip, so that the bus is freed to transfer data from the processor to the memory data inputs. This data is then placed on the bus.

To inform external circuits when the address information on the bus is correct (valid) the processor generates a special control signal on an output control line called ALE (*a*ddress *l*atch *e*nable). This signal indicates to external circuits when addresses can be examined and used. It is described more fully in Chapter 3.

All that is necessary to separate the address information from the shared bus is to take that bus to the input of a set of latches (a latch is a one-bit memory). Sometimes these are included on the memory chip and, as mentioned above, the address is stored inside that chip. Alternatively external latches may be used to provide separate data and address busses as shown in Figure 2.10 which can then be used by all modules in the microcomputer system.

For a 16-bit address bus there must be 16 latches, although this only requires a few integrated circuits since it is possible to obtain up to 8 latches on a single chip (for example the Intel 8282/8283 latch). The

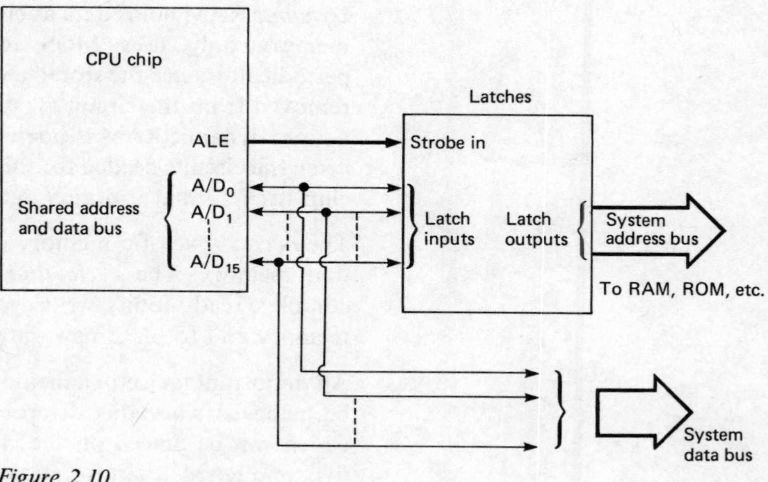

Figure 2.10

ALE control line is used to provide a *strobe* signal. This causes the latches to take in the data on their inputs and hence defines the instant at which the latches 'freeze' the address information. The latch outputs can then be used as the microcomputer address bus.

2.3 Memories

The main types of memory in the microcomputer system, as outlined in Chapter 1, are the fixed program memory and the alterable data memory. In this context, of course, 'fixed' and 'alterable' refer to the memory operation during normal program execution. The program memory uses ROM or PROM and the data memory uses RAM.

The purpose of this section is to identify some examples of memories from manufacturer's literature. However, it is first appropriate to consider some of the important parameters of memory systems.

Semiconductor memory is used in microcomputer systems. The technologies most employed are *bipolar* using bipolar transistors (transistors in which both majority and minority carriers play a part) and MOS, using unipolar field-effect transistors. The commonest technology is NMOS (N-channel MOS).

In random access memory the storage is *volatile*, i.e. any information held in the memory is lost when the power is switched off. There are two types of RAM. *Static* RAM, which may use either bipolar or MOS technology, consists fundamentally of arrays of flip-flops. Data is held permanently in these as long as power is maintained to the circuit. However when power is restored after the circuit has been switched off the individual flip-flops come on in randomly determined states.

Dynamic RAM holds data as charge on capacitors in the circuit. Such memory only uses MOS technology and must be refreshed periodically, since the stored charge decays with time. When power is removed from the circuit all stored charge is lost. Refreshing of the data in dynamic RAM is carried out every few milliseconds and very often the circuits needed for this operation are built into the memory chip itself so that it occurs automatically.

The *access time* of a memory is the time taken to obtain data from that memory. The *cycle time* is the time required to perform a complete read-modify-write cycle, i.e. to obtain information from the memory and to place new data in it.

An important factor in a memory chip is the *packing density* that can be achieved since this determines the amount of storage capacity which can be placed on the chip. Packing densities are higher for dynamic RAMs than for static types.

For dynamic RAMs the *operating power* and the *standby power* are different, i.e. the power requirement of the memory when it is simply retaining data and not being accessed by the processor or any other device is significantly lower than the power used when accesses are being made. This is a considerable advantage of dynamic RAMS over static types. Hence, from both the point of view of storage capacity and power consumption, dynamic RAMS tend to be favoured in applications requiring large memory sizes, low running costs and low capital cost per bit of storage. Static RAMS are particularly applicable for smaller stores and for those in which speed of access is at a premium.

Dynamic RAMs

The memory capacity obtainable in a dynamic RAM chip varies over a wide range. Memories giving storage of 4,096 (4K), 8,192 (8K) or 16,384 (16K) bits have been on the market for a considerable time and a capacity of 65,536 (64K) bits is currently becoming available.

Examples of some dynamic RAMs are shown in Table 2.1. It should be noted that the sizes of these memories are quoted as '$N \times 1$ bits'. This means that the memory integrated circuit can hold N words each of 1 bit. To obtain N words of greater length, for example to have N words of 8 bits, i.e. N bytes, requires eight memory chips to be used, one for each bit in the word. This is elaborated later in Chapter 4.

The figures for power consumption quoted in Table 2.1 are maximum values (except for the 4,164). Typical values are generally lower.

Table 2.1

Memory type	*Capacity/ bits*	*Access time/ns*	*Cycle time/ns*	*Power supplies**	*Package*
Intel 2104A	4,096 × 1	350	500	+12, +5, −5 V	16 pin
Texas TMS 4108	8,192 × 1	100–250	375–515	+12, +5, −5 V 462 mW (O) 20 mW (S)	16 pin
Intel 2109	8,192 × 1	200–250	375–475	+12, +5, −5 V 462 mW (O) 20 mW (S)	16 pin
Texas TMS 4116	16,384 × 1	150–250	375–515	+12, +5, −5 V 462 mW (O) 20 mW (S)	16 pin
Intel 2117	16,384 × 1	150–250	330–475	+12, +5, −5 V 462 mW (O) 20 mW (S)	16 pin
Texas TMS 4164	65,536 × 1	150–326	256–326	+5 V 125 mW (typical) 17.5 mW (S) (typical)	16 pin

*(O) = operating; (S) = standby

It will be noted that 16-pin packages are used for all the integrated circuits listed. To limit the number of pins on the packages to this value necessitates sharing certain pins. For example, in a memory of 16K words such as the 4116 the address specification must use 14 bits, the data output requires one pin, the data input one pin, the power supplies three pins and various control signals three or four pins.

If each address bit used one pin on the package exclusively, the number of pins needed would be $(14+1+1+3+4)=23$. To reduce this, the address is supplied to the package in two halves, each of seven bits. The package thus has only seven pins for address input and these are used twice during every access. Further chips are needed between the memory bus and the address inputs to achieve this.

Static RAMs

A wide range of static RAMs is available on the market. These range from small, high-speed memories of 64-bit capacity and 35 ns cycle time to 8,192-bit capacities with cycle times up to 450 ns. These memories generally require only a single +5 V supply and have power dissipations that vary over a considerable spread depending on the memory speed.

Memory organisation and the packaging used for chips also vary. For example, the 4,096-bit capacity memories are available as 4,096 words of 1 bit (4,096 × 1) or as 1,024 words of 4 bits (1,024 × 4). Memories of 1,024 words can be purchased with word lengths of 1, 4 or 8 bits. Packages use 16, 18, 20, 22 and 24 pins. Some examples from the very wide range of possibilities are shown in Table 2.2.

ROMs and PROMs

ROM and PROM are particularly suitable for program storage because they are non-volatile. For microcomputer applications in which a high volume of a product is to be sold after a design has been

Table 2.2

Memory type	*Capacity/ bits*	*Access time/ns*	*Power supplies*	*Package*
Texas TMS 4008	1,024 × 8	140–450	+5 V, 450 mW	24 pin
Intel 2101A	256 × 4	350	+5 V, 300 mW	22 pin
Texas TMS 4036–2	64 × 8	450–1000	+5 V, 450 mW	20 pin
Intel 2114	1,024 × 4	450	+5 V, 525 mW	18 pin
Texas TMS 4033	1,024 × 1	450	+5 V, 368 mW	16 pin
Intel 3101A	16 × 4	35	+5 V, 525 mW	16 pin

Table 2.3

Memory type	*Capacity/ bits*	*Access time/ns*	*Power supplies*	*Package*
Texas TMS 4700 ROM	1,024 × 8	450	+5, −5, +12 V 580 mW max	24 pin
Intel 2364A ROM	8,192 × 8	—	+5 V	28 pin
Intel/Texas 2708 EPROM	1,024 × 8	450	+5, −5, +12 V 750 mW	24 pin
Intel/Texas 2716 EPROM	2,048 × 8	450	+5, −5, +12 V 550 mW	24 pin
Intel 2732 EPROM	4,096 × 8	450	+5 V 780 mW (O) 160 mW (S)	24 pin

tested and proved correct a *mask-programmable* ROM is used. Programming of such a device is done during manufacture. This allows the cost per bit of the memory to be reduced to a minimum but, of course, allows no possibility at all of later program changes.

Programmable read-only memories (PROMs) allow a little more flexibility than ROMs since the user can program them (once) himself. Eraseable-programmable read only memories (EPROMs) are the most flexible of all since they can be used over and over again. Some ROMs and EPROMs are listed in Table 2.3.

The Intel 2708, 2716, 2732 EPROM range has become an industry standard and circuits are available from several manufacturers.

It is also worth noting that *socket compatability* exists between certain RAMs, EPROMs and ROMs, i.e. the pin connections are such that one type of chip can be unplugged and another substituted for it. This allows design of a system using RAM for writing the software followed by its direct replacement with ROM or EPROM. Thus the TMS 4008 static RAM is socket-compatible with the 2708 EPROM and the TMS 4700 ROM.

Q2.6, 2.7

2.4 Interfacing devices

Chapter 1 introduced the concept of special integrated circuits specifically designed to allow connection of peripheral devices to the microcomputer system. As illustrated in Figure 2.1, these devices can be broadly split into those performing *serial* transfer of information and those performing *parallel* input and output functions. The former of these has already been considered in outline and will be elaborated further in Chapter 9. The latter – parallel input/output – is described in this section.

A block diagram of the facilities typically available in a peripheral

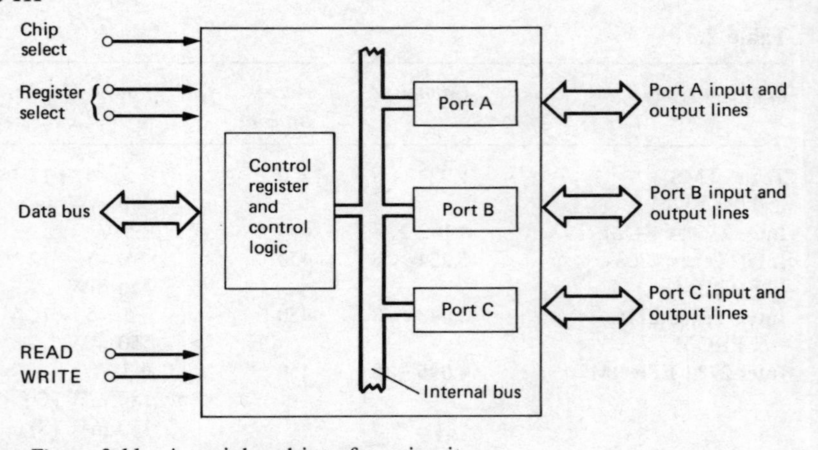

Figure 2.11 A peripheral interface circuit

interface circuit is shown in Figure 2.11. The circuit provides:

1 Three I/O ports: A, B and C.
2 A *control register*.
3 Interfacing circuits which allow the PIC to be connected directly to the microcomputer bus and control lines. These circuits are compatible with the bus driving and loading requirements. Thus, for example, the data bus lines of the PIC use tri-state drivers.

The I/O ports

Each port may act either as an input or as an output. Thus each may be connected to a peripheral device and may receive data from that device or send data to it. Data received from a peripheral is stored (latched) in a data register in the port. Data to be sent to a peripheral comes from the outputs of buffer amplifiers, also in the port.

The control register

The control register holds a bit pattern which controls the functions of ports A, B and C. For instance, one bit in this register is used to determine if A is to act as an input or an output. The control register holds eight bits which are written into it by the microcomputer (as described later).

Addressing the peripheral interface circuit

The microcomputer system may well contain several peripheral interface circuits. In addition there are four places within each PIC which must be separately addressed. These are port A, port B, port C and the control register.

The microprocessor communicates with each PIC using normal input and output instructions such as IN and OUT (Chapter 1). The address part of these instructions is used to select the PIC required and to specify which address in that PIC is to be used.

Selection of a particular PIC is achieved by decoding the address highway signals of the microcomputer and using the decoder output to enable the 'chip select' input of the PIC selected (see Figures 2.11 and 2.16). Selection of a particular address within the PIC is made using the 'register select' control inputs (Figure 2.11).

For example addresses could be arranged as:

Register select lines	*Selected address*
00	Port A
01	Port B
10	Port C
11	Control register

The 'register select' signals are also derived from the address bus.

The address part of an IN or OUT instruction for a system such as the Intel 8085 microprocessor consists of 8 bits. This address is placed on the least significant 8 lines of the address bus, i.e. on lines A_0 to A_7 inclusive.

In a system containing many peripheral interface circuits a decoder may be used to detect unique bus addresses and to drive the select lines accordingly. Commonly, however, the bottom two address bus lines are connected directly to the register select lines of the PIC. This leaves six lines spare for selecting different PICs and thus limits the total number of such circuits possible in the system to 64. Connection of the PIC to the microcomputer is shown later in outline in Figure 2.16.

The 'read' and 'write' control inputs to the PIC determine the direction of data transfer. 'Read' causes information to be read by the computer from the PIC and 'write' sends data from the computer to the PIC.

Sometimes, in a microcomputer system, the peripheral I/O facilities are provided by one or more specialised PIC chips. Alternatively, in some systems, I/O facilities are included within other chips, in particular within the memory chips of the system. For instance the Intel 8155 integrated circuit contains a 2,048-bit static RAM plus two programmable 8-bit I/O ports and one programmable 6-bit I/O port. It also contains a timer. The use of such multipurpose circuits reduces the total number of integrated circuit packages required to make up a complete system and hence the system cost.

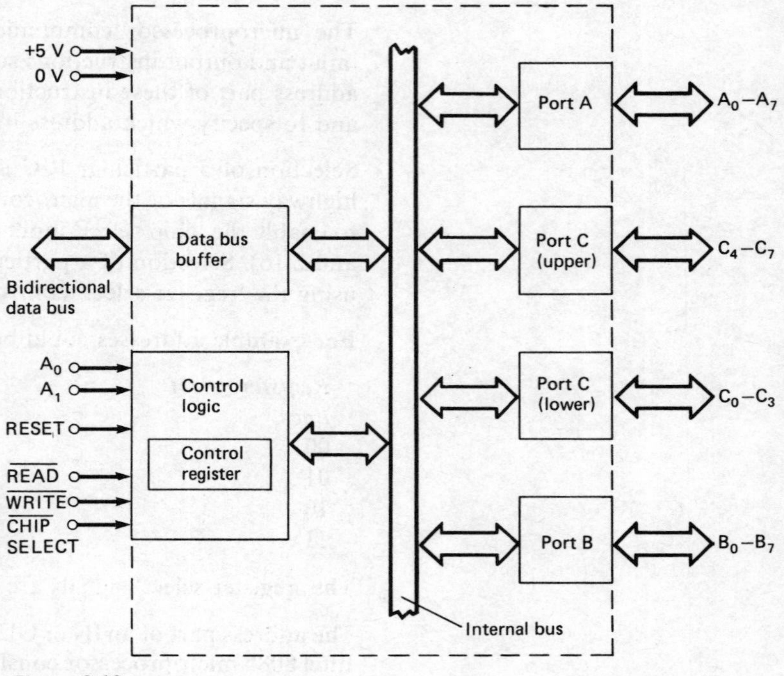

Figure 2.12

Facilities of peripheral interface circuits

It is now appropriate to consider some of the facilities available in a practical peripheral interface circuit. The Intel 8255A programmable peripheral interface (PPI) is used as an example of such a device and a block diagram showing its principal features is given in Figure 2.12.

The chip is contained in a 40-pin package. Connection is made to the microcomputer system via an 8-bit bidirectional data bus using tri-state drivers. Data to be sent to the microcomputer, e.g. data from the tape reader used in an earlier example, can be held in the *data bus buffer* ready for onward transmission. Similarly data received from the computer is written into the buffer. All data flow is thus through this buffer.

Control signals

The control signals linking the peripheral interface and the micro-computer are also illustrated in the figure. Three of these signals, namely READ, WRITE and CHIP SELECT are active in the *low* state, i.e. the computer causes the signal on any one of these lines to go low when the function controlled by that line is to be made to happen. Conventionally such active-low signals are written as $\overline{\text{READ}}$, $\overline{\text{WRITE}}$, etc., the bar over the name of the signal indicating its active-low nature.

A_0 and A_1 are the register-select lines discussed earlier and the $\overline{\text{CHIP SELECT}}$ line is used to enable a particular peripheral interface circuit in a system containing several. The RESET control signal is used to initialise the PPI. A signal on this line sets the contents of the control register to zero and thus, as will be shown, sets all the peripheral ports to the input mode.

Modes and I/O ports

The interface circuit provides three I/O ports called A, B and C, each of 8 bits. It can operate in any one of three *modes* called mode 0, mode 1 and mode 2, as will be described shortly. The mode chosen and the exact function of each port is determined by the pattern of binary digits in the control register.

As shown in Figure 2.12, port C is divided into two 4-bit sections called port C (upper) and port C (lower). Port C (upper) works together with port A for most operations and port C (lower) works with port B.

The control word format

The format of the control word placed in the control register is shown in Figure 2.13.

Bits 0, 1 and 2 (the 'group B control' bits) control the functions of port B and port C (lower).

Bits 3, 4, 5 and 6 (the 'group A control' bits) control the functions of port A and port C (upper).

Bit 7 is used for a special 'bit set' mode of operation. This will not be considered further here.

All ports, A, B, C (upper) and C (lower), can act as inputs or outputs, as determined by bits 0, 1, 3 and 4.

The modes are controlled by bit 2 – for port B and port C (lower) – and bits 5 and 6 – for port A and port C (upper).

Mode 0 This is the basic I/O mode. The system effectively provides four ports, namely the 8-bit port A, the 8-bit port B and two 4-bit ports from C (upper) and C (lower). Each of these can act as an input or an output.

To perform an output the computer simply sends data (an OUT instruction with appropriate address) to the chosen port, and to take information from a peripheral it simply reads the relevant port using an IN order. There is no handshaking. Data output from the PPI is staticised in a register in the port so the speed with which the peripheral device can accept it is not critical.

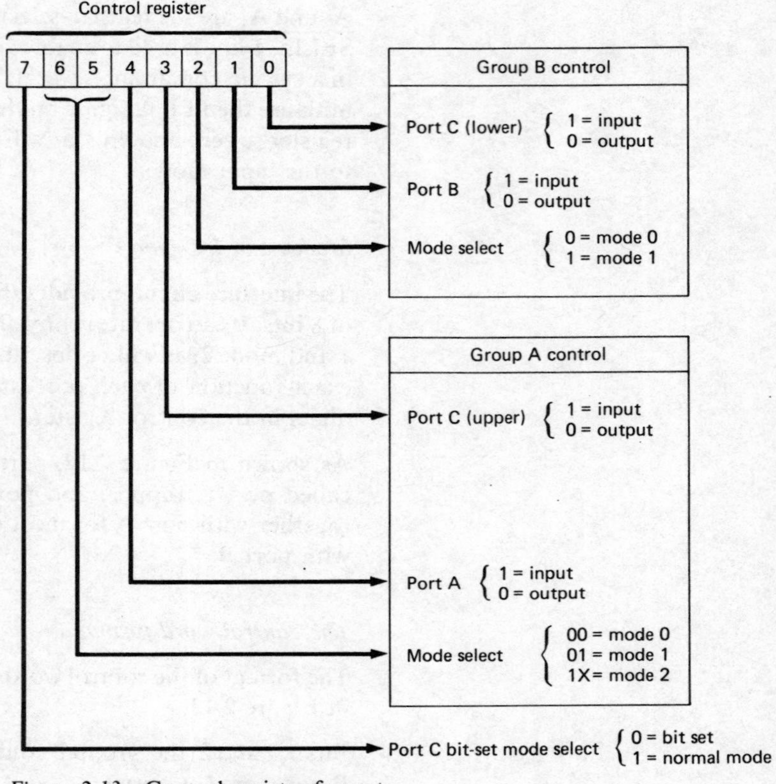

Figure 2.13 Control register format

Mode 1 In mode 1 operation the I/O ports function in two groups A and B as implied by Figure 2.13. Port A is grouped with port C (upper) and port B with port C (lower). Ports A and B operate as 8-bit inputs or outputs whilst the 4 bits of port C grouped with each of them function as control signals to allow handshaking to be used.

In this mode data sent from a peripheral device into either port A or port B is stored in an input register within the port. Similarly data to be output to a peripheral is stored in an output register until the device accepts it.

A diagram illustrating mode 1 operation of the group B section of the PPI is given in Figure 2.14. The group A section operates in a similar manner.

To output data via port B, in mode 1, the following sequence of operations must occur:

1 The microcomputer sends the data to the PPI along the data bus.
2 The PPI puts the data into the port B output register and causes the output control line $\overline{OBF}$ (bit C_1 of port C) to go low.

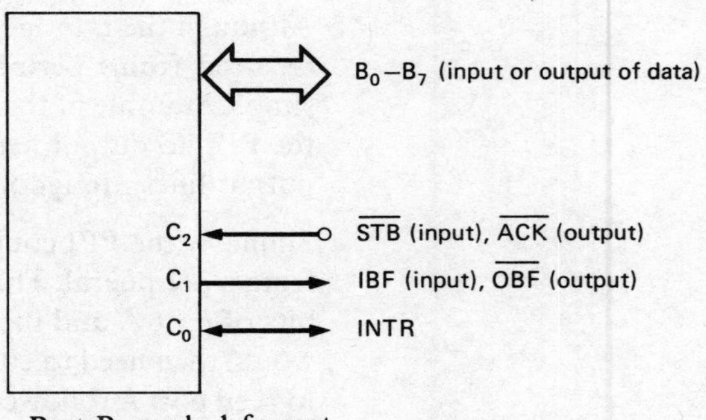

Figure 2.14 Port B, mode 1 format

3 The device connected to port B, i.e. the peripheral, takes the data and causes the PPI input control line $\overline{ACK}$ to go low to show that it has done so.
4 $\overline{OBF}$ goes back to high. The signal $\overline{OBF}$ comes from bit 1 of a 4-bit register in the C port. This register is reset to 0 when data is sent to port B (step 2 above) and is set to 1 by $\overline{ACK}$.

The control lines $\overline{OBF}$ and $\overline{ACK}$ form the handshaking system.

A similar procedure is followed when data is input through port B to the microcomputer. The control signals used in this case are called $\overline{STB}$ and IBF.

In both input and output of data via port B, bit 1 of the C port register is used to show the state reached in the information transfer process. For example, in the input of data to the microcomputer, bit 1 can be used as the *status bit* which indicates that data from a peripheral has been placed in the port B register. A normal IN instruction to read the contents of the port C register allows the microcomputer to examine this bit.

Other bits of the port C register are used in mode 1 operation for indicating the state of other I/O transfers and for controlling the interrupt facilities of the PPI. This latter point will be expanded in the section later in the book which deals with interrupts. It is only important to note here that the port C register acts as a *status register* for mode 1 (and mode 2) operation.

Q2.14

Mode 2 Use of the programmable peripheral interface in modes 0 and 1 provides I/O facilities for the microcomputer as has been outlined. These modes, do however, possess one significant restriction. Each port can act as either an input or an output, but cannot act as both, i.e. it is not possible to implement a *bidirectional* port. Mode 2 allows this possibility. In mode 2 port A can operate in bidirectional mode in conjunction with handshaking signals using port C as described above.

Although the interface ports are 8 or 4 bits wide, the data sent to (or received from) peripherals can, within limits, be of any width. A simple example of this would be the use of an 8-bit port, say port A of the PPI, to output just 6 bits of data to a peripheral. Two of the port output lines are ignored.

Similarly the PPI could be used to receive data of width, say, 16 bits from a peripheral. The information for input could be placed on the 8 bits of port A and the 8 bits of port B. The microcomputer program would then need to contain two IN instructions, to allow the machine to read port A followed by port B. Thus it can be seen that the number of wires in the computer data bus need not be the same as the number of connections to the peripheral device; the programmable peripheral interface can be used to perform a conversion from one format to another.

Finally it should be noted that the PPI can be used with mixed modes. Thus the group B section can be organised to operate in mode 1 whilst the group A section operates in mode 2. Or group B can be in mode 0 whilst group A is in mode 1.

Q2.8, 2.9, 2.11

2.5 Real-time clocks and interval timers

It has already been mentioned (Section 1.3) that the operation of a microcomputer system is synchronised and timed by a crystal-controlled *clock oscillator* and an example was given in Section 1.8 of the use of the microprocessor instruction execution time in the generation of time delays. Such a system possesses some disadvantages. Firstly the microcomputer spends most of its time in the execution of timing loops. Insertion of sections of program to perform other functions is possible but is difficult to achieve since the time occupied by such sections must be precisely calculated. Secondly, the effect of external events which interfere with straight-forward program execution (for example interrupts) must not be allowed to upset the timing function.

An alternative, and better, method of generating precise time periods under the control of software is to use a specialised chip known as an *interval timer*. A block diagram of such a device is shown in Figure 2.15.

Fundamentally the interval timer contains one or more counters. Figure 2.15 shows three of these, all operating in an identical manner. Consider counter 0. The microcomputer can load a value into the counter, under program control. Application of pulses from an external time reference source to the CLOCK (0) input then causes the counter to decrement. For each applied timing pulse unity is taken away from the stored value.

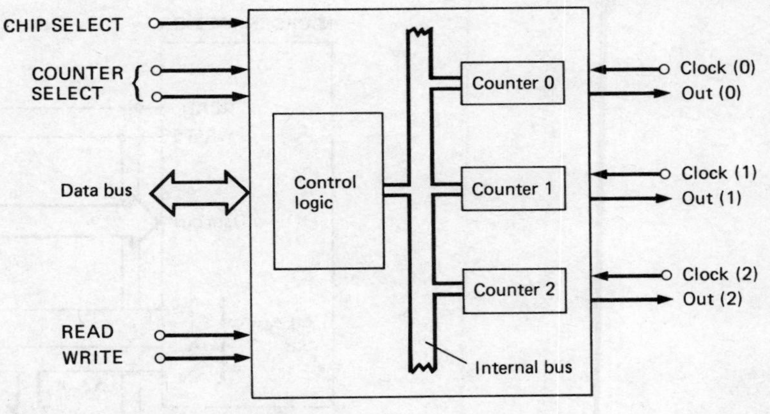

Figure 2.15 An interval timer

When the contents of the counter reach zero, logic in the chip generates an output signal on the OUT (0) line. Normally this signal is used to interrupt the microprocessor. Thus the processor can set up the timer so that it generates interrupt signals at precisely defined intervals. These intervals depend on the frequency of the reference source and on the value initially placed in the counter, and are thus under program control.

The interval timer is interfaced to the processor data, address and control busses as shown in Figure 2.16. As can be seen there is a close parallel between the computer interface of this device and that of a peripheral interface circuit.

The interval timer is connected to the microcomputer data bus using tri-state drivers and receivers. The selection of a particular timer is achieved by enabling the 'chip select' device input using a signal decoded from the address bus. And selection of internal addresses within the timer chip (for example, to set an initial value into counter 0, counter 1, or counter 2) is achieved using the 'counter select' chip input lines. In Figure 2.16 these are assumed to be connected directly to address bus lines A_0 and A_1.

Data can be placed in the counters, to initialise them as has been described, or the values in the counters can be read into the computer. The direction of transfer is determined by the 'read' and 'write' control lines and these, in turn, are activated by an IN or an OUT instruction in the program. The provision of several counters allows the simultaneous timing of a number of separate periods.

The ability of the computer to read the values held in the timer-counters enables the circuit to be used as an *event counter*. In this the signal representing the occurrence of the events to be counted is fed into the clock input of one of the counters. If another counter is fed with a reference clock input from an oscillator so that a precise period

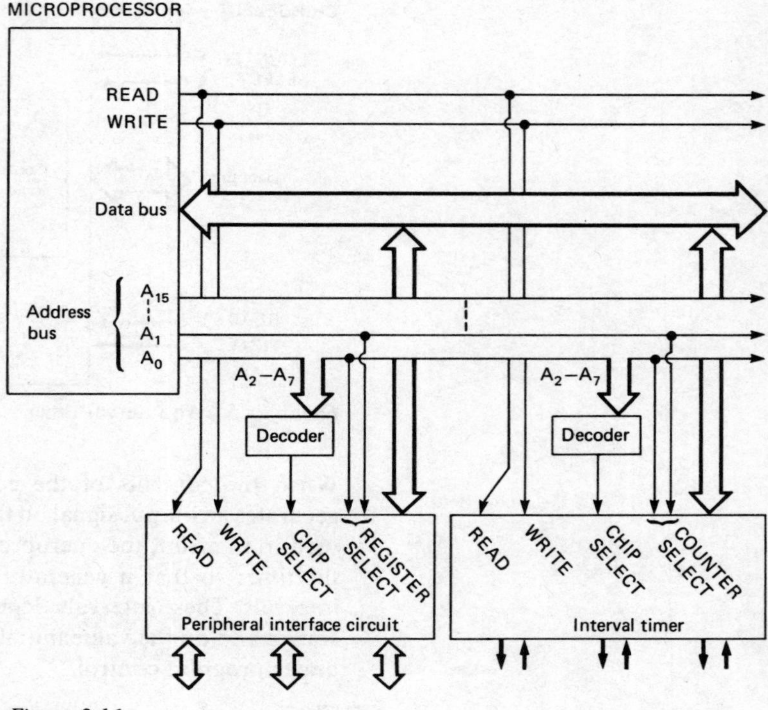

Figure 2.16

can be defined, the microcomputer can read the number of events occurring in that interval. Each time that an interrupt arrives from the period-defining counter the processor reads the event counter; a little arithmetic then yields the count in any period.

It can be seen from the foregoing that an interval timer is a valuable adjunct to a microcomputer system. In addition to its basic property of interval timing it can act as an event counter, as described, or as a *real-time clock*. This latter simply generates timing pulses to synchronise the computer to real-time events.

Q2.1, 2.12, 2.13

2.6 Support chips

Many support chips are available for use in microcomputer systems, ranging from sophisticated devices such as controllers for floppy disk backing stores, for visual display units or for systems for implementing communication network protocols, to relatively simple circuits such as bus drivers, decoders, clock generators, seven-segment decoders for numerical displays, bus buffers and so on.

Many of these are provided to assist in connecting the microcomputer to other systems or to equipment which the computer is controlling. Others, however, form an integral part of the microcomputer itself.

Bus drivers, bus buffers, decoders and clock generators fall into the latter category.

Bus drivers and bus buffers

The microcomputer data bus is a bidirectional information highway via which, as we have seen, the system modules communicate with each other. Connection to this bus, to place information upon it, is made using tri-state drivers.

Reception of data from the bus also uses tri-state circuits. Bus *transceivers* (transmitter–receivers) specially designed to allow easy connection to the microcomputer bus and containing several (usually four) driver/receivers in a package are available. A schematic diagram of such a driver/receiver is shown in Figure 2.17.

Such bidirectional transceivers can be used either as bus drivers, to connect a peripheral device or memory to the microcomputer bus, or can be placed in series in the bus lines to expand the bus capability. The number of gate inputs which the bus control outputs of the microcomputer can drive is limited and it is thus often necessary to add buffer driver/receivers when the system is being expanded by the addition of more memory or peripherals.

The driver/receiver shown in Figure 2.17 can operate as a bus driver with the inputs and outputs on the left-hand side of the figure separate. Thus a device may place data on input 0, input 1, etc., and receive data from output 0, output 1, etc. The right-hand side of the

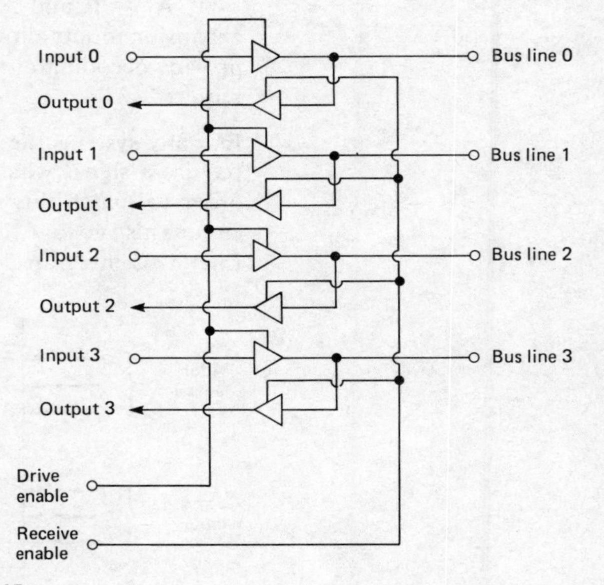

Figure 2.17

figure shows the common bidirectional bus used to connect to the microcomputer highway.

Gating of data on to the highway is achieved using the 'drive enable' control input and reception from the highway is controlled by the 'receive enable' control line.

Since both receivers and drivers are tri-state, the inputs and outputs on the left of the figure may be linked: input 0 to output 0, input 1 to output 1, and so on. This allows the chip to be used as a bidirectional bus buffer in series with the bus. Bus transceivers of this type include the Intel 8216, Texas Instruments SN 75136 and Signetics N8T26 devices.

Decoders

Address decoders are required in a number of places in the microcomputer. They have been shown in Figure 2.16 to derive the 'chip select' signal for interface circuits and interval timers. They are also needed (as will be discussed in Chapter 4) in the development of memory systems.

A typical decoder chip takes in a number of binary-coded input lines and produces separate output 'select' lines to drive the 'chip select' inputs of memory and I/O circuits. This is shown schematically in Figure 2.18.

Three address input lines A_0, A_1 and A_2 are decoded as illustrated. For example, when $A_0 = A_1 = A_2 = 0$, line OS_0 is activated; when $A_0 = 1$, $A_1 = 0$ and $A_2 = 1$, line OS_5 is activated and so on. The expansion inputs allow several decoder chips to be inter-connected to provide decoding of more than three address inputs should this be required.

In many systems the 'chip-select' lines of memory and I/O circuits require a signal which goes low to activate them (Section 2.4). In order to match this requirement the decoder outputs of available circuits also go low when active. A decoder of the type described is the Intel 8205 integrated circuit.

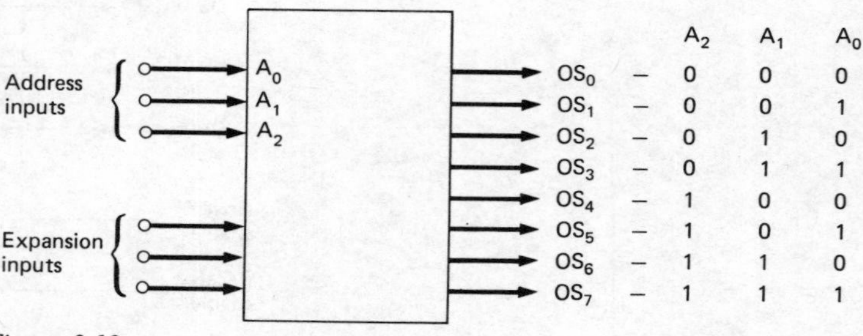

Figure 2.18

Questions

2.1 List the principle modules of a microcomputer system and outline the functions of each of them. By examining manufacturers' literature discuss whether the functions of two or more modules can be combined in a single integrated circuit.

2.2 Describe the advantages to be obtained by the adoption of a standard bus for microcomputer systems. Are there any corresponding disadvantages?

2.3 What are the important facilities offered within the processor chip of a microcomputer system? Compare and contrast the facilities of the Intel 8085, the Zilog Z80 and the Motorola 6809 microprocessors. (This question will require examination of manufacturers' literature.)

2.4 What are the main extra facilities offered by fourth-generation microprocessors over and above those of their third-generation predecessors? Discuss how these facilities affect the likely areas of application of fourth-generation machines.

2.5 Write a short description of the address modes available in a typical fourth-generation microprocessor, paying particular attention to the possible use of each mode in a program.

2.6 Explain the meaning of the following terms: *(a)* segment register; *(b)* static RAM; *(c)* Dynamic RAM; *(d)* access time; *(e)* volatility.

2.7 What are the principle characteristics of the various types of storage device used in microcomputer systems? Distinguish between read/write and read only memory access and briefly discuss the packing density and power consumption of available memory chips.

2.8 What are the principle components of an interfacing device? Explain the functions of:
(a) The data input register.
(b) The data output register.
(c) The status flags.
(d) The control register.
Describe how the microprocessor is able to communicate separately with each of these.

2.9 A programmable peripheral interface is to be used to connect peripheral devices to a computer. If the internal registers of this device are addressed by the 'register select' lines on the chip in accordance with the codes shown in Section 2.4 and if the address of the PPI itself is to be 08 (hex), show how the least significant eight address bus lines of the system can be used to select the required function. Using the instruction format of Appendix 1 write a short program to configure the PPI so that port B is an input, port A is an output and port C is used for handshaking. The control word format shown in Figure 2.13 may be assumed.

2.10 A microcomputer system is to contain six PPIs and two timer-counters. These are to occupy the address range 00 (hex) to 1F (hex) of the system address bus. Each device, either a PPI or counter-timer, possesses four separately addressable internal registers or counters. Draw a block diagram of the system showing how selection of each device is achieved and explain the address organisation used.

2.11 Explain how the data register in a programmable peripheral interface chip can be used to perform an m to n conversion where m is the number of lines in the microcomputer data bus and n is the number of lines to or from a peripheral device.

2.12 Discuss the structure of an interval timer integrated circuit and show how such a circuit can be used as either a real-time clock or an event counter. Distinguish between this type of peripheral device, used as a clock circuit, and the main crystal-controlled system clock in the microcomputer.

2.13 In an experiment in high-energy physics it is necessary to count the number of nuclear 'events' that occur during a 5 second period. It is expected that this number will be in the range of 100 to 120. The counting function is to be performed by a microcomputer system containing a simple timer-counter. This device possesses two internal 8-bit count registers selected by a single 'counter select' connection on the chip. A 'high' level on this line selects one counter and a 'low' the other. The timer-counter address within the system is 02 (hex) and an external clock pulse generator of frequency 25 Hz is also available. Write a program to use the microcomputer to perform the required counting function. Assume that numbers can be written into the counters by OUT instructions and that the counters can be read by IN instructions.

2.14 A tape punch is to be connected to a computer using an 8255A programmable peripheral interface. The punch places 8-bit characters on paper tape. When it is ready to accept a character for punching the device sends a 'high' logic level on an output control line called 'ready'. A character must then be placed on the eight data input lines to the punch and a 'high' level must be placed on its 'data available' input control line. The punch then takes the data into the input buffer and resets 'ready' to a low level. If a high level should already exist on 'data available' when 'ready' goes 'high' the punch takes the data immediately.

Discuss how a PPI can be used to implement this interface and write sections of program code to configure the PPI and to transfer data to the punch.

Chapter 3 Timing diagrams and requirements

Objectives of this chapter *When you have completed studying this chapter you should be able to:*

1. *Appreciate that a microcomputer system consists of a number of complex large-scale integrated circuits which exchange data via the central system highway.*
2. *Appreciate that several steps are involved in the exchange of an item of data:*
   (a) between the processor and a memory chip and
   (b) between the processor and peripheral interface devices.
3. *Understand that the fetch–execute instruction cycle of a microcomputer is divided into a number of short periods called states, each state allowing time for a defined part of the cycle to occur.*
4. *Understand the use of timing diagrams and timing signals, including the fact that timing diagrams may be used to define periods during which information is valid, invalid and uncertain.*
5. *Understand that all events occurring within the microcomputer are controlled by a single system clock, which is normally a crystal-controlled oscillator, and that different microcomputer systems have differing clock requirements.*
6. *Specify the timing requirements of a data transfer between the processor and the memory for:*
   (a) a transfer in which data is written into the memory and
   (b) a transfer in which data is read from the memory, including the use of the various control lines employed within the system to support the operations which occur during the memory read or write cycle.
7. *Understand the use of the WAIT or READY control inputs to the microprocessor chip to allow that chip to be connected to slow memory devices in which the processor must wait for data to become available.*
8. *Draw timing diagrams for memory read, memory write and peripheral transfer operations.*
9. *Understand the use of timing signals as strobes to define the point at which addresses or data are valid and may be latched for further use.*
10. *Appreciate that buffering, or any other logical operation, necessarily introduces a time delay into the signal path and that such delays must be taken into account when the system timing is considered.*

3.1 Why clocks are used

Clock signals are needed in microcomputers to control the system timing so as to synchronise the operation of the various units (processor, memories, I/O, etc.) which make up the system. There are several reasons why such synchronisation is needed.

System structure and operation

It has been seen that a microcomputer system consists of a number of large-scale integrated circuits interconnected by a highway or bus. The circuits themselves contain complex logical functions and have internal data paths for transfer of information. For instance, the processor chip possesses internal registers and an arithmetic logic unit (Figure 2.3), data being continuously swopped between these during program execution. In addition the processor includes other registers which are used to hold the operation code of the instruction being executed, the memory addresses of the operands involved in that instruction, the memory address of the next instruction, the processor status and so on.

Thus the microprocessor chip itself is made up of a complex interconnection of logical units exchanging data via an internal bus and the microcomputer is an assembly of such chips exchanging information through the main computer highway.

To execute an instruction in the machine it is necessary for the control circuits in the processor to:

1 Obtain the instruction from the program memory.
2 Transfer this instruction into the instruction register.
3 Decode the instruction to determine the operation to be performed.
4 Obtain the operand or operands of the instruction.
5 Perform the instruction.

Each of these operations may itself involve several steps. For instance, obtaining an operand from memory requires sending an address to the memory, setting the memory into a read state and transferring the output data from the memory over the highway into the processor.

It is apparent from this discussion that the microcomputer spends a considerable amount of its program execution time in data transfer operations of one sort or another. As well as these, however, it performs the logical, arithmetic and test functions inherent in any program. Many of these also involve the processor in the execution of several intermediate steps and it is clearly necessary for all such operations to occur in the correct time sequence.

In performing a register-to-accumulator ADD instruction, for example (Section 1.6), the processor must:

1 Apply the operands, from the register selected and from the accumulator, to the inputs of the adder.
2 Send a signal to the adder to cause it to perform the addition.
3 Cause the result to be written back into the accumulator from the adder outputs.

Correct sequencing of operations in the microcomputer, whether such operations involve data transfers between system modules or just control of the processor internal functioning, requires the use of *timing* or *clock* pulses in the system.

Highways and timing

Transmission of information in the computer system requires the provision of data paths – the highways already discussed. There are several ways in which these highways can be implemented, the exact method chosen also affecting system operation very considerably.

A shared data and address highway, as outlined in Section 2.2 for example, necessitates the use of the bus to transfer *both* the data and address involved during a single instruction execution and thus extends the time required to perform that instruction. Similarly the use of an 8-bit wide data bus in 16-bit systems necessarily involves two successive hardware transfers between memory and processor to pass a single 16-bit word. Again this increases instruction execution time.

A single-byte instruction in an 8-bit microprocessor system involves a single memory-to-processor transfer during the instruction-fetch phase (Section 1.2). A 2-byte instruction requires two such transfers and a 3-byte instruction requires three. These too must be sequenced in the correct order, and each uses several time periods on the system bus, especially if the latter is shared.

Thus the picture emerges of a system, the microcomputer, that operates in discrete units of time, such units being used to define what is happening in the system and to sequence the correct order of operation. Every microcomputer fetching instructions from a memory external to the CPU chip requires several of these time periods for the execution of each instruction. The exact number is variable and depends on a multitude of parameters, a few of which have been mentioned in the preceding examples.

Q3.1, 3.2

States

It is convenient in microprocessor systems, therefore, to subdivide the fundamental instruction fetch–execute time into shorter periods (called *states*), each period allowing time for one defined operation such as the transmission of an address to memory or to a peripheral interface circuit, the transmission of data on the bus to memory or peripherals and so on. The number of states required varies from one microcomputer to another, because of their different architectures, and from one instruction to another within a particular microcomputer.

A simple example of the use of states is shown in the *timing diagram* of Figure 3.1. The diagram illustrates the signals on various lines in the microcomputer system and, in particular, shows when signals are *valid*, i.e. when they can be used by the system. The horizontal axis of the figure thus represents changes in time. This topic is discussed further in the next section.

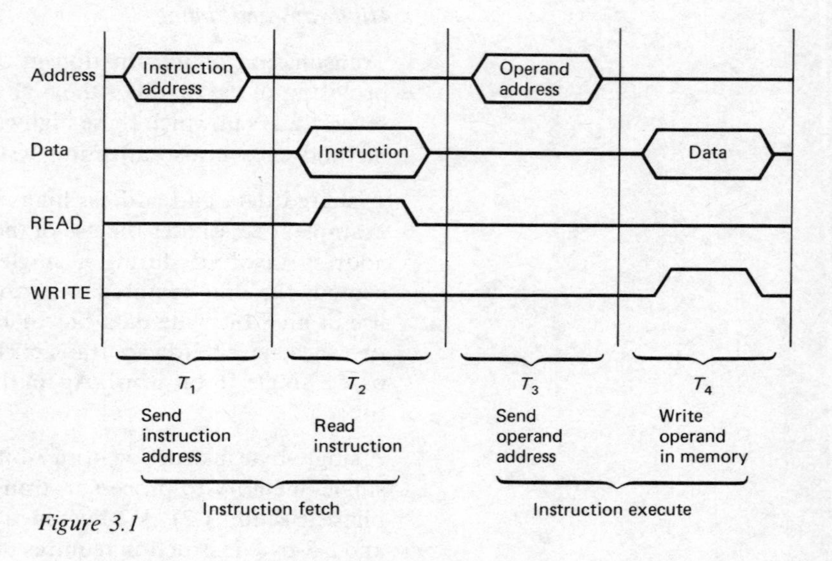

Figure 3.1

Figure 3.1 assumes that a single-byte instruction which requires to write an operand to memory is being executed. There are four states labelled T_1, T_2, T_3 and T_4. The operations occurring in these states are as follows:

During T_1 the instruction address is sent to memory.
During T_2 the instruction is fetched.
During T_3 the operand address is sent to memory.
During T_4 the operand is written into memory at that address.

Also shown in the figure are the signals on the two control lines, READ and WRITE, which define the direction of data transfer as discussed in the previous chapter. These signals are generated by the processor. When a processor input is being performed the READ line goes to logical 1 and when an output is being performed WRITE goes to 1.

The signals on the address and data lines may be either 1 or 0 since addresses and data contain both zeros and ones. Hence the representation of these signals in the figure is both up and down as shown.

3.2 Timing diagrams and timing signals

At this point it is worth discussing the meaning of timing diagrams (such as Figure 3.1) in slightly more detail. It has been mentioned already that such diagrams are used to illustrate the timing relationships between signals in the microcomputer system and to define when a signal is valid.

This can now be stated a little more precisely. The exact period for which the instruction address is valid is shown by the length of the 'instruction address' box. The rise and fall times of the signals representing the address on the address highways are, similarly, shown by the sloping edges of this box. Hence to sense the address information correctly any device needing that information must examine the address lines at some instant after the rise period and before the fall period, i.e. somewhere near the centre of the 'instruction address' box of Figure 3.1. In the same way the data representing the instruction is valid on the data highway during the period marked by the 'instruction' box of Figure 3.1.

The precise instants at which data transfers occur in the microcomputer are governed by the *timing signals* in the system. Examples of these occur in later sections.

3.3 The clock generator

All operations occurring in the microcomputer are synchronised and timed from a master *clock oscillator*. This device produces output pulses which are fed into pins on the CPU chip and are used in that chip to establish the basic periods just discussed.

The clock oscillator, or clock *generator*, is usually crystal-controlled and may be a separate chip in the microcomputer system as has been shown in Figures 1.5 and 2.1. Alternatively the clock circuits may be included on the processor chip itself. The Z80, the 8080 and the TMS 9900 microprocessor chips, for example, all require clock signals to be supplied to the processor from an external oscillator. The 8085 and the TMS 9940, on the other hand, have clock generation circuits in the processor.

Processors that include a clock generator only require connection of a suitable frequency-determining circuit to pins on the processor chip. A crystal or an inductance/capacitance circuit can be used for this. The processor chip in these systems also possesses a clock output to supply synchronising signals for use with external hardware.

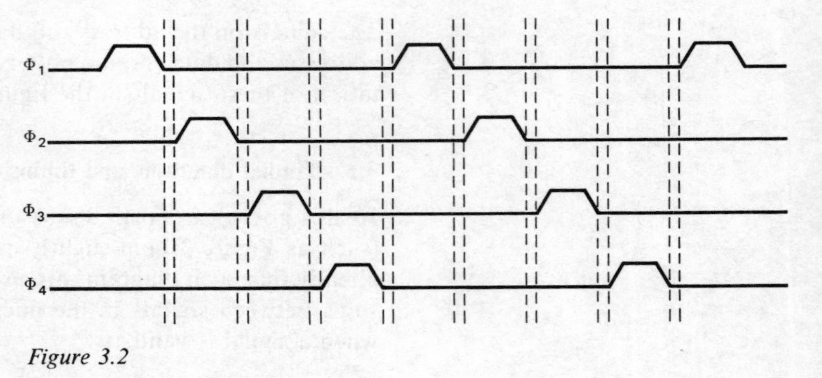

Figure 3.2

The clock pulse requirements of different microprocessors are varied. The Texas TMS 9900, for example, needs a *four-phase* clock signal as shown in Figure 3.2. As can be seen from the diagram there are four separate trains of pulses staggered in time. Since the TMS 9900 does not include a clock generator in the processor, the pulse trains Φ_1, Φ_2, Φ_3 and Φ_4 are fed into four separate pins on the processor chip. The pulses must not overlap and there are specifications of the rise and fall times and the pulse width required. The frequency of the clock can vary between 2 and 3 MHz. Generation of these pulses in a TMS 9900 system can be achieved using a TIM 9904 single-chip clock generator and driver.

The Intel 8080A requires a two-phase clock signal. Two pins are provided on the processor chip for input of these phases and a clock generator circuit, the 8224 clock generator and driver, can be used to generate the necessary signals. Figure 3.3 shows the relationship between these signals and the processor states.

It can be seen that each state occupies one complete cycle of each clock pulse. The processor provides, on an output pin, a signal

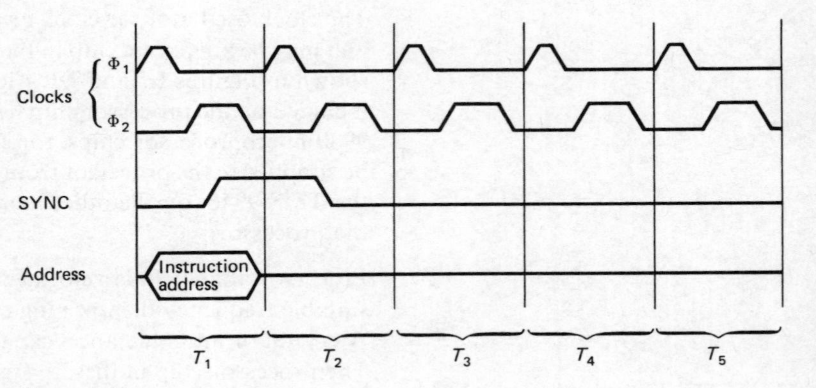

Figure 3.3

SYNC, also shown in the diagram, which serves to define the beginning of each cycle.

Some microprocessors need only a single-phase input clock, i.e. the clock generator produces just a single pulse train. The Zilog Z80 and Z8000, the Intel 8086 and the Motorola 68000 are examples of these.

Q3.5, 3.7

3.4 Memory access-time requirements

Some figures showing the access times of sample memory chips have been presented in Section 2.3, the access time of a memory having been defined as the time taken to obtain data from that memory. More precisely it is the time elapsing between the instant when a request for information is sent to the memory and the instant when that information becomes available.

As shown in the tables presented in Section 2.3 the access times of different memories vary over a considerable range. For example the dynamic RAMs have access times up to approximately 500 ns whilst a small static RAM can operate as fast as an access per 35 ns. The EPROMs tend generally to have access times of around 450 ns.

The effect of long memory access time

The processor chip must be capable of functioning with memories of different speeds and it is thus necessary to provide a method whereby the processor can operate with *slow* memories. *Fast* memories, where the access time is less than one processor clock cycle are, in general, not a problem.

The difficulty involved in using slow memories arises because the processor sends the request to read data to the memory during one processor state, for example during T_1, and takes in the data a little later, for example during T_2 as shown in Figure 3.1. As long as the memory is fast enough to have the required data available before it is needed by the processor there is no problem. It is when the memory has a long access time, and hence requires several processor states to elapse whilst it accesses data, that special steps are needed.

Wait states

Basically in this situation the processor must be held up in its operation until the data is available. This is achieved by the insertion of so-called WAIT states in the processor cycle.

An example should make this clear. Consider a normal instruction fetch cycle for a microcomputer having *separate* 16-bit address and 8-bit data busses. If the machine uses a single-phase clock system the situation may typically be as shown in Figure 3.4. A small change to

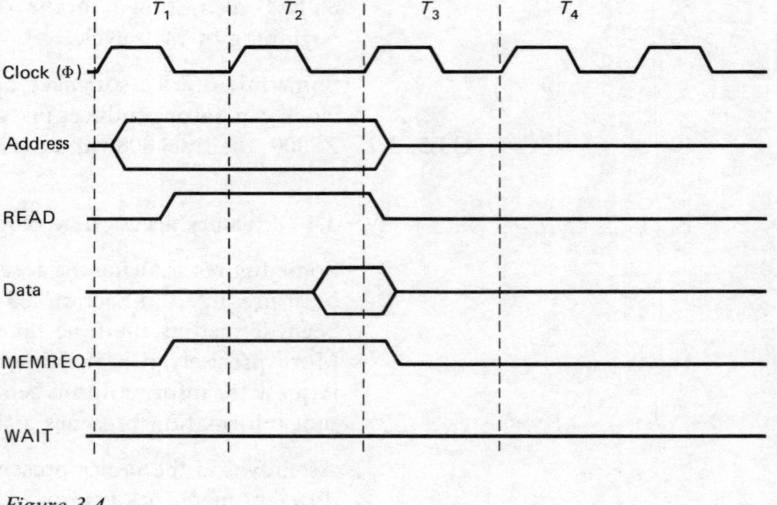

Figure 3.4

the timing has been made in this figure. As before (Figure 3.3), the address of the required memory location is gated on to the address lines of the computer highway during state T_1. The rising edge of the signal MEMREQ (memory request) indicates when the address is valid. This edge occurs about half a clock cycle after the address is set up on the highway, thus allowing time for it to settle.

Following T_1, in state T_2, the processor now *waits* for data to become available from the memory. During this period the processor does not attempt to take data from the memory but simply monitors an input control line WAIT which is used to indicate to it that valid information is available on the data bus.

If WAIT is inactive when the processor examines it, i.e. low (as in Figure 3.4), the memory *is* fast enough to access the data without any problems. However, if WAIT is active when it is examined, the processor must pause in its operation to allow time for the memory to operate.

The precise operation of the system is as follows. The processor senses the signal on the WAIT line at the instant defined by the falling edge of the clock pulse in period T_2. If at this moment WAIT is *inactive* (as shown in Figure 3.4) it is assumed that the memory is fast and that it is able to access the requested data and to place it on the data highway during period T_2. The data is then taken into the processor when the rising edge of the clock pulse in T_3 occurs, i.e. at the beginning of state T_3. Inside the processor the data which, of course, represents an instruction, is placed in the instruction register where it is decoded and used to initiate the execution cycle.

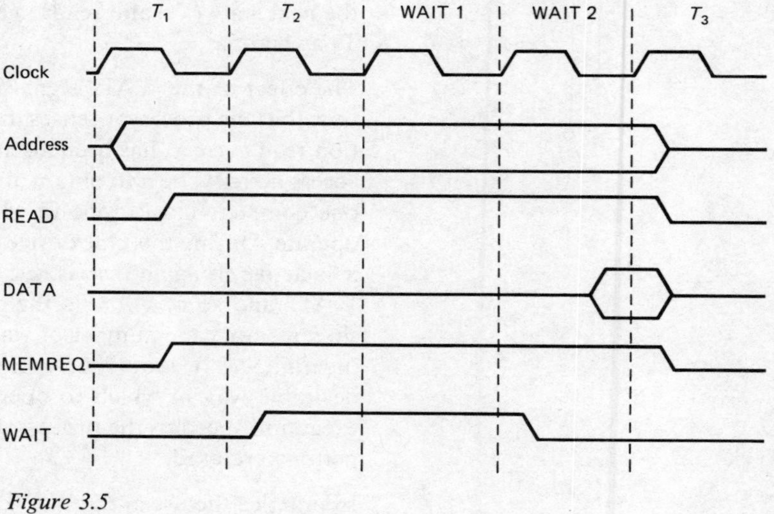

Figure 3.5

The sequence just described represents the fastest instruction cycle that can be achieved with this system. A minimum of three states are required to fetch the instruction from memory. If, however, the memory is slow, the cycle can be lengthened by the insertion of further WAIT states into the cycle. Figure 3.5 shows the timing diagram of another instruction fetch cycle, but this time a slow memory, unable to access data during just state T_2, is assumed.

Again the memory address of the required information, i.e. of the instruction to be accessed, is placed on the address highway during state T_1. As before MEMREQ is set active by the processor to indicate that this address is valid. And again the processor inspects the WAIT line during period T_2, at the instant when the falling edge of the clock pulse occurs.

In Figure 3.5 it has been assumed that the WAIT line becomes active during T_2, before the falling edge of the clock. Thus when it is examined it is at the active (logical 1) level. If this occurs the processor simply inserts one extra *wait state* (WAIT 1, Figure 3.5) into the cycle, i.e. it does not read the data lines on the rising edge of the next clock pulse as it did before, but rather pauses in its operation, doing nothing until the falling edge of the WAIT 1 clock occurs.

At the time of the falling edge of WAIT 1 the processor again inspects the WAIT signal. In the example shown this is still active. In response the processor inserts a second wait state (WAIT 2, Figure 3.5).

On the falling edge of the WAIT 2 clock the WAIT signal is inspected once more. This time it is inactive, having returned to logical 0 during the early part of WAIT 2. When this occurs the processor proceeds to the next state (T_3) and reads in data on the rising edge of clock pulse T_3 as before.

The effect of the WAIT signal is thus simple to understand. Every time that the processor senses that WAIT is active, during an instruction read cycle as has been discussed or, indeed, during any memory access activity, be it to obtain an instruction or an operand, it inserts one complete clock cycle in which it just waits for the memory to operate. During this clock cycle it again tests the WAIT signal and, if it is active, it again inserts one wait state. During this state it tests WAIT and so on. Should the processor have to operate with very slow memory the number of wait clock cycles used can be increased indefinitely. It should be mentioned, however, that this is not a desirable way in which to operate the system since the instruction execution speed of the processor is greatly reduced if too many wait periods are used.

In practice the use of the WAIT control input to the processor is not limited only to memory transfers. Although it has been described in this section in the context of synchronisation between the processor and memory it can also be used in peripheral transfers. Hence it is possible to slow the processor operation to allow it to interlock with I/O chips of the type described in Chapter 2 should this prove, in a particular application, to be required.

One further point is also worth mentioning. This is that in the present context, as in many aspects of microcomputer systems, different manufacturers use different names for similar functions. Specifically the WAIT processor-control input may be replaced by an equivalent alternative. For instance some microprocessors possess a control input called READY. The function of this is, in reality, very similar to WAIT, except that it is the logical inverse of it (if the processor has to *WAIT* it is because the memory or peripheral is *not ready*). Its function is the same, namely to allow the processor to synchronise with slower circuits connected to it.

Q3.4, 3.8

3.5 Control signals used in memory transfer operations

It has been seen that the processor can obtain data from the microcomputer memory and some details have been discussed concerning the synchronisation of these two modules within the microcomputer system. It is now appropriate to consider the operations of reading from and writing to the memory in more detail, and to pull together the separate strands of information on these topics which have been outlined so far.

A block diagram of the microprocessor chip is shown in Figure 3.6. This diagram highlights the control signals used in memory transfers.

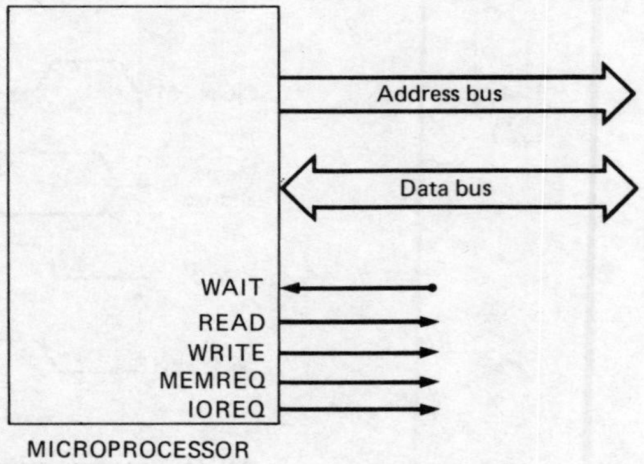

Figure 3.6

Many of these signals have been discussed earlier, but it is worth summarising their functions once more:

1 The address bus carries the address of the memory location to be accessed either for reading or for writing information.
2 The data bus carries the data to be placed in memory or the data coming from memory.
3 READ and WRITE, as defined previously, are used to indicate the direction of a transfer.
4 MEMREQ and IOREQ are used by the processor to indicate the type of transfer required. If the transfer is an exchange of data with the memory then MEMREQ defines when the memory address is valid (Section 3.4). If the transfer is to be an I/O exchange then IOREQ defines when the peripheral address (usually on the least significant eight address lines) is valid.

Thus a memory location is read when its address is placed on the address bus *and* MEMREQ carries a valid signal *and* READ is valid.

Data is written into a memory location when its address is valid *and* MEMREQ is valid *and* WRITE is valid.

Information is taken into the processor from a peripheral device when the address of that device is valid on the address bus *and* IOREQ is valid *and* READ is valid.

Finally data is written to a peripheral device when the device address *and* IOREQ *and* WRITE are all valid.

Timing diagrams showing a memory read operation, a memory write operation and an I/O operation are shown in Figures 3.7, 3.8 and 3.9, respectively. These diagrams assume that the memory (Figures 3.7 and 3.8) and the peripheral (Figure 3.9) are fast enough to supply or receive data without the insertion of extra WAIT states into the cycle. If these are needed they are, however, put in as described earlier.

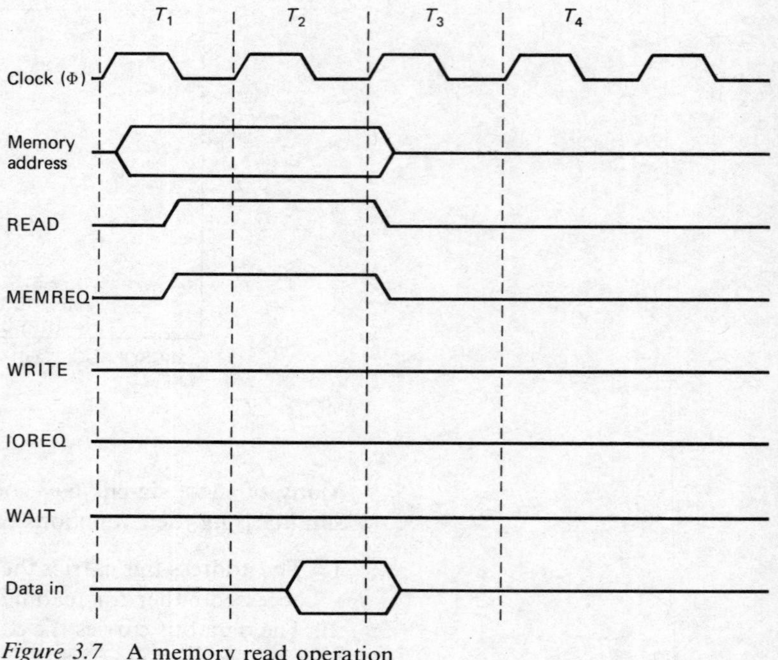

Figure 3.7 A memory read operation

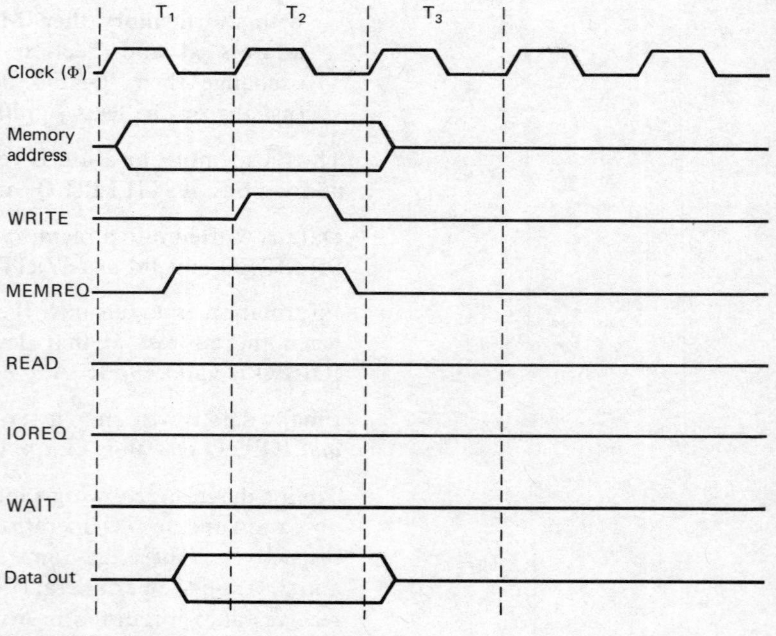

Figure 3.8 A memory write operation

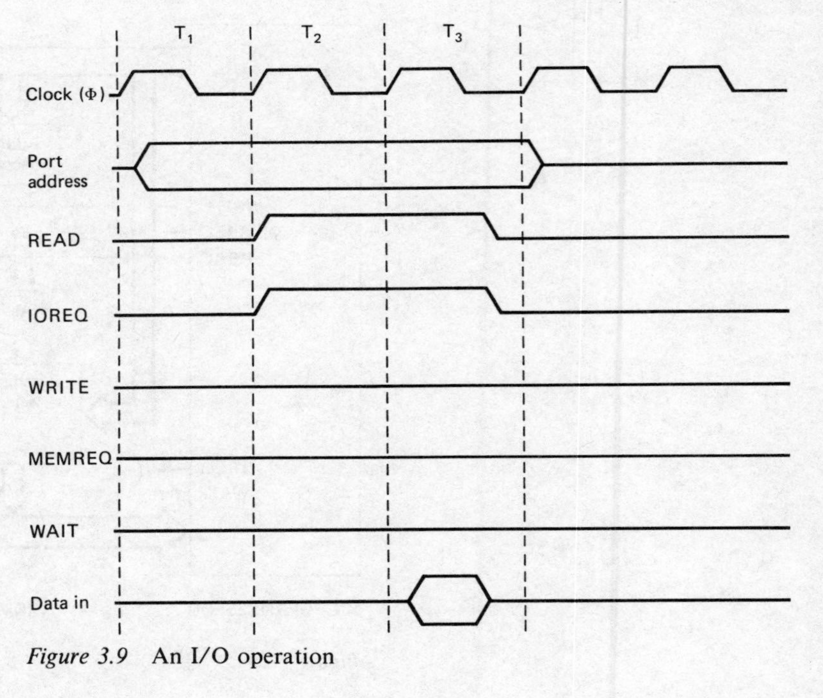

Figure 3.9 An I/O operation

In the memory write operation the data to be placed in memory is set up by the processor as early as possible in the cycle in order to ensure that it is stable by the time the WRITE pulse is made active. During this pulse the data is taken into the memory.

The peripheral transfer operation, Figure 3.9, has been shown as taking one more clock period than the memory operations of the previous figures. The IOREQ signal, the rising edge of which signifies that a valid device address is on the address bus, occurs half a cycle later in this operation than did the MEMREQ signal in the previous memory operations. This allows more time for the address to stabilise, should this be needed.

The system block diagram

The interconnection of the microprocessor chip with ROM and RAM is illustrated in Figure 3.10. The least significant address-bus lines are used to select the location to be accessed in a block of the memory. For example, if the ROM in the figure contains 1,024 bytes of storage, the ten least significant address bus lines (lines A_0–A_9) are connected to the memory address inputs (a non-multiplexed memory address is assumed here – see Section 2.2). The higher-order address bits are decoded and used, when MEMREQ and READ are in the active (high) state, to select the ROM chip. When READ is not high, that is,

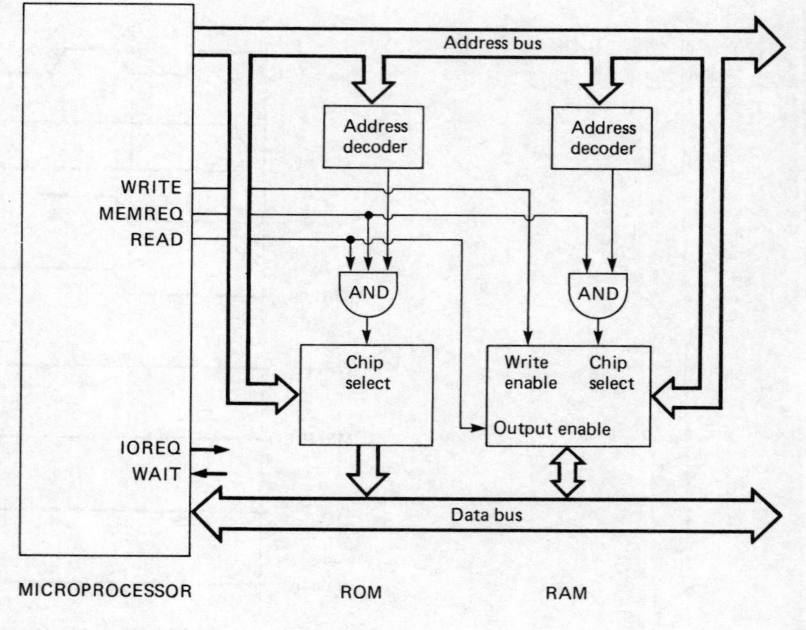

Figure 3.10

for instance, when a write to memory is being performed, the ROM is not selected.

Locations in RAM are selected when the high-order address bits are appropriate to produce an output from the address decoder and when MEMREQ is also high. Thus the RAM is selected irrespective of whether a read or a write is to be performed. The WRITE signal is then used to activate a separate 'write enable' input on the RAM chip, thus allowing data to be placed in the chosen address.

Whenever the RAM chip is enabled, be it for reading or writing, data is read from the selected location. However, this data must only be placed on the data bus of the microprocessor when a *read* operation is being performed, and not during a *write* operation. In the latter case the bus is already being used to transfer the data to be stored to the memory and this information must not be corrupted. The READ signal from the processor is thus used to activate a further input on the RAM, the 'output enable' control input (Figure 3.10). When this input is driven high by the READ signal, and the chip is selected, the RAM output data is connected to the data bus. However, when this input is low, as it is during any operation other than a memory read, the RAM output is isolated from the bus.

In many systems the external logic, i.e. the two 'AND' gates shown in Figure 3.10, is not needed. Instead the memory chips contain internal logic and possess two or more 'chip select' inputs which are 'anded' together inside the chip.

The names used to describe the control lines also vary from system to system. Often signals which are active in the *low* state, as described in Section 2.4 on interfacing devices, are used. Using the same names as previously the control signals then become $\overline{\text{READ}}$, $\overline{\text{WRITE}}$, $\overline{\text{MEMREQ}}$, $\overline{\text{IOREQ}}$, etc. The principles of operation of the system are, of course, not changed at all by this, but the timing diagrams reflect the active-low nature of the signals. A negative-going excursion is used to show the period of validity of a signal.

Q3.9

3.6 Strobing to define transfer period

Having considered the control signals used in memory read or write operations it is appropriate to return briefly to the topic of the time relationships between these signals and to the use of timing diagrams.

In general a timing diagram defines *three* states of a signal in a system. The signal may be *valid*, it may be *invalid* or it may be *uncertain whether the signal is valid or not*. This is best illustrated by use of an example.

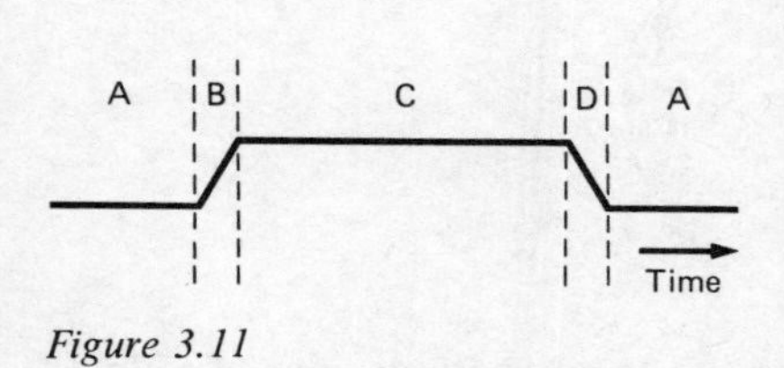

Figure 3.11

Figure 3.11 shows a typical signal of the type used previously. During the periods labelled as A the signal is in the *low* state. During the period labelled as C it is in the *high* state. During periods B and D it is in an intermediate state between low and high. In these latter periods it is uncertain what the precise state of the signal is at any instant. All that *is* certain is that it starts the period in one state and ends it in another.

Thus the computer must only examine signals during periods when their state is unambiguously defined. This is achieved, as we have seen, by using the rising or falling edge of timing signals to signify when the information on data lines is correct. An example is the use of MEMREQ to specify when the memory address information is correct.

There are a number of ways in which such signals can be applied in a system. For example the MEMREQ signal can be used to strobe the address data into a number of *latches*, in the way mentioned in Section 2.2. If this is done, and if signals have the polarity of Figures 3.7 and 3.8, MEMREQ is used as the clock input to a set of latches which take in and store data on the positive-going edge of the clock pulse. This process is known as *staticising* the data. It does not matter that the precise state of the clock is unknown at particular instants during its rise period as long as the address data is valid during the whole of that period.

Q3.3

An alternative and more common method of strobing data into

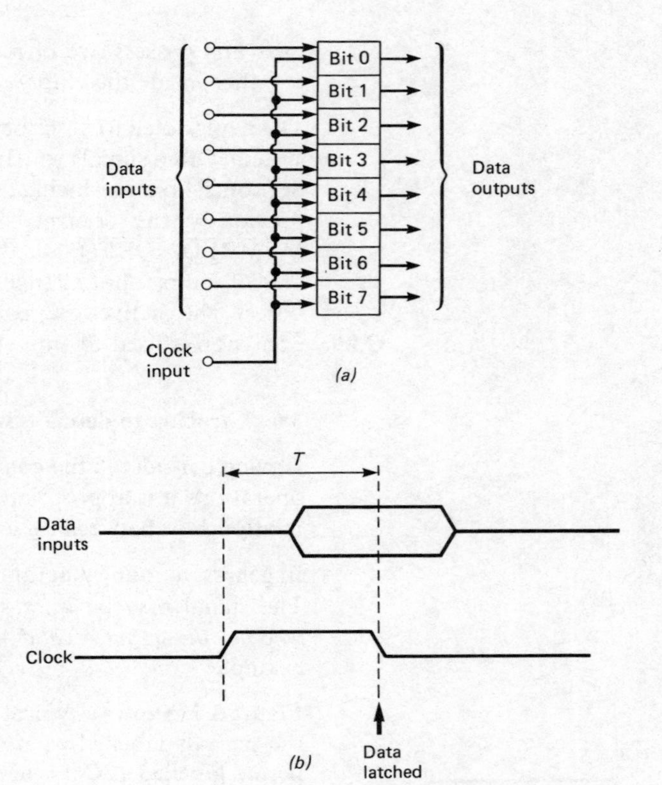

Figure 3.12

latches is to use a system in which the negative-going edge of a clock pulse staticises the data. Figure 3.12(a) shows a block diagram of an integrated circuit which contains eight latches and which, therefore, can store eight bits (see Section 2.2). Each bit possesses a data input and a data output and all bits share a common clock input line. Part (b) of the figure illustrates the timing diagram of the latches. During the period when the clock pulse is high (T) each latch is said to be *transparent*, that is the output is always in the same state as the input. If, during this time, the input to a latch changes the output follows it.

When the clock signal goes low, at the end of period T, the data on the inputs is staticised in the latches. After this time any further change in the input data is ignored. The exact instant at which the data is staticised is the one at which the falling edge of the clock passes through a high-to-low threshold. However, as stated earlier, this is not a critical parameter as long as the data inputs are stable during the whole clock-fall period.

Latches of this type are commonly used in microcomputer systems. They do not always appear as separate components, however, and are frequently included in other modules. The input lines to a memory chip, for example, are latched (staticised) within that chip. Moreover, as has been seen in the previous chapter, data is often staticised in the ports of a programmable peripheral interface, and the processor chip itself contains input and output latches.

3.7 Buffering and timing

It is important to realise that any logical operation performed upon a signal in a microcomputer system or, indeed, in any digital logic system, inevitably introduces a time delay into the signal path. This is because a circuit must be placed in the path to effect the operation and this takes time to function. If, for example the inputs of a NAND gate are connected together and taken from the logical 0 to the logical 1 level the output goes from 1 to 0 a little later, after the *propagation delay* of the gate has elapsed. The actual value of propagation delay depends on many factors, but principally on the type of logic which is being used.

The delay introduced into information paths by buffering must be taken into account in system design. For instance, if the data or address bus lines of the computer are buffered as has been outlined in Section 2.6, the extra delay introduced into these lines must not be forgotten.

Buffering the address bus has the effect of moving the period at which the address information is valid to the right on the timing diagram (Figure 3.7 or 3.8). This means that the point at which the information is strobed into the memory latch moves nearer to the instant at which the address information is set up, since the MEMREQ signal is not delayed in a comparable manner (unless it, too, is buffered). Insertion of too great a delay in the data or address lines may, therefore, reduce the timing tolerance of the system. A strobe point too near to the data set-up time may not allow sufficient time for the data signals to settle and may thus cause errors to occur.

Buffering is frequently required when peripheral devices are to be used at a distance from the computer system. In such instances it may be necessary to use special *line-driver* chips to develop the currents and voltages required to drive the wires to the peripheral in a controlled way. The programmable peripheral interface is not able to perform this function since it does not contain the appropriate circuits. Again the delay introduced by the drivers and by any long connecting wires used must be taken into account.

Q3.6, 3.10

Questions

3.1 List the steps involved in executing a single program instruction in a microcomputer system. Explain the functions of the operations making up each of these steps and outline how the execution of a single-byte instruction differs from that of a 2- or 3-byte instruction.

3.2 'A microcomputer system is a complex interconnection of registers, memory and arithmetic circuits using parallel data highways.' Discuss the above proposition.

3.3 How are timing diagrams useful in describing the operation of a digital logic system? Discuss how such diagrams are used to show when signals are:
(a) valid
(b) invalid
(c) uncertain
and outline the way in which timing control signals can be used to ensure that data is only used when it is in a valid state.

3.4 Discuss how the cycle of operation of a microcomputer can be divided into a number of distinct time intervals and describe the steps which take place in these intervals during
(a) an instruction-fetch cycle and
(b) an execution cycle in which data is written into a memory location.

3.5 Write a short description of the function of the clock oscillator in a microcomputer.

3.6 Discuss the need for buffering in a microcomputer and outline how its use can alter the timing tolerances within the system.

3.7 If manufacturers' data is available, look up the characteristics of some commercial clock-generator circuits and list:
(a) How many phases of clock are generated.
(b) The pulse width of each phase of the clock.
(c) The minimum delay between the pulses from different phases.
(d) The rise and fall times of the output clock pulses.
Minimum, typical or maximum values may be used in the answer, and all three should be quoted if they are available. It is suggested that the Intel 8284 and 8224 and the Texas Instruments TIM 9904 clock generators should be included in the answer.

3.8 Why is it necessary to cause the microprocessor cycle to be lengthened during some memory access operations? Outline how this can be achieved. A microprocessor which uses a single-phase clock of frequency 3 MHz is to be connected to:
(a) A ROM having an access time of 400 ns.
(b) A random-access memory having a read-write cycle time of 550 ns.

The clock pulse mark-space ratio is assumed to be unity. Draw timing diagrams showing the system operation in:

(a) Reading from both memories into the processor.
(b) Writing data into the RAM.

3.9 List the control lines used by the microcomputer system in:

(a) Memory access operations.
(b) Peripheral I/O operations.

How does the system distinguish between a processor output operation which:

(a) Writes data into a memory location, or
(b) Sends data to a programmable peripheral interface circuit?

3.10 Different types of logic circuit possess different propagation delays. By examining manufacturer's literature (if it is available) compile a table of typical propagation delays for NAND gates, NOR gates, INVERTERS and buffer amplifiers using:

(a) Normal transistor–transistor logic (TTL).
(b) Low-power TTL.
(c) Schottky-clamped TTL.

Which is the fastest type of logic?

Chapter 4 **Memory mapping and memory organisation**

Objectives of this chapter *When you have completed studying this chapter you should be able to:*

1. *Understand the organisation of the microcomputer memory.*
2. *Use hexadecimal notation for writing memory addresses and transfer numbers between binary and hexadecimal forms.*
3. *Understand the concept of the address space of the microcomputer.*
4. *Understand that the total address space can be occupied with different types of memory and that not all this address space need be filled with memory chips.*
5. *Use a memory map to illustrate the composition of the memory.*
6. *Distinguish between memory data transfers and peripheral data transfers including:*
   (a) The use of special IN and OUT instructions.
   (b) Memory-mapped input/output.
7. *Understand the principle of mapping the peripheral address space into the memory address space.*
8. *Recognise the need for decoding in microcomputer systems.*
9. *Understand the principles of decoding.*
10. *List the advantages to be gained by using coded information, for example for addresses, so as to reduce the number of interconnections required between units.*
11. *Understand the use of decoding to select one of eight memory locations from a three-bit coded address.*
12. *Understand the application of practical decoder chips.*
13. *Explain the method by which memory chips of width* m *bits can be assembled to form a store of width* n *bits where* n *is greater than* m.
14. *Explain the way in which several groups of memory chips can be combined, together with suitable decoders to increase the number of words of storage that are available.*
15. *Explain how a decoder can be used to select a range of store addresses, e.g. how a range of 1K addresses can be located.*
16. *Recognise that if a large number of memory chips are to be connected to the microcomputer bus, bus drivers are required to alleviate possible loading problems.*
17. *Explain the way in which a number of two-state switching devices can be interrogated by the central processing unit.*

4.1 The microcomputer memory

The memory of the microcomputer has been discussed a little in earlier chapters and details of the types of integrated circuits used in its construction have been presented together with an outline of the timing methods and control signals used to synchronise processor and memory operation.

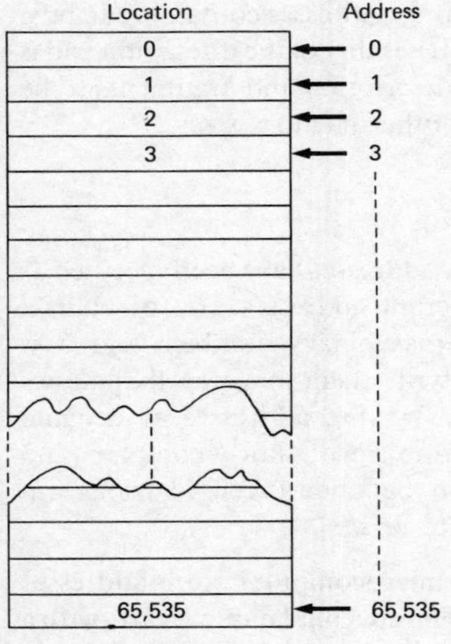

Figure 4.1

The memory, as has been seen, consists of a number of *locations* or *words*. This is illustrated in Figure 4.1. This diagram has been drawn with the low-address end of the memory, i.e. addresses 0, 1, 2, and so on, at the top and the high-address end at the bottom. It should be noted that this is the convention that will be used in this book but it is not always adopted in all publications. Sometimes the high-address end of the memory is drawn at the top of the diagram. Either method is, of course, satisfactory, the choice between them being a matter of personal preference.

Memory width

Each location is capable of holding either data or part or all of an instruction and each is characterised by the number of bits it contains, i.e. by its *width*. In microcomputer systems the width of a word is frequently 8 bits. Thus the memory consists of a sequence of *bytes*, this being the commonly accepted name for an 8-bit unit. In such systems the processor instructions manipulate, in the main, 8-bit quantities. For instance, the order LDA (address), i.e. load the accumulator from 'address', fetches an 8-bit data value from the memory and places it in the accumulator.

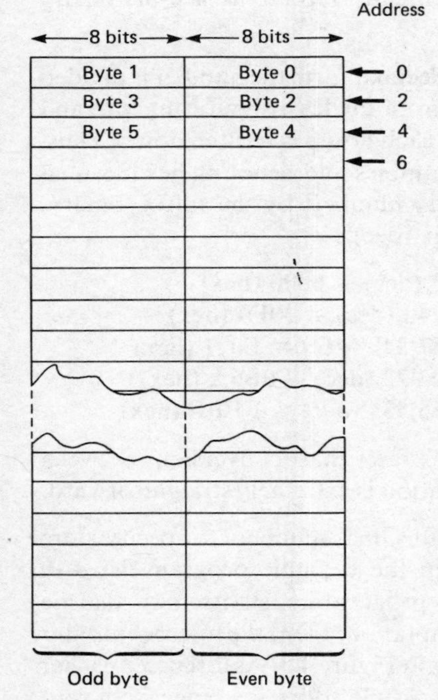

Figure 4.2

Some machines, however, are more flexible than this. The manipulation of different data types – bytes, characters, bits, words, long words – has already been mentioned in Section 2.2. Another, rather less general, but still very useful, approach is to build instructions into the processor which can handle either bytes or 16-bit words. In such a system the memory can be considered to be organised as shown in Figure 4.2. Each word consists of two bytes and word addresses are always even. Instructions that refer to words thus contain even addresses. Instructions that refer to bytes can directly access either the even- or odd-addressed bytes. For instance, LDA 2 would obtain the even byte at address 2 and LDA 3 would obtain the odd byte at address 3. This possibility has been included in the description for completeness, but will not be discussed further. Subsequent sections assume that a store made up of successive bytes, as shown in Figure 4.1, is being used.

Assumptions

The address range of the memory has also been mentioned in earlier

Table 4.1 *Hexadecimal number representation*

Binary pattern	*Hexadecimal representation*
0000	0
0001	1
0010	2
0011	3
0100	4
0101	5
0110	6
0111	7
1000	8
1001	9
1010	A
1011	B
1100	C
1101	D
1110	E
1111	F

chapters and it has been pointed out that ranges as large as 8 Mbytes are available in fourth-generation microprocessors. In these systems the memory address must contain up to 23 bits ($2^{23} = 8,388,608$). For the purposes of this chapter, however, a memory address range of 64K (65,536) will be assumed, requiring addresses containing 16 bits. This assumption does not lessen the generality of the discussion and is made purely for convenience. The description and arguments to be presented are equally applicable to other memory sizes.

Hexadecimal addresses

In the examples given so far memory addresses have been specified as decimal numbers. In practice program addresses are, of course, always held in the microcomputer as binary numbers and it is convenient for the programmer to write them in a way that allows easy translation into binary form. Writing addresses as decimal numbers does not satisfy this criterion since a fairly complex (and tedious) translation process has to be undertaken to transform between decimal and binary and *vice versa.*

Hexadecimal representation of the microcomputer store addresses does, however, satisfy the criterion. Hexadecimal numbers are, with a little practice, easy to write and interpret and they do allow direct transformation to and from binary form. The latter point is achieved because each hexadecimal digit directly represents a 4-bit binary pattern as shown in Table 4.1.

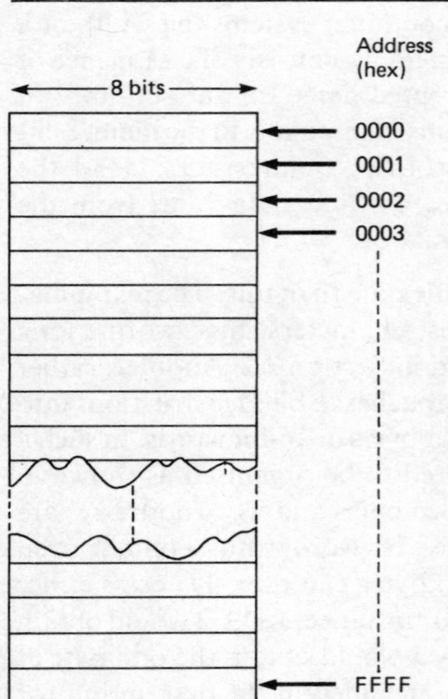

Figure 4.3 Hexadecimal memory addresses

To write a binary number in hexadecimal form the number is divided into groups of four bits, starting from the least significant end, and the hexadecimal representation of each group is written down. Thus, using 16-bit binary numbers as examples and denoting hexadecimal numbers by the suffix (hex), binary numbers by the suffix (binary) and decimal numbers by the suffix (dec):

0000000000000000 (binary) = 0 (dec) = 0000 (hex)
0000000011110000 (binary) = 240 (dec) = 00F0 (hex)
1110000000000001 (binary) = 57,345 (dec) = E001 (hex)
0000101101101010 (binary) = 2,922 (dec) = 0B6A (hex)
1111111111111111 (binary) = 65,535 (dec) = FFFF (hex)

A little practice should demonstrate that conversion between hexadecimal and binary representation is extremely straightforward.

It is common practice to use hexadecimal numbers to specify store addresses as was done, in fact, in the example program listed in Table 1.2. In machine language, program constants may also be specified in this form. Using this notation, then, the microcomputer memory may be redrawn as shown in Figure 4.3. As discussed earlier a width of 8 bits is assumed. The possible addresses range from zero to 65,535 (dec) or to FFFF (hex).

Q4.2

Filling the memory space

In practice, the microcomputer system may not contain enough memory chips to provide storage at all these addresses, i.e. although the *possible* number of bytes in memory can be up to 65,536 if a 16-bit address is used, the *actual* number in a real system, especially in a system intended for use in an application requiring only a short program, may be much less than this. Thus just a part of the available memory space may be 'filled' with real memory chips.

In such a system only a section of the total number of addresses can be actually used in a program, the remainder being, with the exception of the case discussed later in the chapter, invalid.

A further complication is that the microcomputer memory can, as has been seen, be composed of a mixture of memory types. Part of the memory may, for instance, be read only (ROM) and part may be read write (RAM). Some method of showing what the memory composition is, i.e. how much RAM is included, how much ROM is included and how much unused address space exists, is clearly desirable.

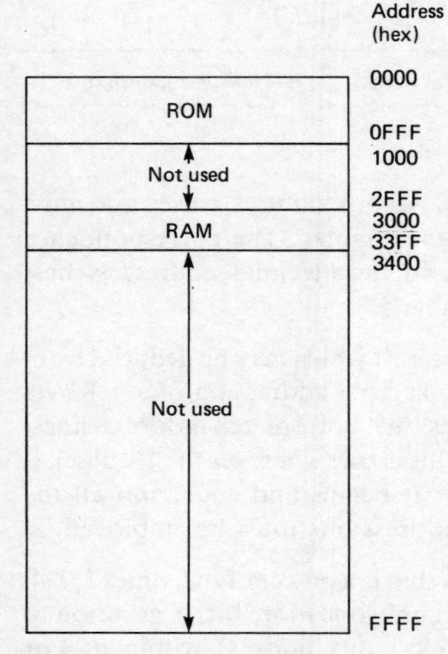

Figure 4.4 A memory map

4.2 The idea of a memory map

A *memory map*, as drawn in Figure 4.4, is used to show these points pictorially. The map illustrates the total range of addresses available in the microcomputer system, together with the use to which any particular address is put. Thus the system represented contains 4 Kbytes of ROM and 1 Kbyte of RAM. The former occupies the address section from 0000 (hex) to 0FFF (hex) and the latter occupies addresses from 3000 (hex) to 33FF (hex). The addresses between 1000 (hex) and 2FFF (hex), and between 3400 (hex) and FFFF (hex), the end of the memory, are unused.

To put this in the, perhaps, more familiar decimal form (for reference) the ROM occupies addresses 0 to 4,095, there is then a gap from addresses 4,096 to 12,287, the RAM occupies addresses 12,288 to 13,311 and the rest of the address space, from 13,312 to 65,535, is spare.

Use of the memory map

The memory map allows the system user to see, at a glance, what memory capacity is available in the system and what addresses are, and are not, used. In the example given it should be noted that the highest address that is used is 33FF (hex).

If the system address bus lines are labelled A_0 (the least significant line) to A_{15} (most significant), then lines A_{14} and A_{15} are never

Table 4.2

Address line	A_{15}	A_{14}	A_{13}	A_{12}	A_{11}	A_{10}	A_9	A_8	A_7	A_6	A_5	A_4	A_3	A_2	A_1	A_0	
Significance	32,768	16,384	8,192	4,096	2,048	1,024	512	256	128	64	32	16	8	4	2	1	
Address (hex)																	
0000	0	0	0	0	0	0	0	0	0	0	0	0	0	0	0	0	
0FFF	0	0	0	0	1	1	1	1	1	1	1	1	1	1	1	1	} *
1000	0	0	0	1	0	0	0	0	0	0	0	0	0	0	0	0	
2FFF	0	0	1	0	1	1	1	1	1	1	1	1	1	1	1	1	} *
3000	0	0	1	1	0	0	0	0	0	0	0	0	0	0	0	0	
33FF	0	0	1	1	0	0	1	1	1	1	1	1	1	1	1	1	} *
3400	0	0	1	1	0	1	0	0	0	0	0	0	0	0	0	0	
FFFF	1	1	1	1	1	1	1	1	1	1	1	1	1	1	1	1	
	Hexadecimal digit 3				Hexadecimal digit 2				Hexadecimal digit 1				Hexadecimal digit 0				

* Consecutive

required since they are always zero. All other lines are used and must be decoded as described later in the chapter. The correspondence between memory address lines and hexadecimal address is best shown diagrammatically, as in Table 4.2.

There are some points of general interest which may be deduced from a consideration of the map. For example addressing of a 1 Kbyte block of memory always requires the bottom ten address lines, namely lines A_0 to A_9, to be used. This is true wherever the 1K block is situated in memory, i.e. wherever it begins and ends, and all the combinations of the bottom ten address bits must be employed.

If the 1K block starts at an address that is a power of two times 1,024, say at 2,048, 4,096, 8,192, etc., then only one more bit, in addition to the bottom ten, is required to select any address within it. For instance, if it lies between addresses 1,024 and 2,047, only line A_{10} is used in addition to A_0–A_9, if it lies between addresses 8,192 and 9,215 only line A_{13} (and not lines A_{10}, A_{11} or A_{12}) is needed, and so on.

Should the block not begin at such an address, however, more lines are required. A block of 1 Kbyte in the address range 8,200 to 9,223, for instance, uses *all* the address lines up to A_{13} (including A_{10}, A_{11} and A_{12}).

The arguments presented above can equally well be applied, with suitable changes in the values involved, to other block sizes. A 2K block of memory, for example, requires the use of lines A_0 to A_{10} and, if sited at a starting address which is a power of two times 2,048, say 4,096, 8,192, etc., needs only one more line for selection.

From the foregoing arguments it is clear that if the address space of a microcomputer system is not fully populated, so that there are alternative positions in that address space at which a block of RAM, say, may be placed, then economies in hardware can be obtained by selecting the RAM starting address with care. The aim should be to position it so that the address decoding required to select the block is minimised. This will be discussed further in Section 4.5.

Q4.1

4.3 The distinction between memory transfers and input/output

In the discussion of I/O facilities included so far it has been assumed that all I/O operations are performed by the special peripheral transfer orders such as IN and OUT included in the microcomputer instruction set. This is *programmed* I/O.

During the execution of these I/O instructions the processor generates an output control signal IOREQ (Section 3.5) which informs peripheral devices connected to the address bus of the system that the request is directed to them and that they must decode the information on the address lines. During a memory transfer instruction, on the other hand, IOREQ remains inactive and the control line MEMREQ (Section 3.5) becomes active to inform the memory system that the address information is directed towards it.

Thus the distinction between a peripheral address and a memory address is made by IOREQ and MEMREQ and the full range of addresses obtainable using the address bus may be applied to *either* peripheral devices *or* to memory. With a 16-bit address bus, therefore, there are 65,536 possible memory addresses and, in addition, 65,536 possible peripheral addresses.

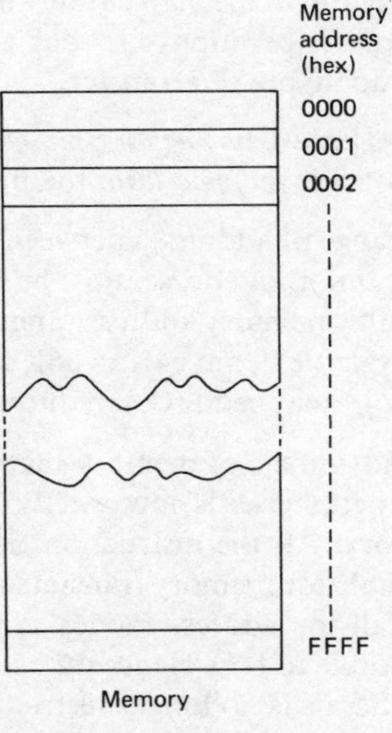

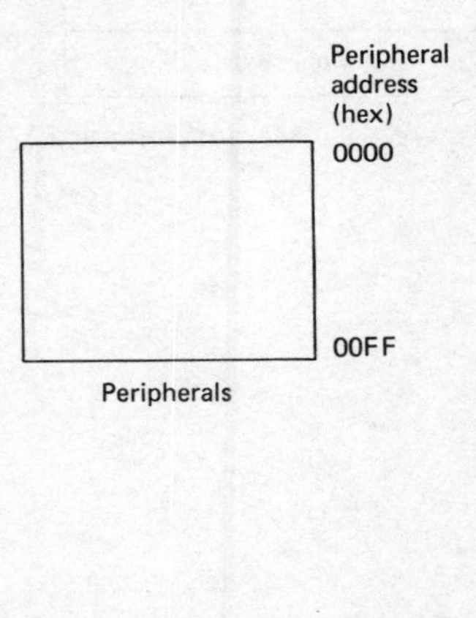

Figure 4.5

Usually it is not necessary to have such a large range of peripheral addresses (very few computers, if any at all, have 65,536 separate peripherals) so only the bottom eight address lines (A_0–A_7) are used in conjunction with peripheral transfer instructions.

It should be noted that the effect of MEMREQ and IOREQ is to *separate* the peripheral address space from the memory address space, as shown in Figure 4.5. This figure assumes an 8-bit peripheral address as discussed above.

4.4 Allocation of memory space to input/output

When there is spare space available in the memory address map an alternative approach to I/O can be adopted. This is to divide the available memory address space into two parts; one to be used, as before, to access memory locations and the other to be used to address peripheral devices. Using this method, the memory map of Figure 4.4 can be redrawn as illustrated in Figure 4.6.

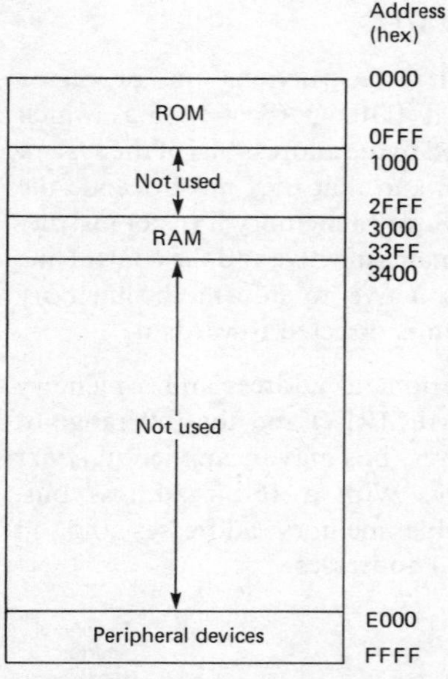

Figure 4.6 Memory-mapped I/O

In this diagram part of the previously unused address space, from E000 to FFFF (hex), i.e. from 57,344 to 65,535 (dec), has been allocated to peripheral devices. When an address within this range is detected on the address bus it is used to select a peripheral operation.

The control signals, IOREQ and MEMREQ, still function exactly as before but now peripheral selection is signified by MEMREQ being active together with an address between E000 and FFFF (hex). Thus *all* transfers of data, whether to memory or to I/O occur with MEMREQ in the active state and separation of I/O operations from memory operations is achieved wholly through the *address* accompanying the transfer.

This is known as *memory-mapped* I/O because the I/O addresses are part of, i.e. *mapped into*, the memory address space.

The range of addresses between E000 and FFFF (hex) being used for I/O cannot, of course, now be used for memory accesses. Hence the available memory address range of the microcomputer is reduced, in the example, from 64K to 56K addresses. This is the disadvantage of memory-mapped I/O; it reduces the maximum possible memory size.

The advantage of memory-mapped I/O is that transfer of data to or from peripherals is now exactly the same as transfer of data to or from memory. All the instructions in the machine order code which are available for memory transfers are now also available for I/O. Moreover all the address modes available for memory accesses are also applicable to I/O. Hence the exchange of data between processor and peripherals is no longer restricted to simple IN and OUT orders and can be made more flexible than it was before. An example of I/O is given at the end of this chapter in Section 4.8. For the moment it is better, here, to continue with the discussion of addressing.

The choice made in Figure 4.6 of a peripheral address range of 8K is, of course, arbitrary. It has been made on the basis that 8,192 addresses for peripherals is likely, for most systems, to be more than adequate whilst, at the same time, not too much memory space is lost.

If only a few peripherals are required a smaller range of addresses can be allocated to them, for instance from F000 to FFFF (hex) (4,096 addresses) or from F800 to FFFF (hex) (2,048 addresses). The possible memory size is increased accordingly.

Returning to the original example of memory-mapped I/O, with 8,192 addresses from E000 to FFFF (hex) reserved for peripheral use, it can be seen that any address having the three most significant bits, namely A_{13}, A_{14} and A_{15}, at '1' refers to peripherals. Any other address refers to memory. A single four-input AND gate, as shown in Figure 4.6, can thus be used to distinguish between a peripheral transfer and a memory transfer.

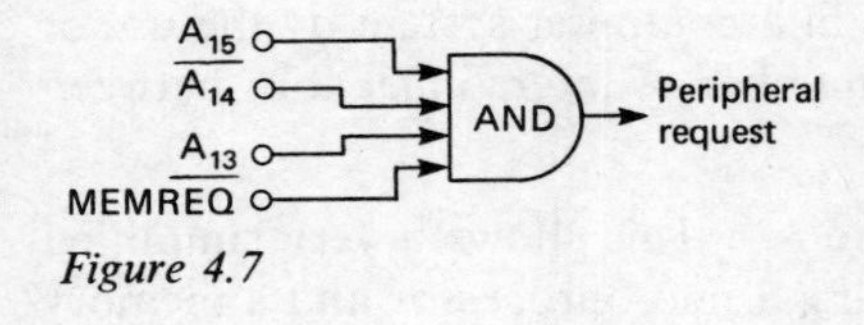

Figure 4.7

It should be noted that this simple distinction between memory and peripherals is possible only because the peripheral address range has been chosen to lie at one end of the address map. A peripheral address range within the map would be more complicated to separate out, i.e. it would require more *decoding*.

4.5 Decoding

Decoding, in the context of microcomputer systems, is the use of a logic network to detect unique combinations of binary numbers. It is worth digressing a little to consider this before returning to the question of memory organisation.

Consider a 3-bit binary number. This can represent 2^3, i.e. eight possible combinations as illustrated in Table 4.3. The binary digits have been called A, B and C.

Table 4.3

Binary Number			*Combination Number*
A	*B*	*C*	
0	0	0	0
0	0	1	1
0	1	0	2
0	1	1	3
1	0	0	4
1	0	1	5
1	1	0	6
1	1	1	7

Each combination is a unique grouping of A, B and C. Writing A for the situation where A = 1 and $\overline{A}$ for the situation where A = 0 it is possible to write

Combination 0 = $\overline{A}$ and $\overline{B}$ and $\overline{C}$
Combination 1 = $\overline{A}$ and $\overline{B}$ and C
Combination 2 = $\overline{A}$ and B and $\overline{C}$
and so on up to
Combination 7 = A and B and C

Signals corresponding to the individual combinations can be obtained by using AND gates to implement the groupings in the

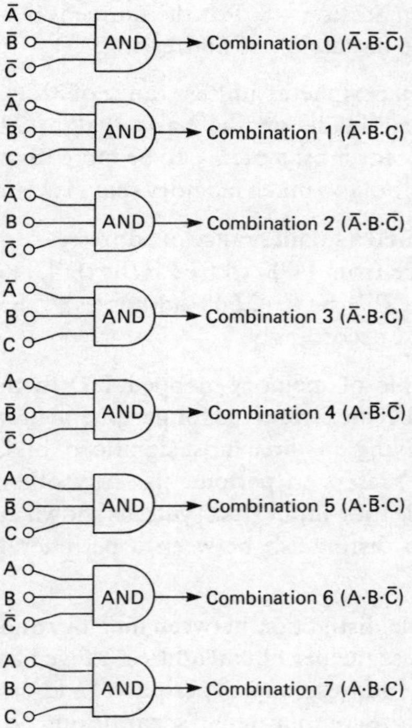

$\bar{A}$, $\bar{B}$, $\bar{C}$ — AND → Combination 0 ($\bar{A}\cdot\bar{B}\cdot\bar{C}$)
$\bar{A}$, $\bar{B}$, C — AND → Combination 1 ($\bar{A}\cdot\bar{B}\cdot C$)
$\bar{A}$, B, $\bar{C}$ — AND → Combination 2 ($\bar{A}\cdot B\cdot\bar{C}$)
$\bar{A}$, B, C — AND → Combination 3 ($\bar{A}\cdot B\cdot C$)
A, $\bar{B}$, $\bar{C}$ — AND → Combination 4 ($A\cdot\bar{B}\cdot\bar{C}$)
A, $\bar{B}$, C — AND → Combination 5 ($A\cdot\bar{B}\cdot C$)
A, B, $\bar{C}$ — AND → Combination 6 ($A\cdot B\cdot\bar{C}$)
A, B, C — AND → Combination 7 ($A\cdot B\cdot C$)

Figure 4.8 A three-bit to eight-output decoder

above list. Using eight AND gates, as shown in Figure 4.8, a unique signal can be obtained for each binary number combination. In this figure the AND operation is represented by a median point, so A *and* B *and* C is written as A·B·C. The figure represents a complete three-bit to eight-output decoder.

It is, of course, possible to expand the size of such a decoder. A group of four binary digits, for example, possesses sixteen unique combinations. A complete four-bit decoder would thus require sixteen AND gates and would have four input and sixteen output lines. Each AND gate in this decoder would have to possess four inputs.

Advantages of decoding

The great benefit to be gained in a computer system by the use of decoding is that it allows the number of interconnections between units to be reduced.

Consider the diagram of Figure 4.9. This shows a very simplified microcomputer system possessing a microprocessor and a memory (ROM) containing just 8 bytes of information. It is thus the same structure as we have seen before for the microcomputer, for example in Figures 1.2 or 1.5, but with a very small number of addresses.

The memory has been assumed to contain a three-bit to eight-output decoder. This is used to select individual bytes of memory when a 3-bit address is placed on the address bus. Thus an address of:

000 selects Byte 0
001 selects Byte 1
010 selects Byte 2, etc.

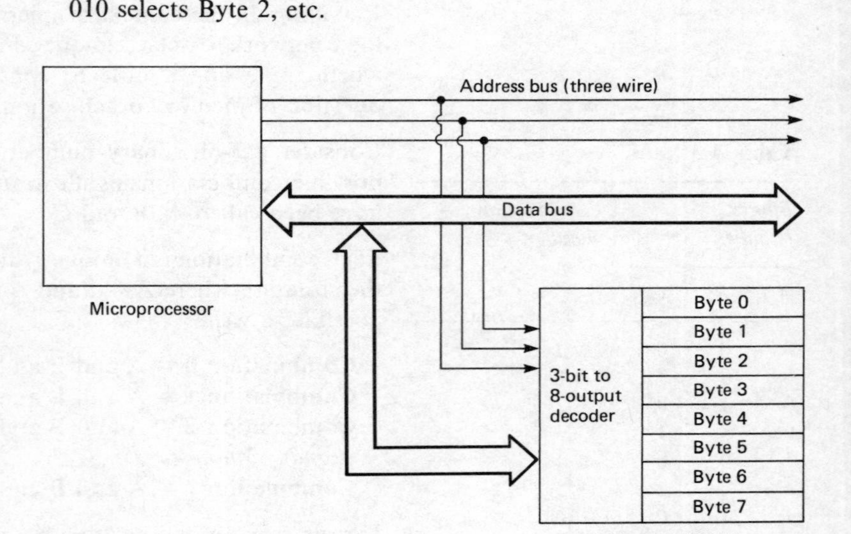

Figure 4.9

Because the memory contains this decoder it is only necessary, as implied in the above discussion, to have *three* address bus wires. Any address sent on these wires is transmitted as one of the eight combinations obtainable with three bits and is decoded *in the memory* to select an individual byte.

It is interesting to consider what would be required if the memory did not contain the decoder. It would then be necessary to send a separate signal to select each of the eight bytes, i.e. the address bus would need eight wires instead of three.

This may not seem too severe in this simple example of a very small memory. However if the memory is a practical size containing, say 1,024 or 2,048 bytes, it is clear that the decoder is essential. With 2,048 bytes of memory and a *coded* address there must be 11 wires for transmission of addresses. Without coding 2,048 wires would be required; clearly not a practical proposition.

Practical decoder chips

Special decoder integrated circuits, having the necessary logic to decode three inputs to eight outputs on a single chip, are available as support circuits for microcomputer systems. These have been mentioned previously, in Chapter 2. Schematically they are represented as shown in Figure 4.10.

The binary pattern to be decoded is placed on inputs A, B and C and causes one of the output lines OUT 0 to OUT 7 to become active, i.e. it causes a '1' signal to appear on one of these lines.

The expansion inputs are used to select one decoder chip from a number, should several be used in a particular application. For example it may be necessary to decode a binary pattern of 5 bits. Since $2^5 = 32$ this will result in 32 output lines. A possible system is shown in Figure 4.11(a).

Four three-bit to eight-line decoders, D_1, D_2, D_3 and D_4 are used. For this example it has been assumed that each of these has just one

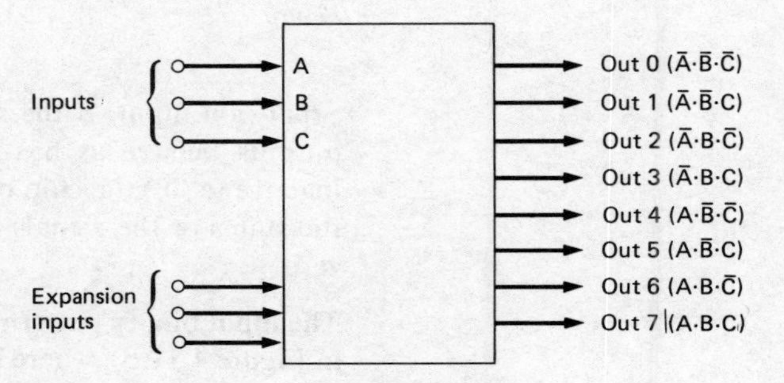

Figure 4.10

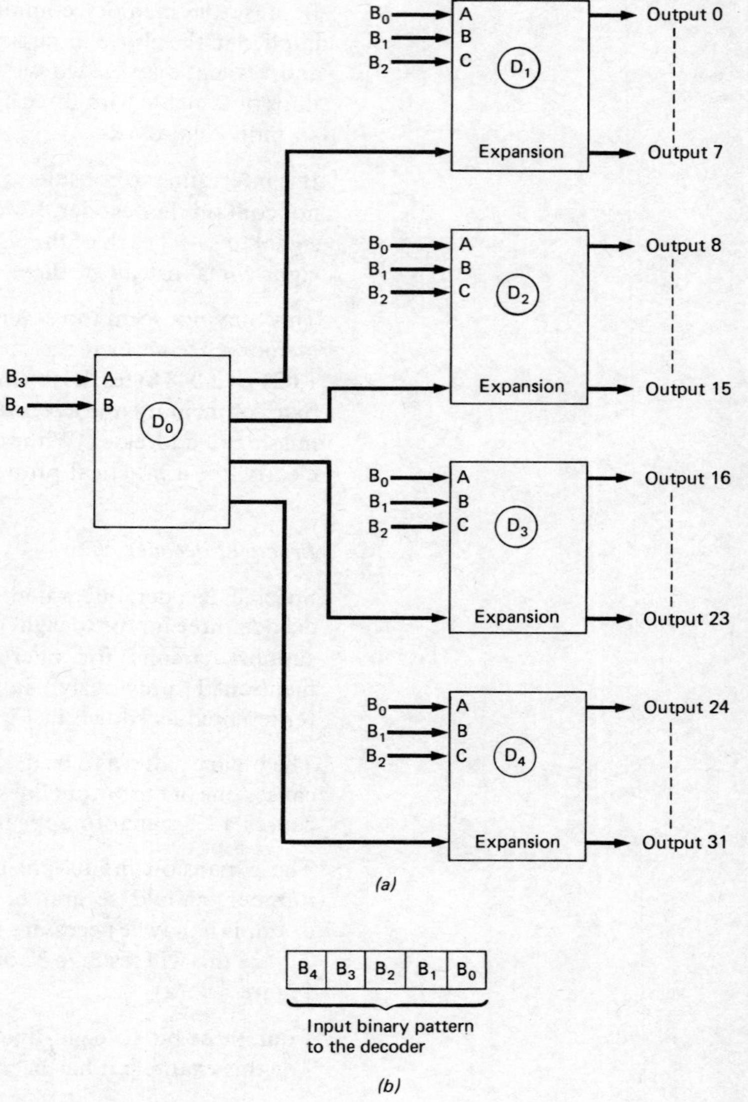

Figure 4.11

expansion input. If the signal on this input is active (a '1') the chip outputs behave as has been explained. If, however, this input is inactive (a '0') the chip outputs are all forced to be inactive *whatever* the states of the signals on A, B and C. Thus the outputs are all at zero.

The input binary pattern to the decoder of Figure 4.11(a) is as shown in Figure 4.11(b), where bits B_0, B_1 and B_2 are the least significant and B_3 and B_4 are the most significant bits.

Bits B_0, B_1 and B_2 go in parallel to the A, B and C inputs of all the four decoders. Bits B_3 and B_4 are connected into a separate two-bit to four-line decoder (D_0) and the outputs of this feed the expansion inputs of the other four chips. Thus:

(*a*) when $B_3 = 0$ and $B_4 = 0$, chip D_1 is selected (outputs 0–7)
(*b*) when $B_3 = 1$ and $B_4 = 0$, chip D_2 is selected (outputs 8–15)
(*c*) when $B_3 = 0$ and $B_4 = 1$, chip D_3 is selected (outputs 16–23)
(*d*) when $B_3 = 1$ and $B_4 = 1$, chip D_4 is selected (outputs 24–31).

In other words the whole circuit acts as a five-bit to thirty-two-line decoder.

The three expansion inputs of a practical decoder provide logical combinations for use in expansion of the decoder inside the chip itself and thus give greater flexibility.

Q4.9

Decoding in microcomputer systems

The use of decoding has been illustrated in this chapter by considering the very simple example of an 8-byte memory. Selection of an individual byte was performed by a three-bit to eight-output decoder inside the memory chip.

Practical memory chips generally contain many more than 8 bytes, of course, but the principles outlined earlier still hold. Thus a memory chip of capacity, say 1,024 bytes, must be supplied with a 10-bit binary-coded address to access any location. The memory chip itself uses the ten address bits to select the byte required, i.e. it performs the 10-bit to one-in-1,024 decoding operation.

A total memory for a microcomputer is built up of many such chips to achieve total capacities of 64 Kbytes or more. The function of decoder chips as components in these systems is, as has been outlined in Chapter 2, to select individual memory or I/O circuits from the total number making up the system. They do this by detecting the binary pattern representing the unique address of the required memory or I/O chip on the address bus and using the output signal produced by this pattern to drive the 'chip select' control input of the memory or I/O circuit.

Q4.6, 4.7

4.6 Memory organisation

Consider a microcomputer memory made up of eight type 2708 EPROM chips. Each chip (Table 2.3) contains 1,024 bytes. The total memory size is thus 8,192 bytes and the memory map is as shown in Figure 4.12. This figure assumes that the total memory address space is 64 Kbytes and that the top 8K addresses are being used for memory-mapped I/O as discussed earlier.

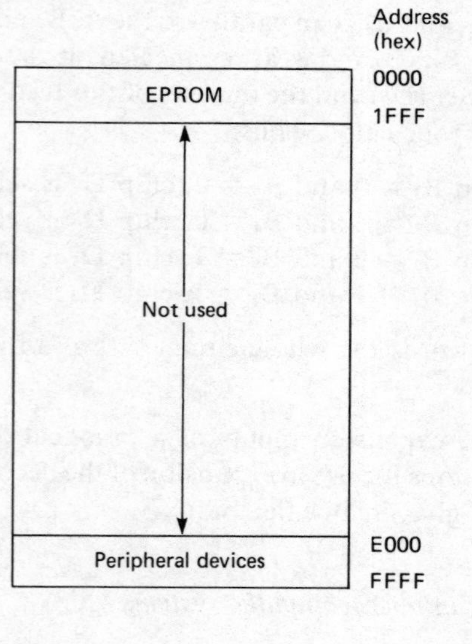

Figure 4.12

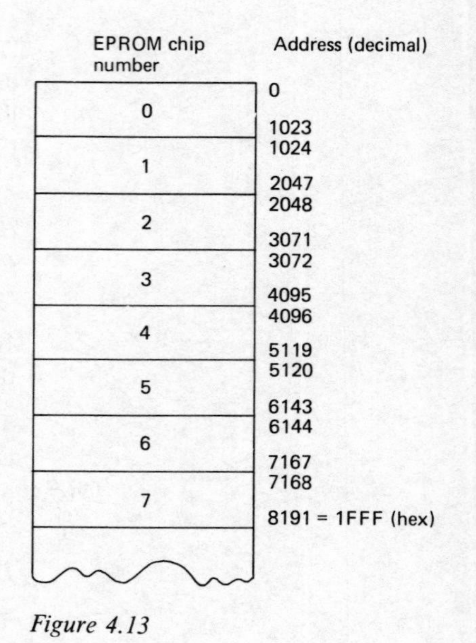

Figure 4.13

Table 4.4

	Address (dec)	*Address (hex)*	*Address (binary)* 15	14	13	12	11	10	9	8	7	6	5	4	3	2	1	0
Chip 0	0	0000	0	0	0	0	0	0	0	0	0	0	0	0	0	0	0	0
	1,023	03FF	0	0	0	0	0	0	1	1	1	1	1	1	1	1	1	1
Chip 1	1,024	0400	0	0	0	0	0	1	0	0	0	0	0	0	0	0	0	0
	2,047	07FF	0	0	0	0	0	1	1	1	1	1	1	1	1	1	1	1
Chip 2	2,048	0800	0	0	0	0	1	0	0	0	0	0	0	0	0	0	0	0
	3,071	0BFF	0	0	0	0	1	0	1	1	1	1	1	1	1	1	1	1
Chip 3	3,072	0C00	0	0	0	0	1	1	0	0	0	0	0	0	0	0	0	0
	4,095	0FFF	0	0	0	0	1	1	1	1	1	1	1	1	1	1	1	1
Chip 4	4,096	1000	0	0	0	1	0	0	0	0	0	0	0	0	0	0	0	0
	5,119	13FF	0	0	0	1	0	0	1	1	1	1	1	1	1	1	1	1
Chip 5	5,120	1400	0	0	0	1	0	1	0	0	0	0	0	0	0	0	0	0
	6,143	17FF	0	0	0	1	0	1	1	1	1	1	1	1	1	1	1	1
Chip 6	6,144	1800	0	0	0	1	1	0	0	0	0	0	0	0	0	0	0	0
	7,167	1BFF	0	0	0	1	1	0	1	1	1	1	1	1	1	1	1	1
Chip 7	7,168	1C00	0	0	0	1	1	1	0	0	0	0	0	0	0	0	0	0
	8,191	1FFF	0	0	0	1	1	1	1	1	1	1	1	1	1	1	1	1
						Select chip			Select address within each EPROM									

The eight chips making up the EPROM have individual start and finish addresses as shown in Figure 4.13. These have, for clarity, been written in decimal form. They are shown in hexadecimal and binary form in Table 4.4, from which it can be seen that the bottom ten address bits (bits 0–9) are used to select addresses *within* every chip. For instance bytes in Chip 5 start at address 5,120 (dec), i.e. 1400 (hex) and finish at 6,143 (dec), i.e. 17FF (hex). At the start of this block of memory address bits 0–9 are all zero (see entry for 5,120 in Table 4.4) and at the end of the block they are all one (see entry for 6,143 in Table 4.4).

The address of the chip itself is given by the next three most significant bits, i.e. bits 10, 11 and 12. For Chip 5 these three bits are 101 (5). For Chip 7 they are 111 (7).

This memory is connected to the address bus as shown in Figure 4.14. Address bits 0–9 go to the address inputs of every memory chip. Address bits 10, 11 and 12 are decoded by a three-bit to eight-line decoder, the output lines of this device being used to select the chip required.

As discussed earlier the memory space of the computer need not be filled with real memory, i.e. gaps can be left in it as was shown in Figure 4.6. If this is done not all the outputs of the decoder used to select the memory chips need be used. Only those corresponding to addresses at which real ROM, RAM or EPROM exists are required.

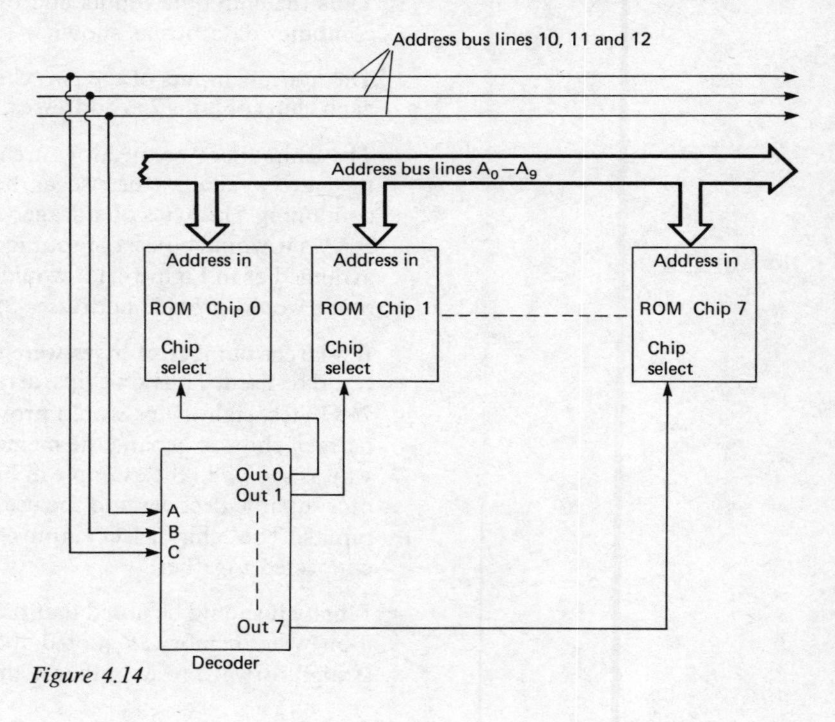

Figure 4.14

4.7 Memory chip size

Memory chips, as will have become apparent, have very variable size. They vary both in the *width* of each location that can be addressed (see Section 4.1) and in the total number of addresses that are available per chip.

The previous section has considered how the number of words of storage, i.e. how the number of addresses in a store, can be increased by the use of many memory chips together with additional address decoder circuits. This section briefly discusses how the width of a memory can be increased.

Expanding memory width

Section 2.3 gave examples of typical memory chip sizes. Consider the Intel 2101A static RAM memory (Table 2.2). This chip has a capacity of 256 words each containing 4 bits, i.e. the width of each chip location is 4 bits. To make up a memory capable of holding, say, 256 bytes requires two chips to be connected as shown in Figure 4.15.

Effectively the two chips are connected in parallel. One chip (labelled chip A in the figure) provides storage for the most significant 4 bits of the byte, i.e. for bits 4 to 7 inclusive. The other chip (labelled chip B) provides storage for the least significant 4 bits, i.e. bits 0 to 3 inclusive. Thus the chip data inputs and outputs are connected to the microcomputer data bus as shown.

The address inputs of the two chips are connected in parallel. Since each chip contains 256 addresses, address bus lines A_0 to A_7 are used.

The 'chip select' connections are not shown in Figure 4.15. However they are available for use as before. For example, if a memory containing 512 bytes of storage were to be constructed using 2101A RAMs it would consist of four memory chips in two pairs. One pair, arranged as in Figure 4.15, would provide addresses 0 to 255 and the other would provide addresses 256 to 511.

If a larger number of bytes were to be required, more pairs of chips could be used. Thus six chips, arranged in three pairs, would provide 768 bytes, eight chips would provide 1,024 bytes and so on. Adding pairs of chips to expand the memory address range works in the same way as shown in the example in Figure 4.14 and requires the addition of a suitable decoder and the use of the 'chip select' memory control inputs. The 'chip select' inputs of the memories in each pair are connected together.

Finally it should be noted that the use of 4-bit wide chips to make an 8-bit wide memory as quoted above is only an example. It is just as straightforward to use other memory widths. For instance, an 8,192

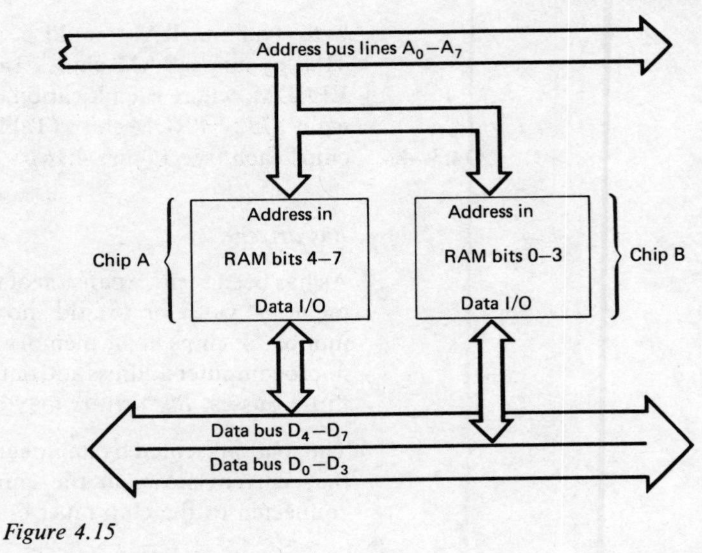

Figure 4.15

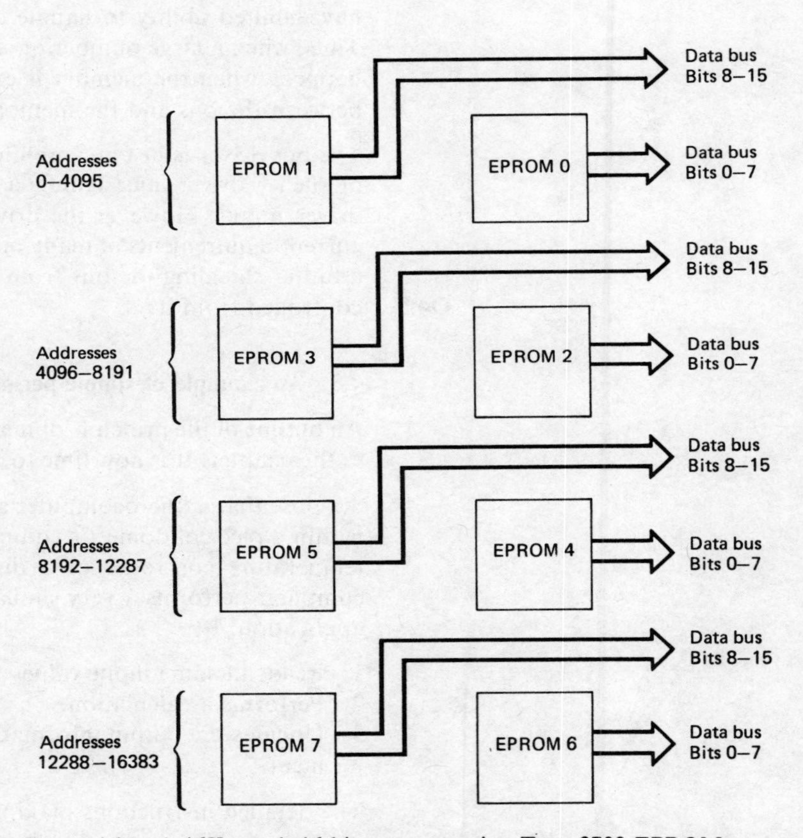

Figure 4.16 A 16K-word, 16-bit memory using Type 2732 EPROMs

byte dynamic RAM could be constructed using eight Texas TMS 4108 dynamic RAM chips (Table 2.1). Similarly a 16,384-location EPROM, where each location contains 16 bits, could be made using eight 2732 EPROM chips (Table 2.3) arranged as four groups of two chips each (see Figure 4.16).

Q4.3, 4.4

Bus drivers

As has been seen, expansion of the memory size, either to increase the memory width or to add more addresses, involves increasing the number of chips in the memory. These chips must be connected to the microcomputer address and data busses and each represents a *load* on those busses. *Bus drivers* may be necessary to cope with this load.

The load presented by an integrated circuit chip is caused by the fact that current flows in the chip inputs and outputs. Any circuits connected to the chip must be able to deal with this current flow.

The circuits inside the microprocessor and other chips which send and receive signals on the address and data highways of the system have limited ability to handle currents in the wires of the busses. Thus, when a large number of chips are connected to a bus, as often happens when the memory is expanded, bus drivers are connected between the bus and the memory.

The bus driver is just an amplifier. A bus line connected to the input of such a driver must handle a small current (that required by the driver input). However the driver output is able to cope with the current requirements of many other chips. The bus driver thus acts as a buffer shielding the bus from the effects of the many chips being controlled from it.

Q4.5

4.8 An example of simple peripheral input operations

An outline of the principle of memory-mapped I/O was given earlier in the chapter. It is now time to consider a simple practical example.

Suppose that a microcomputer system is to be used as a control unit within a piece of domestic equipment such as a washing machine, a temperature controller or a digital clock. In general, the microcomputer performs a very similar cycle of operations, whatever the application. It:

1. Reads in some input values from the external equipment.
2. Performs a calculation.
3. Updates the output information being sent to the external equipment.

The detailed instructions making up these operations vary with the application. The program for a clock is obviously different from that for controlling a washing machine, for instance, but the three major steps above are generally necessary.

In later chapters complete examples of the use of the microcomputer in various applications will be presented. Here a small subsection of such applications, namely the input of information to the microcomputer, is described. Furthermore it is assumed that the inputs to be examined are all simple two-state switching devices. These could be relays, switches or the outputs of latches.

A block diagram of the system is shown in Figure 4.17.

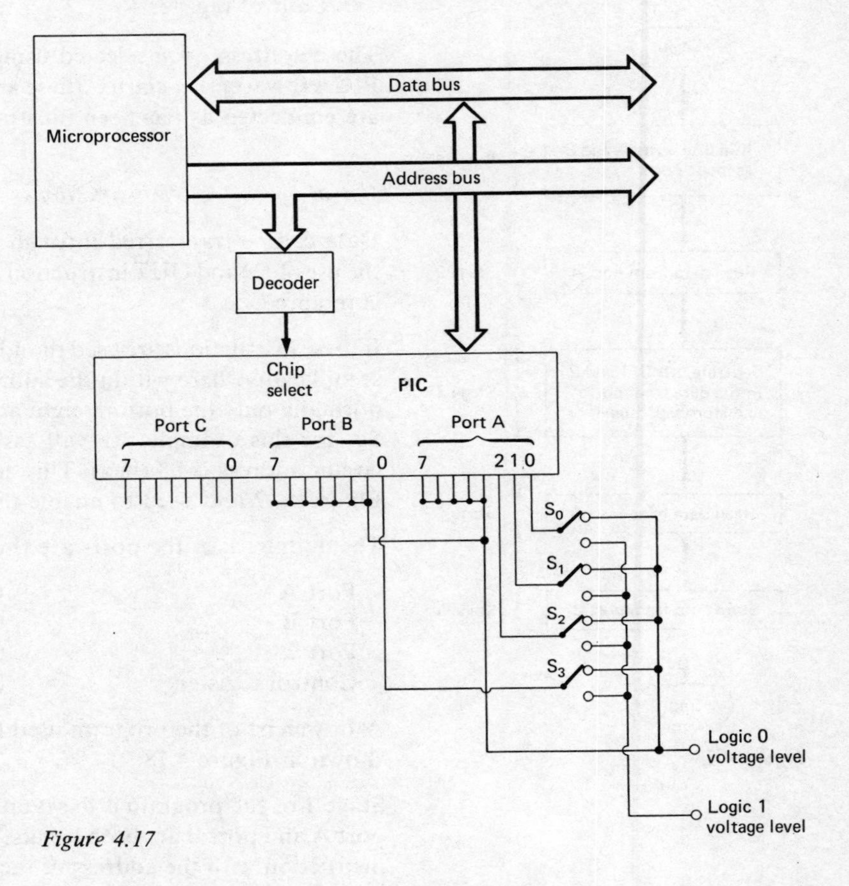

Figure 4.17

For simplicity the input devices to be interrogated by the microprocessor are all simple switches. These are labelled S_0, S_1, S_2 and S_3. They are connected to the microcomputer system using a peripheral interface circuit of the type described in Chapter 2. Each can be switched to logical 1 or logical 0.

The interface circuit contains three ports, each of 8 bits, labelled A, B and C. The switches are assumed to be connected to bits 0, 1 and 2 of port A and to bit 0 of port B. All the other bits of port A (bits 3 to 7 inclusive) and of port B (bits 1 to 7 inclusive) are connected permanently to logical 0.

The peripheral interface circuit contains, as discussed previously, a control register as well as the three ports. The addresses in the unit, as before (Section 2.4) are taken to be:

Port A	0, i.e. 00 (hex)
Port B	1, i.e. 01 (hex)
Port C	2, i.e. 02 (hex)
Control register	3, i.e. 03 (hex)

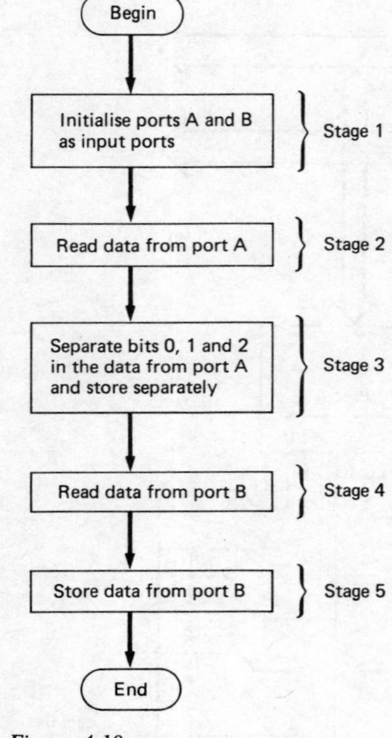

Figure 4.18

These addresses are selected using the 'register select' inputs to the PIC. However, for clarity, these are not shown on the diagram. They are connected as has been illustrated in Figure 2.16.

Use of IN and OUT instructions

Data can be transferred through the peripheral interface circuit by the use of IN and OUT instructions. For reading the switches, only IN is required.

If these instructions are used the address of the circuit can, as has been seen, lie anywhere within the address range of the machine although normally only the bottom eight address lines are used (Section 4.3). So, for this example, we will assume that the peripheral interface circuit address is 08 (hex). This address is sensed by the decoder in Figure 4.17 and used to enable the PIC.

The addresses of the ports are thus as follows:

Port A	08 + 00 = 08 (hex)
Port B	08 + 01 = 09 (hex)
Port C	08 + 02 = 0A (hex)
Control register	08 + 03 = 0B (hex)

A flowchart of the program used to read the state of the switches is shown in Figure 4.18.

Stage 1 of the program is to set up the PIC, i.e. to *initialise* it, so that port A and port B are both inputs. This is achieved by using an OUT instruction with the address of the PIC control register and with the bit pattern to be placed in the control register held in A. Thus:

```
MVI  A,92
OUT  0B
```

The pattern placed in the PIC control register is 92 (hex) i.e. 10010010 (binary) which, as shown in Figure 2.13, makes ports A and B both inputs in mode 0.

Stage 2 of the program reads data from port A. Thus:

```
IN  08
```

The data read goes into the A register. Following this instruction, therefore, the least significant three bits of the A register contain ones or zeros indicating the states of switches S_0, S_1 and S_2. All the other bits in A are zero.

A few program instructions are needed at this stage (stage 3) to separate out bits 0, 1 and 2 and to store their values individually. The section of code to do this will not be considered further here, but examples of similar sequences are given in later chapters.

At stage 4 the state of switch S_3 is read in through port B. Thus:

```
IN  09
```

Again the data goes into the A register. This time however, it can be stored directly as only the one switch is connected to port B. A convenient way of achieving such storage is to transfer the value in A into another register. Thus at stage 5 there may be:

```
MOV  E,A
```

i.e. transfer the value in the A register into the E register.

Memory-mapped I/O

Memory-mapped I/O can be used to transfer data through the PIC instead of IN and OUT orders.

The address of the PIC, in this method, must be arranged to be within the peripheral device address area. Using the address space allocation illustrated in Figure 4.6, therefore, the PIC must have an address between E000 (hex) and FFFF (hex). Suppose it is taken to be E000 (hex). Then

Port A has address E000 (hex)
Port B has address E001 (hex)
Port C has address E002 (hex)
The control register has address E003 (hex)

As explained in Section 4.4 any memory transfer instruction can be used, in this system of input-output, for peripheral data transfer. Thus the PIC initialisation at the beginning of the program could use the instructions:

```
MVI  A,92
STA  E003
```

The second of these writes the contents of the A register 92 (hex) directly to address E003, i.e. to the PIC control register.

Similarly data could be read through port A or port B into registers other than A. For instance:

```
LXI  H,E001
MOV  E,M
```

loads the H,L register pair with E001 (hex), the address of port B, and then takes in information from that address directly to register E.

These possibilities allow more economical programs for peripheral data transfer to be written.

Q4.8, 4.10, 4.11

Questions

4.1 Explain the concept of a memory map and show how it can be used to help the design of a memory system for a microcomputer.

4.2 Describe the organisation of the memory in a microcomputer system explaining what is meant by
(a) the memory width;
(b) the address range.
A microcomputer has a total address space of 32 Kbytes. If the machine is to possess 12 Kbytes of ROM and 8 Kbytes of RAM, where the ROM occupies the low-address end of the memory, starting at address 0000 (hex), and the RAM occupies the high-address end of the memory, express the start and end addresses of each block in hexadecimal notation.

4.3 Explain how an *n*-bit wide memory can be made up from proprietary integrated circuits having a width of less than *n* bits. Using the tables given in Chapter 2 propose ways of assembling the following memories:
(a) A 64-byte RAM with an access time of less than 100 ns.
(b) A 16,384-byte EPROM.
(c) A 16,384-word ROM. Each word is to contain 16 bits.
Show how the address connections to the chips in each of *(a)*, *(b)* and *(c)* can be organised. Are address decoders needed in these systems?

4.4 Sixteen Intel 2114 RAM chips are to be used to make an 8,192-byte memory. Show how an address decoding chip can be employed to enable address lines A_0–A_{12} to be used to select any address in this store.

4.5 What extra circuits are required when a large number of memory chips are used to construct a high-capacity store? Assuming that bus driver chips each containing four drivers are available, estimate the *total* number of chips required for the memory in Question 4.4.

4.6 Discuss how a 1 Kbyte block of memory may be located within a larger (64 Kbytes) store using address decoding. Show how careful positioning of the 1 Kbyte block can minimise the complexity of the decoder circuits required. Express all addresses in the discussion in hexadecimal form.

4.7 A microcomputer having a total address range of 64K addresses is to use memory-mapped I/O in which addresses in the range 62K to 64K are to be used to access peripheral devices. Discuss the address decoding requirements of this system. Is such a choice of peripheral addresses a sensible one?

4.8 Compare and contrast programmed I/O using special peripheral-transfer instructions such as IN and OUT with memory-mapped I/O. List the advantages and disadvantages of each method.

4.9 Why is decoding required in microcomputer systems? Explain how a six-bit to sixty-four-line decoder could be constructed:
(a) Using simple logic gates.
(b) Using three-bit to eight-line decoder chips with a single expansion input.

4.10 A microcomputer is to be used as a controller in a washing machine. In this it must interrogate a number of two-state signals which indicate the state of the wash cycle. Thus:
When signal 1 = 1 the wash tub is full.
When signal 2 = 1 the water heater is on.
When signal 3 = 1 the wash tub is empty.
When signal 4 = 1 the water temperature is hot enough.
Show how these signals can be connected to the microcomputer. Draw a flowchart for the program to interrogate them and, using the code in Appendix 1, write the instruction sequences to examine the washing machine state.

4.11 A microcomputer is to be used to generate a square-wave signal. Four switches are to be connected to the microcomputer to control:
(a) Whether the square wave is switched on or off (if it is off the microcomputer output must stay at the logical 0 level).
(b) The duration of the square wave. The duration is to be set in steps of T. Thus it can be T, $2T$, $3T$, etc., up to $8T$.
Show how the switches can be connected to the microcomputer and draw a flow diagram of the program required to interrogate them.

Chapter 5 Introduction to subroutines and stacks

Objectives of this chapter *When you have completed studying this chapter you should be able to:*

1. *Understand that computer programs often contain sequences of instructions which are repeated many times.*
2. *Understand that such repetition of instructions is wasteful of memory space and represents unnecessary effort for the programmer.*
3. *Understand that the use of subroutines allows a single section of program code to be used many times within a larger program.*
4. *Explain the principles of subroutines.*
5. *Explain the important features of subroutines, e.g.*
   - (a) *they shorten the program object code;*
   - (b) *they improve the program structure by encouraging it to be written in a modular fashion;*
   - (c) *program readibility is improved;*
   - (d) *the program running time is increased;*
   - (e) *they may alter the contents of registers which are in use in the main program.*
6. *Realise that it is necessary to pass parameters or arguments between a main program and a subroutine and that two ways of achieving this are:*
   - (a) *by using the processor registers; or*
   - (b) *by placing the parameters in memory and using one or more processor registers to hold a pointer to the area of store involved.*
7. *Realise that entry to a subroutine and exit from it require the use of special CALL and RETURN instructions.*
8. *Explain that, because of 5(e) above, it may be necessary to store the contents of the processor registers before entering a subroutine.*
9. *Recognise that correct entry to a subroutine and exit from it involves storage of the value of the program counter on entry, and restoration of this value on exit.*
10. *Realise that a stack is a last-in, first-out memory (LIFO).*
11. *Understand that data is pushed on to a stack and popped or pulled from it.*

5.1 Why subroutines are important

Very often within a computer program it is necessary to perform a particular task many times. In this situation a *subroutine* can be used. A subroutine is a single section of program code, i.e. a sequence of instructions, which can be employed over and over again within a larger program.

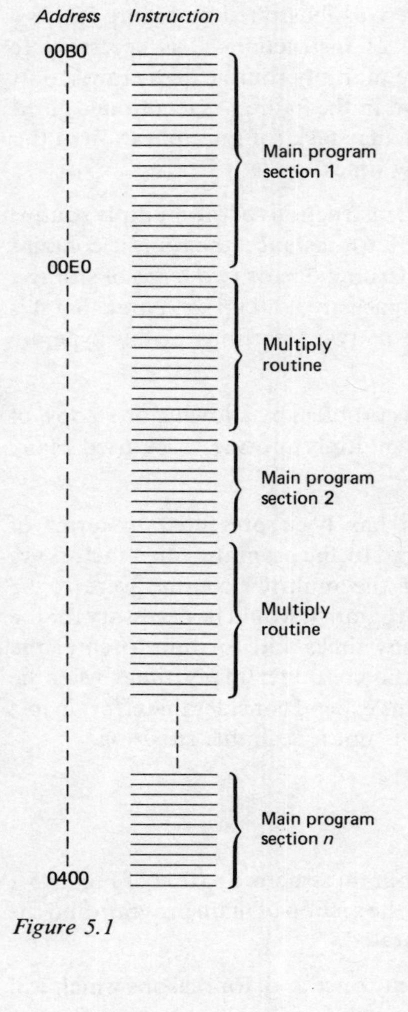

Figure 5.1

The need for subroutines

Consider the situation shown in Figure 5.1. This diagram illustrates a program consisting of a sequence of machine code instructions starting at address 00B0 (hex) and continuing to address 0400 (hex). The program thus occupies 848 bytes of memory space. The instructions in the program are represented, in the figure, by short horizontal lines. This has been done simply for clarity and convenience in drawing the diagram.

The program begins with a sequence of instructions (labelled 'main program section 1') which perform some task or other. Let us suppose that these are part of a scientific calculation.

In such a calculation it is likely to be necessary to form the products of numbers, i.e. to be able to multiply numbers together. However if a microcomputer such as the Intel 8085 is being used for the calculation there is no 'multiply' instruction in the order code. The processor simply does not contain any circuits to do multiplication. In passing it is worth noting that it does not possess a 'divide' instruction either.

Multiplication is, of course, really only a sequence of repeated addition operations. For instance,

$$4 \times 24 = 24 + 24 + 24 + 24$$

Similarly division is only a sequence of repeated subtractions. Thus it is a relatively simple matter to write a short program to perform multiplication, using the processor add instruction, or to write a division program using the subtract instruction (see Appendix 1). Such programs are commonly called *routines.*

Returning to Figure 5.1, then, let us assume that 'main program section 1' calculates the values of two numbers and that these subsequently must be multiplied together. The multiplication, as suggested above, is carried out by a short routine, the 'multiply routine' of the figure, which follows 'main program section 1'.

After this multiplication more manipulations are carried out by the code sequence 'main program section 2' and following this another multiplication is performed. This cycle may continue over and over again using sections of main program code interspersed with multiply routines.

If the complete program is written, as illustrated by Figure 5.1, as a straightforward linear sequence of instructions it is necessary to include the orders making up the multiply routine many times, only the first two of these being shown in the figure. As mentioned at the beginning of this section a particular task (of multiplication in this instance) must be repeated many times.

It is clearly wasteful to include the instructions of the multiply routine over and over again in this way. If, for instance, the routine contains forty or fifty instructions, each needing one or two bytes of storage, forty or more bytes of memory space are used up each time that it is inserted into the program. One or two insertions of this type are tolerable, but more are not.

The use of subroutines avoids this problem by allowing one 'copy' of the instructions making up the multiply routine to be used many times.

Although the above discussion has been presented in terms of reducing the storage space required by the program, other factors are also important. For instance if the multiply routine were to be repeated many times within the program it would be necessary for the programmer to write it out many times and for him to enter the instructions comprising it into the computer many times when he types in his program. He must thus expend considerable effort in just repeating sections of code. This is not a desirable situation.

5.2 Introduction to subroutines

An alternative and preferable program structure to that of Figure 5.1 is illustrated in Figure 5.2. In this the section of main program and the multiply routine have been separated.

The multiply routine is written only once and, for reasons which will become apparent, is now known as the multiply *subroutine*. For the purpose of this example this subroutine has been assumed to be placed in memory with its first instruction at address 0301. The instructions to perform the multiplication within the subroutine are exactly the same as they were before.

The sections of code making up the main program now follow on directly one after the other. Thus 'main program section 1' ends at address 00E0 and 'main program section 2' starts at the next location, that is at address 00E1. Of course, the multiply subroutine and main program must both be stored in the memory at the same time so the addresses in store which they occupy must not overlap. This is why the subroutine is shown as starting at address 0301 after the end of the main program which, now that it does not have the subroutine code inserted in it several times, is assumed to finish at address 0300.

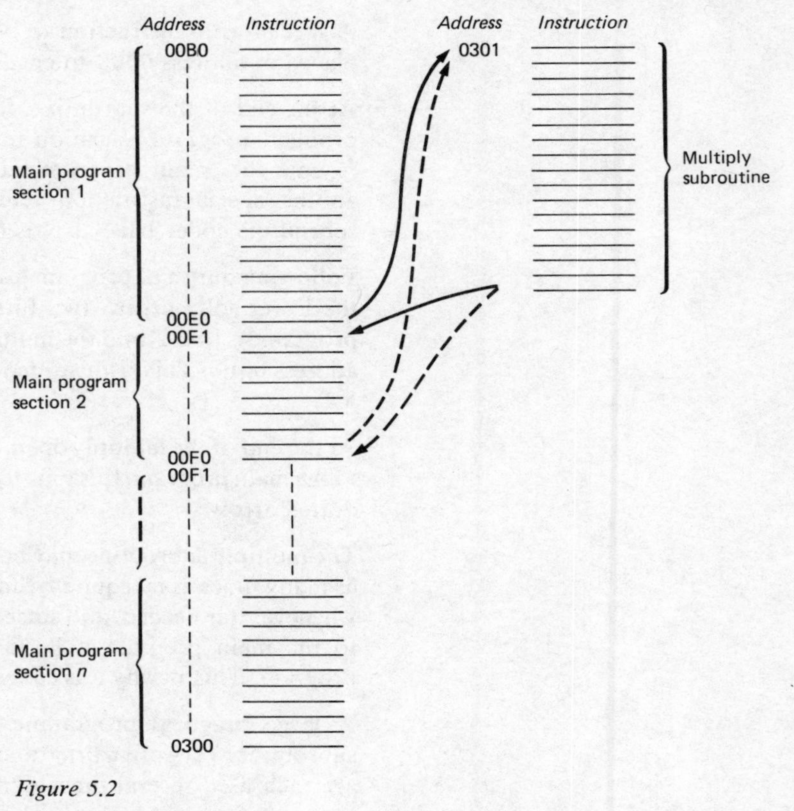

Figure 5.2

Q5.1 The subroutine is drawn beside the main program in this figure only so that the method of entry to it and exit from it can be clearly illustrated.

Program operation using a subroutine

Although the program code making up the multiplication subroutine is placed in the computer memory only once, the multiplication operation which it performs is still required the same number of times as it was before when there were many copies of the code throughout the program. Thus it is necessary for the sequence of execution of the program to be as indicated by the arrows in Figure 5.2.

The 'main program section 1' instructions calculate the values of two numbers as before. To multiply these numbers together it is now necessary for the multiply subroutine to be executed, i.e. for its instructions to be run before 'main program section 2' begins. Hence from address 00E0 program execution must be transferred to the start of the subroutine, at address 0301. This is shown by the upper solid arrow in Figure 5.2, and is called '*entering* or *calling* the subroutine'.

A special 'call' instruction to be discussed in detail in Chapter 7 is placed in address 00E0 to ensure that it occurs.

At the end of the subroutine, following calculation of the required product, program execution must be returned to address 00E1 to resume the 'main program section 2'. There must, therefore, be another special instruction 'return' which is placed at the end of the subroutine code. This, also, is discussed in Chapter 7.

Following return of program execution to address 00E1, as shown by the lower solid arrow, two further values are calculated by 'main program section 2' and the multiply subroutine is entered again from address 00F0. This is illustrated by the upper dotted arrow in Figure 5.2.

At the end of the multiply operation, execution is once more returned to the main program, this time to address 00F1, as shown by the lower dotted arrow.

The multiply subroutine may be used over and over again in this way, as many times as is required. Since it is called from the main program whenever it is needed, and since program flow always returns from it to the main program it is, in a sense, subordinate to the main program. This is why it is called a *sub*routine of the main program.

A large practical programme is not limited to the use of one subroutine. Very often programmes contain many subroutines which are each used several times during a calculation. Subroutines may, moreover, be used for many different purposes. They are not limited to performing only arithmetic operations and later examples will illustrate some of their other applications.

Nested subroutines

Figure 5.2 has illustrated one *level* of subroutining, i.e. it has shown a situation in which a main program calls a subroutine or several subroutines each of which return control to the main program on completion of their task. The main program may be regarded as the top level of program with the subordinate subroutines one level below it.

Often further levels of subroutining are necessary. Figure 5.3 shows a program structure in which the main program calls a subroutine which itself calls another subroutine. There are thus two levels of subroutine involved.

Whenever the main program calls subroutine A that subroutine itself calls subroutine B. Thus the program flow is from the main program to subroutine A and from there to subroutine B.

Subroutine B completes its operation and returns control to sub-

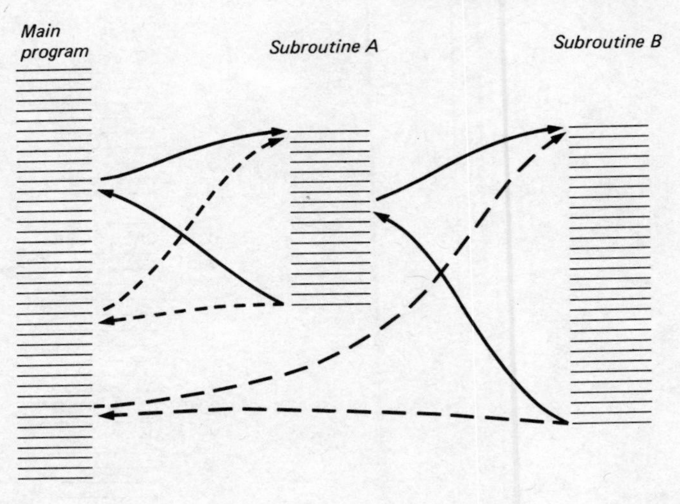

Figure 5.3

routine A at the instruction following the one causing entry to B. Subroutine A then completes its operation (using the results obtained from the operation of B) and returns control to the main program as before.

This process, in which subroutines call other subroutines, is called *nesting* of subroutines. In principle, at least, it may occur to any *depth*. That is subroutine A may call B which, in turn, calls C which calls D, etc., etc. Return is from D to C to B to A as before.

As shown in the figure, subroutine B is not necessarily only called from subroutine A. It may also be called directly from the main program. Such a situation could arise if B were a multiplication subroutine, as discussed earlier, and A were a subroutine which, say, found square roots. Subroutine B is of general applicability whenever multiply operations are needed, including those multiplications involved in taking the square root of a number.

Subroutine entry and exit

The picture emerging from the above description is of a group of subroutines which can be entered in a very flexible way both from the main program and from each other. The manner in which this is achieved is discussed in detail in Chapter 7. It should be noted here, though, that a special mechanism is needed for it. The use of simple branch instructions does not allow the transfers of control which are required. An example will clarify this point.

Consider Figure 5.4. The diagram is very similar to Figure 5.2. It has been assumed that a main program uses a subroutine which it enters twice using the instructions in addresses 00E0 and 00F0. It is desired

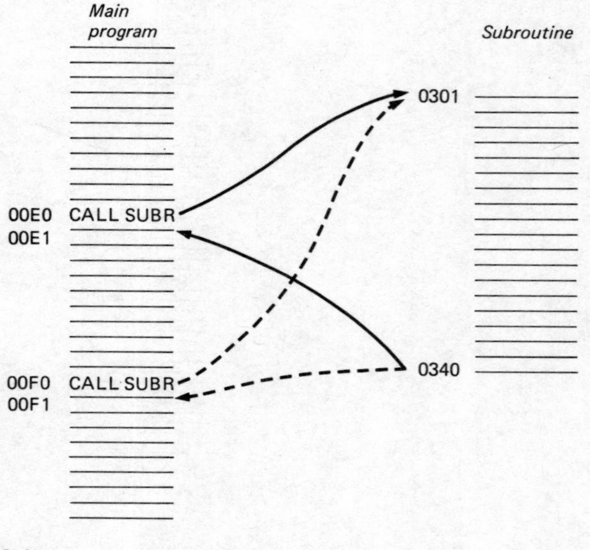

Figure 5.4

to cause the subroutine to return control after the first entry to 00E1 and after the second to 00F1.

Entry to the subroutine from 00E0 could be managed by placing a 'branch to 0301' instruction in address 00E0. Return to 00E1 could be achieved by placing a 'branch to 00E1' instruction at the end of the subroutine in address 0340.

Entry to the subroutine for the second time, from address 00F0, could be achieved by placing a 'branch to 0301' instruction in 00F0. However, correct return from the subroutine is now not possible since in address 0340 there is already the instruction 'branch to 00E1'. And, of course, address 00E1 is not the correct return point for the second exit from the subroutine. The correct point is, in fact, address 00F1.

Thus the use of branch orders for subroutine entry and exit falls down even in the simple case of the single level of subroutining chosen for this example. For more complex structures of subroutines it is wholly inadequate.

The special subroutine entry instruction 'CALL' and return instruction 'RETURN' which were mentioned earlier in the chapter completely overcome these difficulties.

Q5.3

Advantages of the use of subroutines

The use of subroutines in a program confers a number of advantages. First, since the instructions making up the subroutine only have to be included once in the program, the program length is reduced. Hence the amount of storage space needed for the *object code* of the program is minimised. (The object code is the list of machine code instructions making up the program.) Secondly, the structure of the program is improved. It is widely recognised that a good way of writing programs which can be easily debugged and corrected is to make them *modular*. Thus it is good programming practice to write a program as a sequence of modules. Each module consists of a block of program code and should, preferably, have a single entry point and a single exit as shown in Figure 5.5.

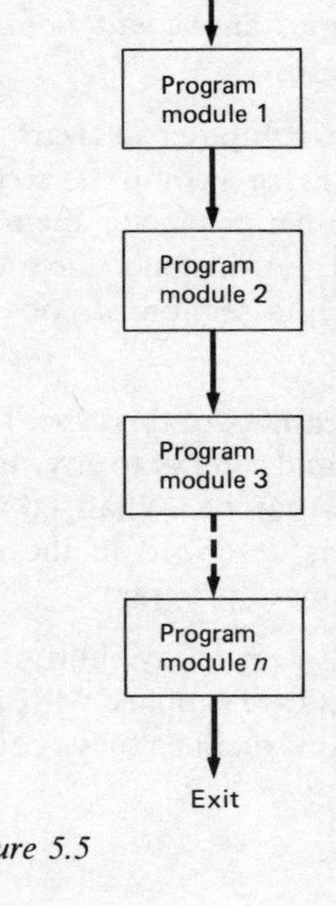

Figure 5.5

The use of subroutines encourages the development of modular programs. Each subroutine forms one module and, usually, each one has only a single entry point and a single return point.

It is possible to write a complete program as a sequence of such subroutines. If this is done the main program is reduced to a list of call instructions which just control the sequence in which the subroutines are invoked.

Debugging, i.e. finding and correcting the errors in such a program, is much simplified because the flow of control through the program is clearly defined.

The third advantage gained from the use of subroutines is that the *readability* of the program is improved. A programmer can examine a listing of the program and can more easily understand what it does if it is written as a sequence of subroutines.

Generally the subroutines are given names which are descriptive of their function. Thus the multiply subroutine considered earlier might be called MULT, a time-delay subroutine might be called DELAY and so on. Reading a program which consists of a sequence of calls to these subroutines, for example:

```
CALL  MULT
CALL  SQROOT
CALL  DELAY
Etc.
```

it is fairly easy to deduce what the program is intended to do. It is certainly much easier than reading through the detailed sequence of instructions which would replace the calls if subroutines were not employed.

If it should be required to inspect the functioning of a particular subroutine module in detail it is always possible to examine the code of that module. Thus splitting up the program into modules does not cause any loss of ability to examine the fine detail within it.

Libraries

The use of subroutines brings one further important benefit; *libraries* of useful sections of program can be built up.

It was realised early on in the development of computer software that it would be beneficial to store useful routines for a computer so that they could be used not only by the programmer producing them but also by other users of the computer system. For instance the multiplication routine discussed earlier is clearly a section of code for which many users would find an application.

Subroutines are well suited to general applicability of this type. They can be entered from anywhere in a program and can exit to anywhere, as just outlined. If information (parameters) can be exchanged with them in a convenient and flexible way, as described in the next section, they become easy to 'slot in' to a main program.

Thus it is possible to have available in a system many subroutines grouped together in a so-called library. Users are supplied with a list of available routines and can employ such of them as they require.

5.3 Parameter passing

The need for parameter passing

One aspect of the use of subroutines which has not been dealt with so far is the question of *parameter passing*. It is often necessary to pass parameters to a subroutine when it is called and to receive back information from it when it completes its operation.

The multiplication routine considered in the previous section takes two input values (the numbers whose product is to be found) and multiplies them together to produce a result. On entry to the subroutine from the main program, therefore, it is necessary for that program to pass the values of the two operands to the subroutine.

When the subroutine passes control back to the main program using the RETURN instruction it must also pass over the result of its operation, that is the product of the input operands. Hence this subroutine has two input parameters and one output parameter. It should be noted that sometimes these parameters are called the *arguments* of the subroutine.

The parameter-passing process is illustrated in Figure 5.6. The number and type of parameters passed to and from subroutines can be very varied. Often, as quoted in the example above, only a few data values need be exchanged. Sometimes, however, as in the case of a subroutine to process a matrix, a large number of parameters are involved.

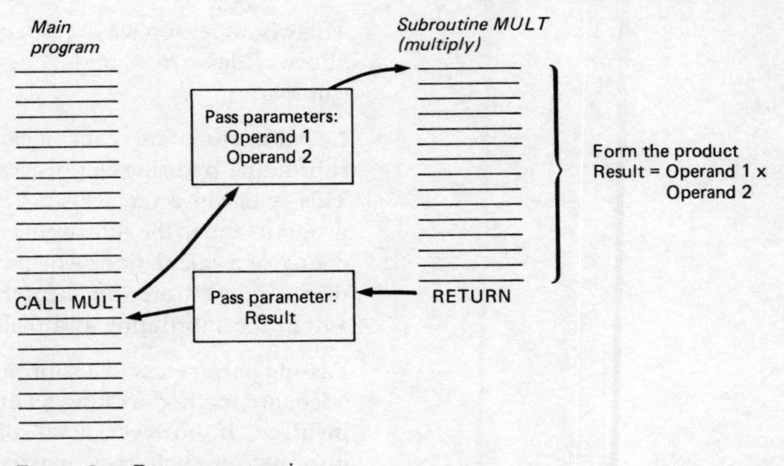

Figure 5.6 Parameter passing

Sometimes the parameters to be passed are not simply numerical values. A subroutine to perform a peripheral transfer, for example, requires information to be passed to it specifying the device to be used and, perhaps, the mode of operation of that device. These parameters define the *way* in which the subroutine (or the devices which it controls) are to function.

Methods of parameter passing

There are various methods by which parameters can be passed to a subroutine.

The first of these is to employ one or more of the processor registers to hold the parameter(s) to be exchanged. Consider the Intel 8085 microprocessor. As has been seen, this possesses registers A, B, C, D, E, H and L. Any of these can be used to hold a parameter to be passed to a subroutine.

To call the multiply subroutine, therefore, a program could:

(a) Place operand 1 in register B.
(b) Place operand 2 in register C.
(c) Call the subroutine.

On return the subroutine could:

(a) Place the upper 8 bits of the result in register B.
(b) Place the lower 8 bits of the result in register C.
(c) Return to the main program.

Two registers (B and C) have been used to return the result to the main program because the product of two 8-bit numbers is, in general, a 16-bit number.

There is no reason why registers B and C have been particularly used above. Registers A and B or D and E would have been equally suitable.

If parameters are exchanged between a main program and a subroutine by using the processor registers care must be exercised. This is because the registers are normally used both in the main program and in the subroutine to hold intermediate results during the course of a calculation. Any parameters passed to a subroutine must, therefore, be stored in memory before use is made of the registers within the subroutine and their value is overwritten.

Passing parameters to a subroutine using the processor registers is an adequate method as long as only a small amount of information is involved. If, however, a subroutine is to be used to process a lot of information such as a matrix containing 64 × 64 (4,096) values another method is required.

In this situation the information to be passed to the subroutine is stored in the microcomputer memory. A *pointer* to the address of the first location of the area of memory involved is then passed to the subroutine in the registers. Figure 5.7 shows this arrangement.

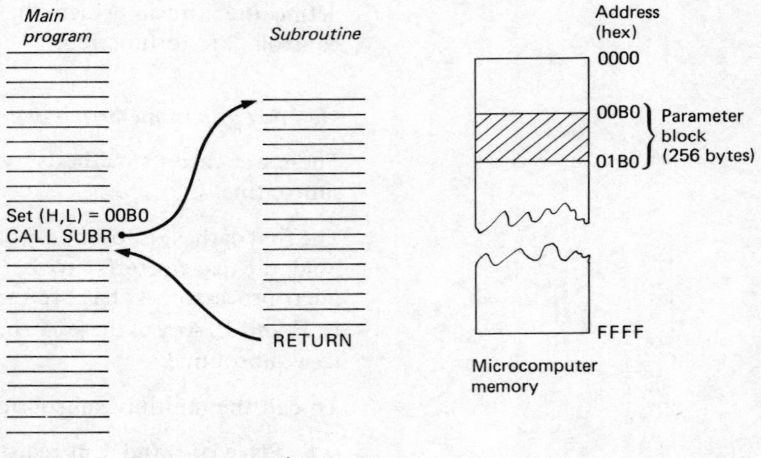

Figure 5.7 Parameter passing

In the 8085 microprocessor the H and L registers are normally used to hold memory addresses. Hence if the parameters to be passed to the subroutine are stored in memory locations 00B0 to 01B0 (this represents 256 bytes) the contents of H and L are set, respectively, to 00 (hex) and B0 (hex).

In other words H holds the most significant half of the address of the first byte of the parameter block and L holds the least significant half of that address. This is commonly described as using H,L to hold a pointer to the parameter block.

The subroutine is easily able to get access to the parameters. For example the 8085 instruction

```
MOV   (register),M
```

where (register) can be A, B, C, D or E causes data to be taken from the memory byte whose address is the number contained in H and L and to be placed in register A or B or C, etc.

There is also an instruction

```
INX  H
```

which increments (adds +1 to) the H,L register pair. Thus it is a simple matter to step through the parameters from 00B0 to 01B0 picking them up into a register one at a time.

To return large amounts of information to the main program the subroutine uses the same method. It

1 Places the results it has calculated in the memory at some suitable position.
2 Sets the contents of H and L to point to the first address of the result area.
3 Returns control to the main program.

Using the memory to exchange parameters between the main program and the subroutine is not necessarily limited to the transfer of large amounts of data. It is also effective when only a few bytes have to be transferred. However, it does have a tendency to add to the time the program takes to run since storing parameters, setting values into H and L and retrieving parameters is a time-consuming process.

Q5.7, 5.8

5.4 Saving and restoring data

The processor registers

Both the main program and its subroutines are likely to use the processor registers during the course of a calculation. Thus when a transfer of control is made from one part of the program to another, say by the main program calling a subroutine, it is important, before the call is executed, to save the values stored in these registers. Then, when control is returned to the main program after the subroutine has run, the register contents can be restored and the program can resume operation exactly where it left off.

Strictly, of course, if the subroutine does not use the registers at all, there is no need to save them as described above. But this would be an unusual situation, especially if the subroutine performs calculations of any complexity.

Q5.6

The program counter and subroutines

The program counter, as has been discussed in earlier chapters (Section 1.2), is a register inside the processor which has a specific purpose. It always holds the address of the *next* instruction to be executed. Thus it is used, during the instruction-fetch cycle of the computer, as the memory address of the instruction to be obtained.

In the context of subroutines the program counter has a special significance. It may be seen from Figure 5.4 that the address to which a subroutine must return control is that which follows the CALL instruction causing entry to the subroutine.

When the CALL instruction at, for example, address 00E0 is executed the return address is 00E1 and, because of the way in which the program counter operates, this is the number which it contains. Similarly at the instant when the CALL at address 00F0 is executed the program counter holds 00F1. Again this is the address to which the subroutine must return control.

If, therefore, the value in the program counter is stored whenever a subroutine call is executed, the correct return address is automatically saved. Return to this address from a subroutine can then be achieved by causing the stored address to be loaded into the program counter by the RETURN instruction at the end of the subroutine code. Specific examples of this operation will be given later.

Summary

To summarise the foregoing sections it can be seen that when a subroutine is called from a main program (or indeed from any other program) the calling program must, in general, store the contents of the processor registers, including the program counter, before the CALL instruction is executed.

Return to the main program, to resume its operation precisely where it was broken off, can then be achieved by restoring the stored register values at the end of the subroutine.

Disadvantages of subroutines

Some of the advantages of the use of subroutines have been outlined earlier. As with most things there are corresponding disadvantages.

The first possible disadvantage has been mentioned in Section 5.3: using subroutines tends to increase the length of time that a program takes to run. Or, to put it the other way around, it tends to reduce the running speed of the program. The reasons for this are fairly clear. Before entry to a subroutine is made, the processor, controlled by the calling program, must save the register values. Before return from the subroutine can be effected these values must be restored.

There are thus *overheads* which are inevitably associated with the use of subroutines. The saving and restoring processes give rise to time overheads and increase program run time. It may not matter if the run time of a program is increased, of course. Not all programs have constraints on the time which they can take. In general it is only programs that are in *real-time* systems, i.e. which are interacting with another process outside the microcomputer, that are in any way time-critical. A good example of such a process is the use of a microcomputer to process an analogue signal varying in time.

The second disadvantage is that the use of subroutines also incurs storage space overheads. The register contents and, perhaps, other values which have to be saved on passing control to a subroutine must be stored somewhere. Usually they occupy memory space.

Q5.2

5.5 Introduction to stacks

So far it has been stated that the register contents must be stored before entry to a subroutine. However there has been no discussion of how this storage takes place. *Stacks* are important in this context.

A mechanical stack

A good way to visualise a stack is shown in Figure 5.8. This diagram represents a stack as a container. In step one, at the left of the diagram, one object has been placed in the stack, i.e. in the container. This is object A and it lies at the top of the container held up by a spring which is between it and the container bottom.

In step two another object, B, has been placed in the stack. Adding B

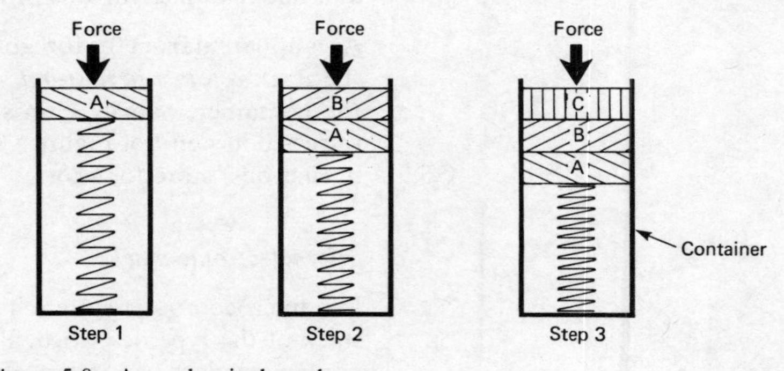

Figure 5.8 A mechanical stack

in this way is a simple operation; B is placed on top of A and the two (A and B together) are pushed downwards, compressing the spring, until the top of B is level with the top of the container.

In step three another object, C, has been added to the top of the stack in the same way. The last object to be added to the stack is thus always the one which is at the top. The first object to be placed on the stack is always at the bottom. The number of objects that can be held is limited by the stack size, in this example by the number that will fit inside the container.

Because of the way in which objects are added to the stack the operation of storing an object is known as *pushing* it on to the stack.

Retrieval of objects from the stack is by *pulling* or *popping* from it. Figure 5.9 shows this operation. This figure is the reverse of Figure 5.8. When the force on the top of the stack is released the object at the

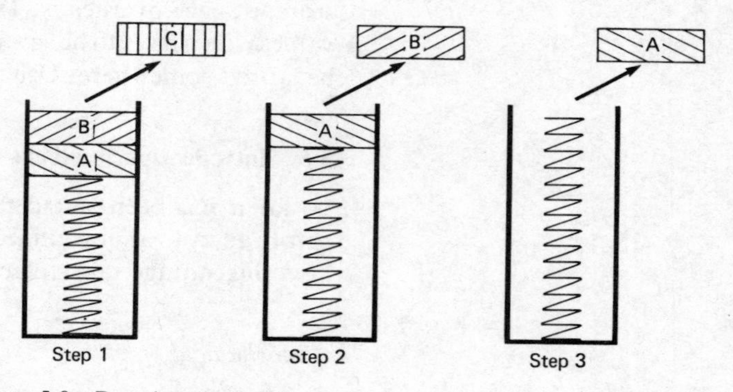

Figure 5.9 Popping the stack

top (C) comes out of the container and is retrieved. B and A both move up one place, B reaching the top of the stack. Next B can be extracted from the stack, with A moving to the top, and finally A can be removed. The stack is then empty. Pulling and popping are alternative names for this process of removing data from the stack.

As is apparent from the foregoing description and from the diagrams, the stack is a *last-in first-out store*. The last object to be pushed into the container, namely C in step 3 of Figure 5.8, is the first to be retrieved in step 1 of Figure 5.9. Such a device is called a LIFO (Last-in first-out) store for short.

Q5.5

Microelectronic stacks

In a microcomputer system it is not, of course, appropriate to use a stack of the type described. Practical microelectronic stacks can be implemented in a number of ways. One of these is to fabricate a special area of memory, which operates as a LIFO store, within the microprocessor chip. Another is to use a part of the normal RAM as a stack in conjunction with a special register known as a *stack pointer*.

These possibilities will be discussed further in the next chapter.

Applications of stacks

Stacks are very convenient for storing the program counter values required to allow return from a subroutine.

When a CALL instruction is encountered in a program the value in the program counter during execution of that instruction is automatically pushed on to a stack. When a RETURN instruction is encountered at the end of a subroutine the value at the head (the top) of the stack is popped from it and loaded into the program counter. This ensures that the main program is re-entered at the instruction following the call to the subroutine.

Use of the stack in interrupt-handling and in nested subroutine program structures is dealt with in later sections.

Q5.4, 5.9–5.11

Questions

5.1 Explain why subroutines are important in the development of large computer programs. Give examples of situations in which it is appropriate to use one or more subroutines.

5.2 List the main advantages and disadvantages of the use of subroutines. Illustrate each item which is listed by the use of appropriate examples.

5.3 Discuss how entry to a subroutine and exit from a subroutine is achieved by the use of CALL and RETURN instructions. Show that it is not possible to perform subroutine entry and exit using only the normal BRANCH or JUMP instructions in the microcomputer instruction set.

5.4 Describe what is meant by 'nesting' of subroutines. Show that entry to and exit from nested subroutines may be achieved by storing the contents of the program counter at the time when a CALL instruction is executed. How can such storage be implemented in practice?

5.5 What is meant by a stack? Show how a stack might be used to store the contents of the program counter to allow subroutine entry and exit. Outline the meanings of the terms PUSH and POP with reference to their use for manipulating the contents of the stack.

5.6 Explain why it is usually necessary to save the contents of the processor registers before a subroutine is entered. Illustrate the answer with examples.

5.7 Draw a flow diagram showing how the expression

$$y = 1 + 3x + 4x^2 + 7x^3$$

can be evaluated for all values of x between 0 and 20. Assume that a multiplication subroutine is available and illustrate how it can be used in the above calculation.

5.8 A set of 100 numbers is stored in a microcomputer memory between locations 0B00 (hex) and 0B63 (hex). Discuss how a subroutine could be written to calculate the mean and variance of these numbers using the formulae:

$$\text{Mean} = \frac{1}{100} \sum_{n=1}^{100} x_n$$

$$\text{Variance} = \frac{1}{100} \sum_{n=1}^{100} x_n^2$$

Outline the way in which the input values can be passed to the subroutine and the output values passed back to the main program.

5.9 Using the Intel 8085 instruction set given in Appendix 1, write the sections of program code involved in passing the parameters described in Question 5.8.

5.10 Draw a flow chart for the subroutine described in Question 5.8. Does this subroutine need to call any other subroutines if it is written to run on an Intel 8085 microprocessor?

5.11 A set of 1,000 numbers are stored in a microcomputer memory. Draw the flowchart of a program that will find the largest and the smallest of these numbers. Are there any sections of this program that could conveniently be written as subroutines?

Chapter 6 The stack mechanism

Objectives of this chapter *When you have completed studying this chapter you should be able to:*

1. *Describe the microcomputer organisation of a stack.*
2. *Describe the capacity of a stack in terms of the number of levels of storage it provides.*
3. *Recognise that the stack is a flexible data storage device and may be used to hold single values or blocks of data.*
4. *Describe the use of the stack to store the return address for a subroutine.*
5. *Understand the use of the stack to store the contents of the processor registers before a subroutine is called so as to enable these values to be restored on exit from the subroutine.*
6. *Understand the use of the stack in holding return addresses and register values to support nested subroutines.*
7. *Recognise that the stack forms a convenient temporary data store.*
8. *Understand the operation of the instructions PUSH and POP which are used to manipulate the contents of the stack.*
9. *Recognise that the stack may be implemented in registers which are either:*
   - *(a) on the processor chip of the microcomputer system; or*
   - *(b) in the system random access memory.*
10. *Recognise that stacks on the processor chip have limited capacity but that stacks in RAM can have very large capacity.*
11. *Explain the function of a stack pointer and its operation:*
    - *(a) during a PUSH instruction and*
    - *(b) during a POP instruction.*
12. *Appreciate the advantages and disadvantages of using a stack in RAM as opposed to a stack on the processor chip.*
13. *Appreciate the instructions typically available for manipulation of the stack contents and the way in which they are used.*

6.1 The stack is a last-in, first-out (LIFO) store

Chapter 5 contained a brief introduction to the concept of a stack using a mechanical analogy. It is described there how objects to be placed in the stack are pushed into it from the top and how objects to be retrieved are pulled off it, also from the top.

Another analogy that could have been used for stack operation in that chapter is that of a pile (a stack) of sheets of paper. Information to be put on the stack, say a new sheet, is placed on top of the pile. When information is to be retrieved sheets are picked from the top of the pile in order.

It can be seen from this example, as well as that in Section 5.5, that the stack is a last-in, first-out store (LIFO). The sheet placed on the pile last is the one on the top and is therefore the first one to be removed in a retrieval operation. Thus at any instant of time it is the last piece of data (the last sheet) to be put in the stack which is the first to be taken out.

The size of the stack is normally described in terms of the number of *levels* it contains. In the case of the pile of paper the number of levels is the same as the number of sheets. In a microcomputer stack the number of levels refers to the number of separate items of information that can be held in the stack.

If, for example, a stack is designed to hold 8-bit values and consists of sixteen memory locations each 8 bits wide, i.e. it is 16 bytes, it is said to be a sixteen-level stack.

Blocks of data

The use of stacks is not restricted to storage of single items of data. Very often in microcomputer systems a number of items of information can naturally be grouped together and are best handled in the system as a group.

We have seen, for example, that when a subroutine is called from a main program the contents of the processor registers, including the program counter, must be stored so as to allow return to the calling program from the end of the subroutine. The processor register contents, in this instance, can be considered as a block of information which must be stored and retrieved in its entirety.

The block contains a number of bytes of information each of which represents the contents of one processor register (an 8-bit system such as the 8085 or 6809 is assumed). The program counter, being a 16-bit register, requires 2 bytes. Thus there may be, say, 10 bytes of data to be saved on entry to a subroutine. These are made up of:

1 byte for (A)
1 byte for (B)
1 byte for (C)
1 byte for (D)
1 byte for (E)
1 byte for (H)
1 byte for (L)
1 byte for (Processor Status Register)

2 bytes for (Program Counter).

where, as before, (A) means 'the contents of register A'.

Very often, of course, it is not necessary to save the contents of all the processor registers since the main program may not be using them all. Hence only a few may contain valid data. However it is generally necessary to save the contents of several registers together in a block.

To do this the block of information can be placed together on the stack as shown in Figure 6.1.

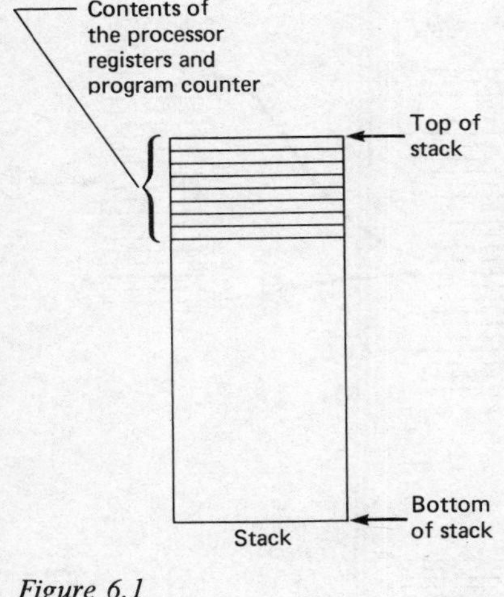

Figure 6.1

To save the information individual items are pushed on to the top of the stack one after another using instructions provided in the computer order code as described later. To retrieve the data, individual items are pulled from the stack, again using the instructions provided.

Use of the stack with nested subroutines

Chapter 5 contained a short outline of the concept of nested subroutines in which a subroutine itself calls another subroutine. The action of the stack as a last-in, first-out memory is well suited to this type of operation.

Consider Figure 6.2(a). This shows a main program which calls a subroutine (subroutine A) which itself then calls a second subroutine (subroutine B). It is necessary, as has been seen, to store the value in the program counter when the call instruction to subroutine A is made so as to allow return to the main program at the end of A. Similarly it is necessary to store the program counter value at the point at which B is called, in order to permit return to A at the end of B. It may also be desirable to store the contents of some of the processor registers both when A is called and when B is called. Figure 6.2(b) illustrates how this can be done using the stack.

When the main program calls subroutine A, instructions within it are used to push those contents of the processor registers which must be saved on the stack. The call to the subroutine then causes the value in the program counter to be stored. Thus a block of data relevant to the return of control from subroutine A to the main program is placed on the top of the stack.

When subroutine B is called from A, a similar procedure is followed. Instructions in subroutine A are used to place register values which must be conserved on to the stack. The call to B then also puts the program counter value appropriate for return from B to A on the stack.

Figure 6.2(b) shows the stack contents after subroutine B has been

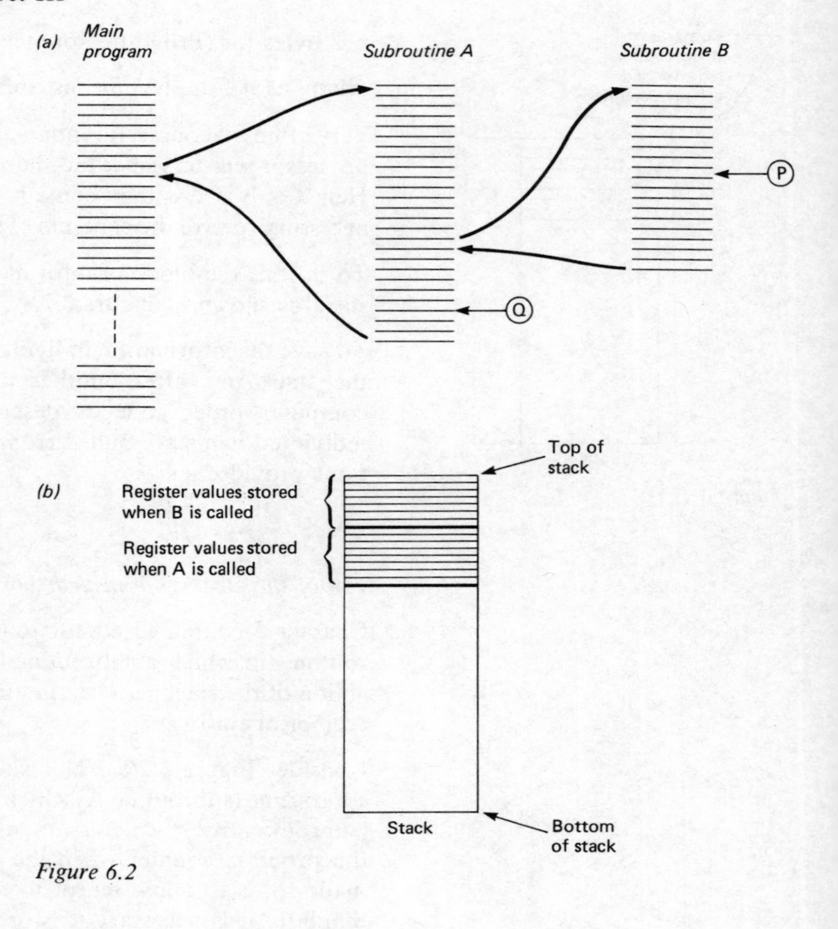

Figure 6.2

entered, say at the instant when execution of the program is at some instruction P within the body of B.

The values on the top of the stack are those which were put there on entry to B, namely the register contents and return address necessary to permit operation of A to be resumed when B finishes.

The register values and return address necessary to allow the main program to be resumed when subroutine A finishes have been pushed down in the stack and lie beneath the values for return from B to A.

When subroutine B completes execution the values on the top of the stack are retrieved. The RETURN instruction at the end of B causes the retrieved program counter value (which was held in the locations at the very top of the stack) to be placed in the program counter. This transfers program execution to the instruction following the call to B in subroutine A. Instructions in subroutine A are then used to extract

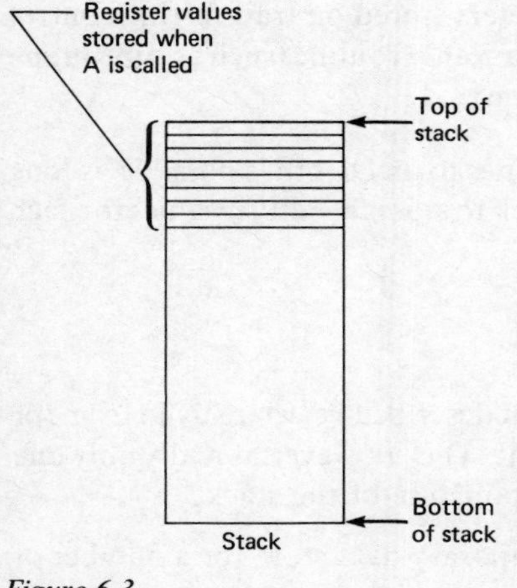

Figure 6.3

the stored register values from the stack and to place them in the appropriate registers. Following this, operation of A can be resumed where it was left off.

Each time that a value is taken from the stack the stored information beneath it moves up one position, as outlined in Section 5.5. Thus when program execution is within subroutine A, for example at instruction Q [Figure 6.2(a)] following return from B, the contents of the stack are as illustrated in Figure 6.3.

The quantity on the very top of the stack is now the return address from A to the main program. Hence the RETURN instruction at the end of subroutine A causes this value to be loaded into the program counter and control is passed to the main program. Instructions within this program extract the required register values and operation is resumed.

Because of the way in which the stack functions as a LIFO memory an orderly transfer of control from main program to subroutine A to subroutine B and then back from B to A to main program is automatically achieved.

The system works correctly for more complicated structures. For example, Figure 6.4 shows a main program and five subroutines called A, B, C, D and E. The states of the stack at various points during program execution are illustrated in Figure 6.5. In this figure the parameters relevant to the return of control to a particular routine are represented by a box with letters in it. Thus

| MP | represents the parameters stored on transferring control from the main program to a subroutine.

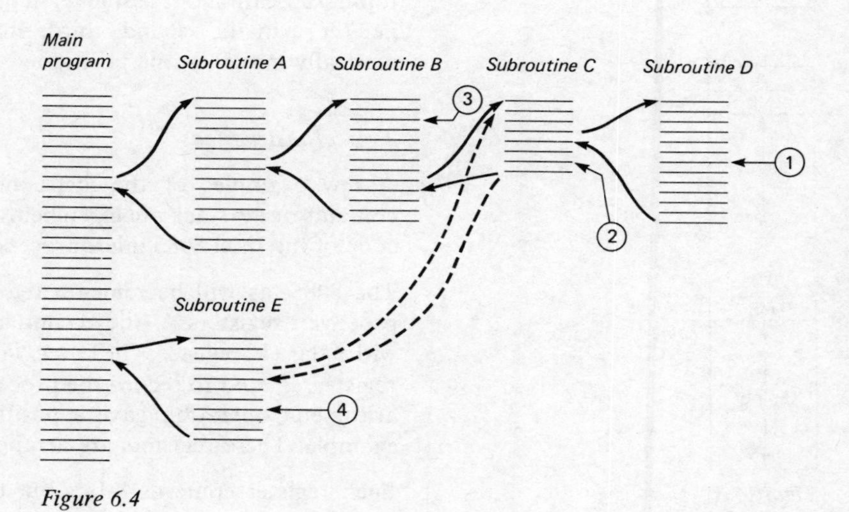

Figure 6.4

A	represents the parameters stored on transferring control from subroutine A to another routine (such as subroutine B or the main program).

It is clear that nesting of subroutines to any depth is possible as long as there is enough space in the stack to store the return values for each level.

Q6.2, 6.3

Stack contents — *Point within program*

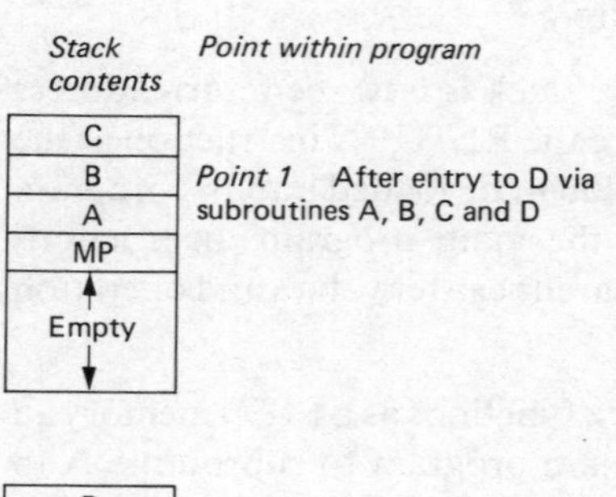

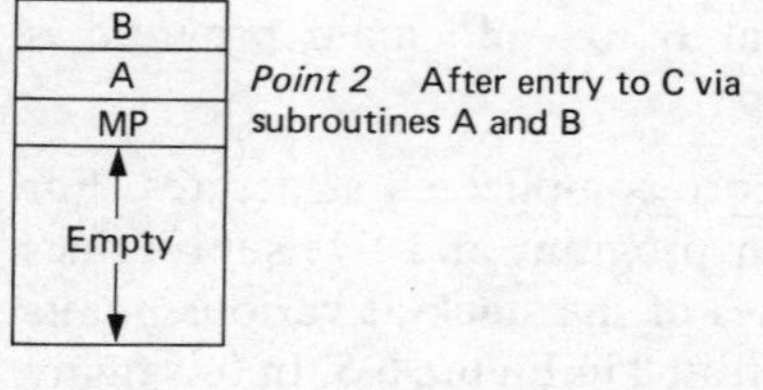

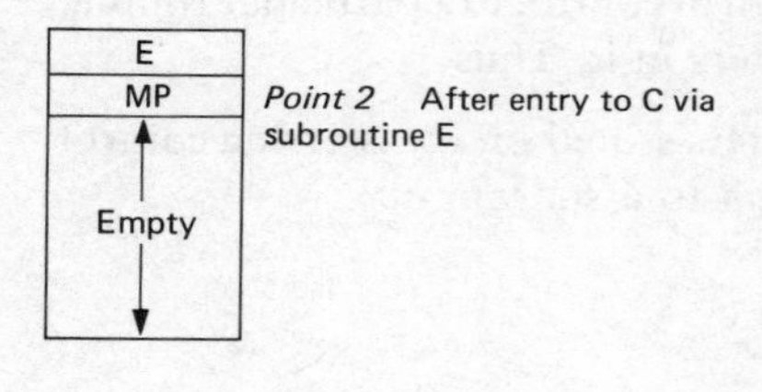

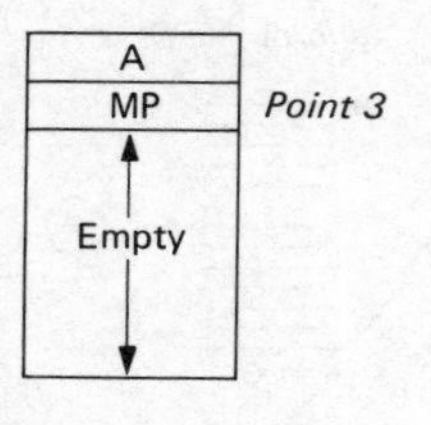

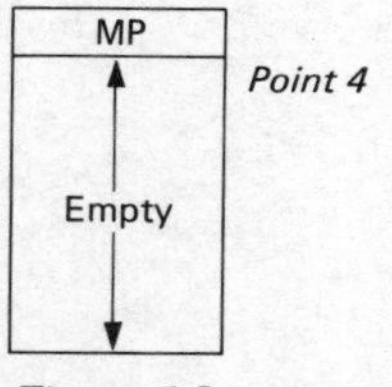

Figure 6.5

The stack as a data store

So far the stack operation has been described very largely in terms of its use for subroutine entry and exit. This, however, is really only one (although admittedly very important) use of the stack.

The stack forms a convenient temporary data store for a number of applications. As long as its last-in, first-out mode of operation suits the manner in which data can conveniently be stored and retrieved there is no reason why it should not be used in this way. In fact this mode of access to data is particularly appropriate in certain applications. One example of this occurs in the manipulation of arithmetic expressions by a high-level language compiler.

6.2 The PUSH and POP operations

The push operation, as outlined in Section 5.5, is used to place a new value on the top of the stack. This value is, in effect, placed on top of any other numbers already in the stack and the whole lot is 'pushed down' one position so that the new information resides in the topmost (or first) stack location.

The pop or pull operation is used to take a data value out of the topmost location of the stack. All the values below the one extracted, i.e. those in the second, third, etc., locations of the stack, automatically move up one position.

Typical instructions

A few examples of the instructions used for manipulating the contents of the stack are given below. These are taken from the order code of the Intel 8085 microprocessor which is listed in Appendix 1.

The 8085, as will be remembered from earlier chapters, contains processor registers A (the accumulator), B, C, D, E, H, L together with a flag (F) register. The latter, which is sometimes called the *status* register, is used to record the processor status – whether a previous arithmetic operation gave a positive, negative or zero result, for example. These registers are arranged as shown in Figure 6.6.

Each register contains 8 bits but they can be grouped in pairs as

8 bits	8 bits
B	C
D	E
H	L
A	F

Figure 6.6

shown. Thus B is grouped with C, D with E, H with L and the accumulator with the flag register. The latter pair are collectively called the PSW (*p*rocessor *s*tatus *w*ord).

The push and pop operations available in the instruction set of the machine include:

```
PUSH  B
PUSH  D
PUSH  H
PUSH  PSW
```

In these instructions B refers to the register pair B and C, D to the pair D,E, H to the pair H,L and PSW to the pair A,F. All instructions operate in a similar manner.

Thus when a PUSH B instruction is executed the contents of the B and C registers are pushed on to the top of the stack, taking up two locations. When a PUSH PSW instruction is executed the contents of A and F are pushed on to the top of the stack, and so on.

The available POP operations are:

```
POP  B
POP  D
POP  H
POP  PSW
```

and each of these performs the inverse operation, as defined below, to the corresponding PUSH instruction. Thus the instruction POP PSW takes the contents of the top two stack locations and places them in A and F. To be precise the contents of the top stack location are popped and placed in F and then a second POP operation is executed with the data obtained being placed in A.

PUSH B – pushes B and then pushes C
PUSH D – pushes D and then pushes E
PUSH H – pushes H and then pushes L
PUSH PSW – pushes A and then pushes F

The POP operations are the inverse:

POP B – pops C and then pops B
POP D – pops E and then pops D
POP H – pops L and then pops H
POP PSW – pops F and then pops A

It is interesting to note that as long as the PUSH and POP operations on any register pair are the exact inverse of one another, as above, the programmer does not really need to know which stack location is used for A and which for F (or for B and C, etc., if the other pairs of instructions are considered).

The registers used during a calculation can thus be saved on the stack when entry is made to a subroutine by executing one or more of the PUSH orders. They can be retrieved by executing the corresponding POP operations.

There is also an instruction:

```
XTHL
```

which causes the contents of the H and L registers to be exchanged with those of the top two locations of the stack. Thus the contents of the top two locations in the stack are popped and placed in H and L whilst the previous contents of H and L are pushed on to the stack, occupying the same top two locations.

Any of these instructions can be placed anywhere within the code of a program to allow the stack to be used as a temporary data store as mentioned earlier.

6.3 Stack implementation in microprocessors

As has been outlined in Chapter 5 there are two ways in which stacks are implemented in microprocessor systems. The first of these is for the manufacturer of the system to include an area of memory which acts as a LIFO store on the processor chip. The second is for an area of the system RAM to be used in conjunction with a *stack pointer* register in the processor.

Stacks on the processor chip

Some microcomputer systems contain registers, organised to act as a stack, within the microprocessor chip. These are used to store the program counter contents when entry is made to a subroutine.

Generally the size of such stacks is rather limited. For example:

1 The Rockwell PPS4 microprocessor chip contains a two-level stack.
2 The Texas TMS 1000 microprocessor chip contains a one-level stack.
3 The General Instruments PIC 1645/1650 microprocessor contains a two-level stack.
4 The Intel 4040 microprocessor chip contains a seven-level stack.
5 The Signetics 2560 microprocessor chip contains a fifteen-level stack.

Because the capacity of the stacks in these devices is limited they are normally intended *only* for storing the contents of the program counter when subroutines (or interrupt service routines) are entered. They are not intended for use in storing any other information.

Hence the Intel 4040 microprocessor, for example, allows seven levels of subroutining. The Texas TMS 1000 microprocessor has only one register in which the program counter contents can be stored (this is not really worthy of the name stack) and, consequently, allows only one level of subroutine call.

Since the restricted stack, as has been indicated, is intended solely for holding the contents of the program counter, i.e. subroutine return addresses, any processor register contents which must be saved have to be stored elsewhere. This is perfectly acceptable, however, since they can be written as normal variables into memory.

The microprocessors listed above are, in the main, at the least sophisticated end of the range of available devices. They are intended for use in simple, undemanding applications and in these the restriction on the number of levels of subroutining possible is not too serious. However, for the larger, more sophisticated third- and fourth-generation systems the limited stack size obtainable when the stack is fabricated from processor registers may be a serious limitation. For these systems the alternative of using a part of the RAM as a stack is an attractive proposition. **Q6.5**

Random access memory used as a stack

The most common way of implementing a stack in later generations of microprocessors is to use the RAM in conjunction with a stack pointer. The stack pointer is simply a register in the processor of the microcomputer which is used in a rather special way. It holds the address of the location in RAM which is at the top of the stack. Thus it *points* to the top of the stack, as illustrated in Figure 6.7.

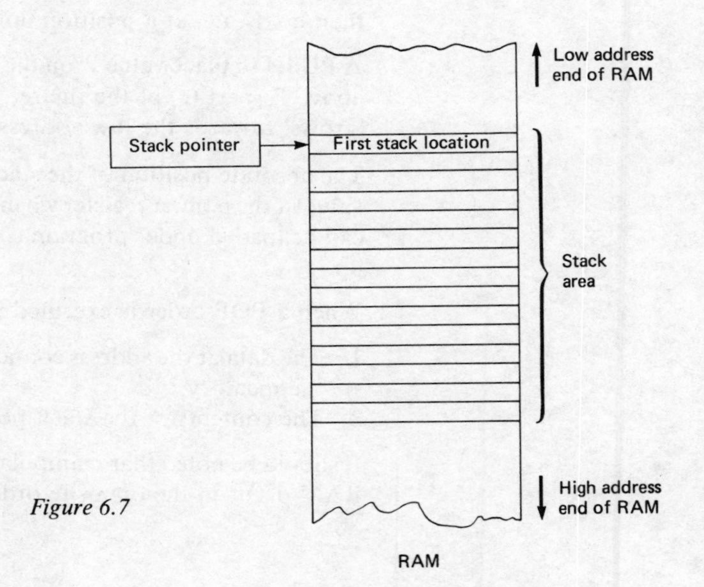

Figure 6.7

The stack consists of an area of the RAM. The size of this area may be as big or as small as is desired by the programmer and he can place it anywhere within the memory address space. These points will be elaborated shortly.

When a PUSH instruction is executed in the microcomputer the following operations occur:

1 The contents of the stack pointer are decremented.
2 The data to be placed in the stack is stored at the address held in the stack pointer.

This process is illustrated in Figure 6.8. Initially, as shown in part (a) of the figure the quantity labelled A is at the top of the stack. The stack pointer register contains the address of the location holding A.

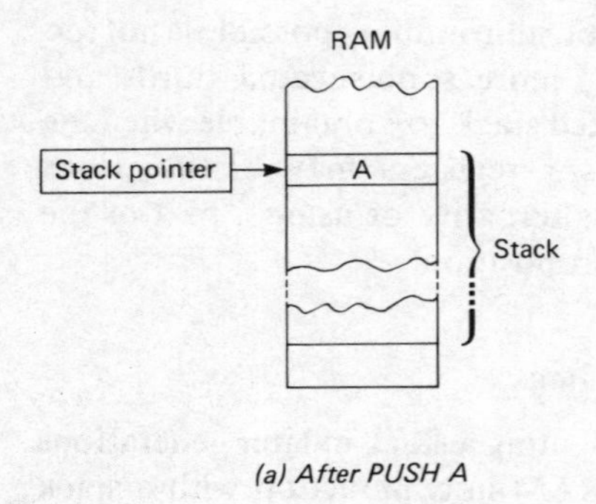

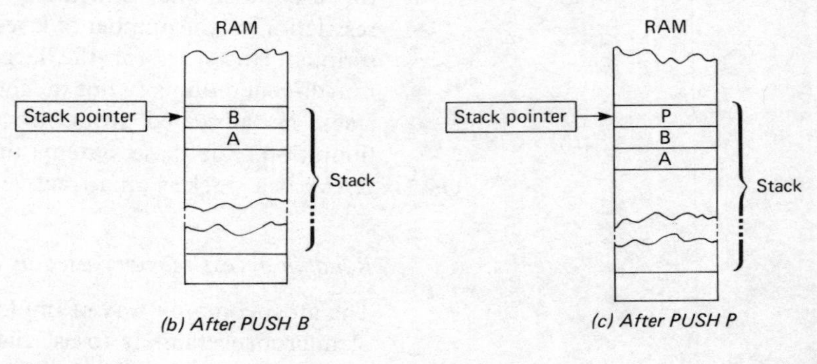

Figure 6.8

When a PUSH order is executed to place the value B on the stack the pointer is decremented, moving it one location towards the low-address end of the memory, and B is stored at the address which it then holds, i.e. at a position immediately above A.

A PUSH to place value P on the stack operates identically placing P above B [part (c) of the figure]. Thus it may be seen that the stack 'grows' towards the low address end of the memory.

The absolute position of the stack in the memory is governed by the value in the pointer register when stack operations begin. The register can be loaded under program control to allow this position to be set up.

When a POP order is executed in the microcomputer:

1 The data at the address contained in the stack pointer is read from the memory.
2 The contents of the stack pointer register are incremented.

It should be noted that manipulation of the pointer and access to the RAM occur in the opposite order in PUSH and POP operations.

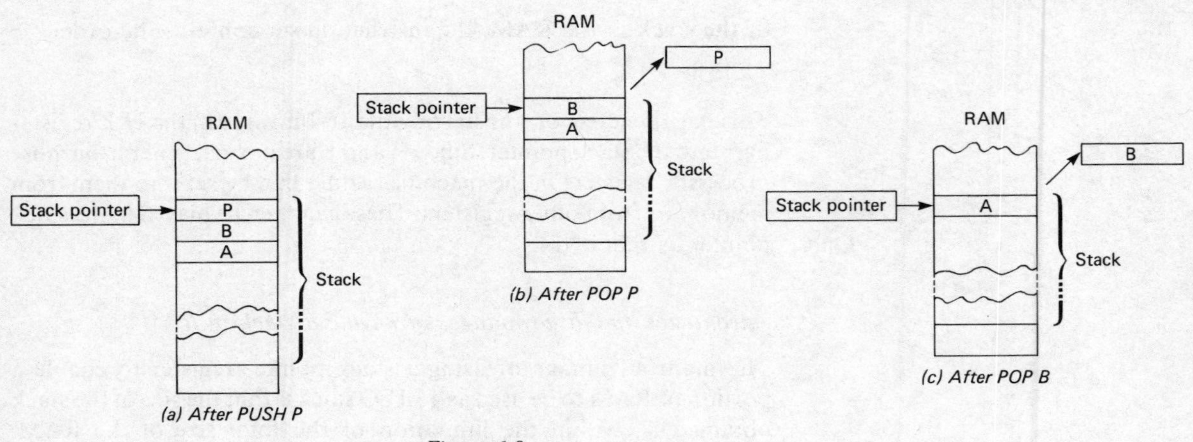

Figure 6.9

Q6.4 Figure 6.9 shows a sequence of POP operations. It is assumed that the stack begins in the state shown in Figure 6.8(c).

Practical stack pointer operation

The PUSH and POP operations available in the Intel 8085 microprocessor system have been described in Section 6.2. These are, in practice, executed using a stack pointer register in conjunction with the RAM. Thus when the instruction PUSH B is encountered during program execution the processor performs the following steps:

1. It decrements the stack pointer by 1.
2. It stores the contents of the B register at the address held in the stack pointer.
3. It decrements the stack pointer by 1.
4. It stores the contents of the C register at the address held in the stack pointer.

Overall, during execution of this instruction the stack pointer is decremented by two.

When a POP B operation is encountered the processor:

1. Reads the data in the memory location whose address is in the stack pointer. This data is placed in the C register.
2. Increments the contents of the stack pointer by 1.
3. Reads the data in the memory location whose address is in the stack pointer. This data is placed in the B register.
4. Increments the contents of the stack pointer by 1.

Overall, as can be seen, the stack pointer is incremented by 2.

So that a value can be set into the stack pointer to define the position of the stack in the RAM, the instruction set contains the order

```
SPHL
```

This has the effect of transferring the 16-bit value in the H,L register pair into the stack pointer. Since H and L are normal general-purpose processor registers in the machine, values can be set into them from memory or from other registers. These can then be placed in the stack pointer as required.

Q6.6

Advantages and disadvantages of having a stack in RAM

The main advantage of using a stack pointer register to enable a portion of RAM to be used as a LIFO stack is that the size of the stack obtained is, within the limitation of the total size of the RAM, unrestricted. Thus the stack is not constrained to holding only return addresses for subroutine calls or interrupt handling routines but can be used for other purposes.

Storage of the processor register contents when a subroutine is entered is one such application of the stack. Passing of parameters between a program and a subroutine is another.

The disadvantage of a stack in RAM is that its use requires transfer of data along the main computer highway. Storage of information in RAM is slower than storage directly within the processor chip and therefore the time taken to enter a subroutine is likely to be longer when a stack in RAM is involved.

6.4 Introduction to using a stack

Parameter passing

We have discussed two ways in which parameters can be passed between a main program and a subroutine. The methods described were:

1 By using the processor registers.
2 By using an area of memory to hold the parameters and by passing a pointer to this area in the processor registers.

Another possibility is to pass parameters between one program and another by using the stack.

Since the stack is usually in the RAM, this method is, in one sense, similar to (2) above. But the method by which the RAM is addressed is quite different. In one case the memory is accessed by normal MOV orders using the address pointer. In the other PUSH and POP instructions are used.

Consider the multiplication routine already used as an example in

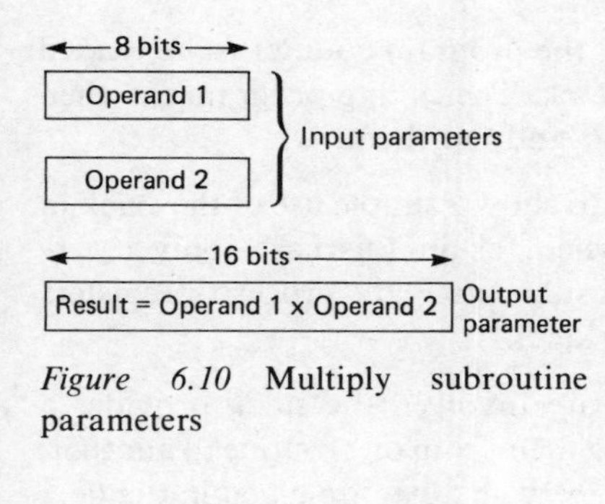

Figure 6.10 Multiply subroutine parameters

Sections 5.2 and 5.3. This subroutine has two input operands and one output operand. Suppose that the input operands each contain 8 bits. Then the output operand contains 16 bits. This is because the product of two numbers each of *n* bits is a number of $2n$ bits. Thus the parameters to be exchanged between the multiply subroutine and the program calling it are as shown in Figure 6.10.

To enter the subroutine the calling program performs the operations

Push Operand 1
Push Operand 2
Call multiply subroutine.

In terms of actual instructions this may be achieved using the register PUSH instructions listed earlier.

For example, when the calling program requires a multiplication to be performed it can place the operands in a suitable register pair, say B and C. Operand 1 can be stored in B and operand 2 in C. Then a

```
PUSH B
```

instruction stores B (operand 1) followed by C (operand 2) on the stack. The program next contains the CALL instruction to the multiply subroutine. This places the contents of the program counter (PC) on top of the stack. Hence when the subroutine is entered the top of the stack is as shown in Figure 6.11(a).

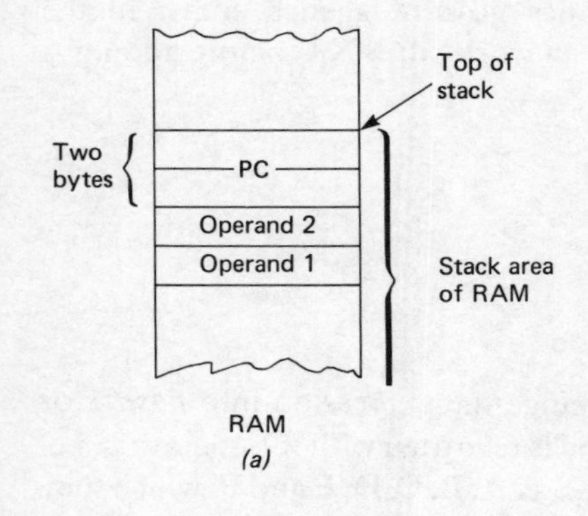

The subroutine requires to use the operands, which are in positions 2 and 3 on the stack. To get to them it must first POP the return address (that is the program counter value) off the stack and store it somewhere for future use. A possible sequence (there are a number of ways in which this can be achieved) is:

Instruction *Comment*
```
POP   B  ;Place (PC) in B and C registers
POP   D  ;Place operand 2 in E and operand 1 in D
```

The subroutine must next contain the sequence of instructions to multiply (E) by (D). Suppose that these are present and that the result, when it is obtained, is placed in registers H and L, the most significant half of the result being in H and the least significant in L. Then to return to the calling program the last instructions in the subroutine are:

Instruction *Comment*
```
PUSH    H  ;Push the result on to the stack
PUSH    B  ;Replace (PC) on the stack
RETURN     ;Return to calling program
```

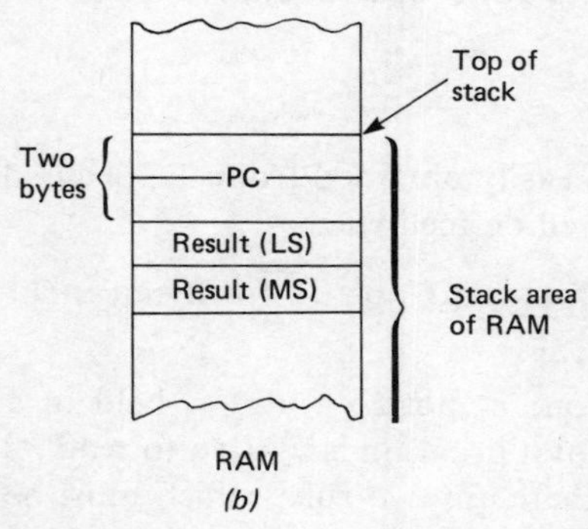

Figure 6.11

After the PUSH H and PUSH B operations the top of the stack is as shown in Figure 6.11(b).

The RETURN instruction causes the program counter to be loaded with the value at the top of the stack. The calling program can then extract the two bytes of the result and use them.

This example has been described to show a simple use of the stack in parameter passing. Normally when, as in this case, only a few parameters have to be passed to a subroutine, the processor registers are used without recourse to the stack.

However, if several parameters are involved the stack provides a convenient method of transferring them from one routine to another. Further examples of subroutine entry and exit are given in the next chapter.

Q6.1, 6.7

Evaluation of arithmetic expressions

One of the tasks that a compiler for a high-level language has to perform is to produce the machine code instructions required to work out arithmetic expressions such as:

$$\text{Result} = A + B \times C + (D + E) \times F$$

The machine code program must evaluate these expressions in accordance with the normal rules governing such sums. In the example above, for instance it must work out $B \times C$ before adding A to it, i.e. it must evaluate

$$A + (B \times C)$$

and not

$$(A + B) \times C$$

for the first part of the expression.

A way of achieving this is to change the expression into *postfix* or *Polish* form. In this, the expression is rewritten with the operators, i.e. $+, -, \times$ and $\div$, after the variables, i.e. A, B, C, D, E and F, which they affect rather than in between them. In this form the expression above becomes:

$$\text{Result} = ABC \times + DE + F \times +$$

This looks curious at first, but is easily obtained from the original (*infix*) expression using a set of well defined rules.

When the expression has been put into postfix form it can be evaluated using a stack.

Let us assume that the expression, in postfix form, is held in a sequence of bytes in RAM and that a program is written to read its terms one after the other. Then there are two rules which must be followed:

1 Whenever a variable is read from memory it is pushed on to the stack.
2 Whenever an operator is read from memory the last two values are removed from the stack, the operation required is performed, and the result is put back on the stack.

Consider the expression used earlier:

$$ABC \times + DE + F \times +$$

The sequence is as follows:

a Variable A is read from RAM and, according to rule (1) above, is pushed on the stack.
b Variable B is read and pushed on the stack.
c Variable C is read and pushed on the stack. At this point the top of the stack is as shown in Figure 6.12(a).
d Operation $\times$ is read. In accordance with the second rule, above, this causes:
C to be popped from the stack.
B to be popped from the stack.
$B \times C$ to be formed.
$B \times C$ to be pushed on to the stack.

At this point the top of the stack is as shown in Figure 6.12(b).

e Operation + is read. This causes:
$B \times C$ to be popped from the stack.

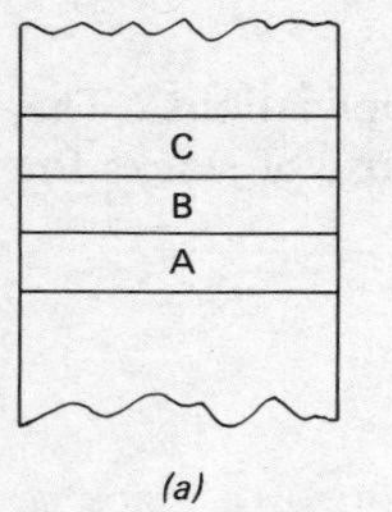

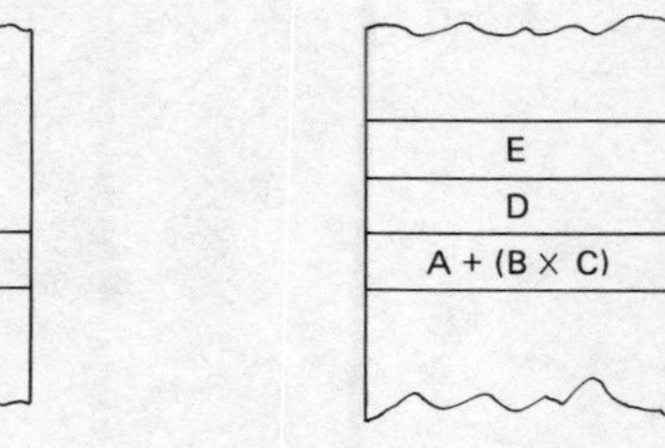

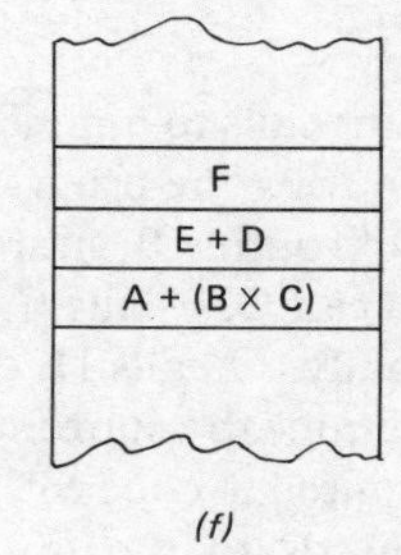

Figure 6.12

A to be popped from the stack.
(B × C) + A to be formed.
(B × C) + A to be pushed on to the stack.

At this point the top of the stack is as shown in Figure 6.12(c).

f Variable D is read and pushed on to the stack.

g Variable E is read and pushed on to the stack. At this point the top of the stack is as shown in Figure 6.12(d).

h Operator + is read. This causes D + E to be formed and pushed on to the stack in a similar way to that described in *(e)* above. Thus the stack, at this point, is as shown in Figure 6.12(e).

i Variable F is read and pushed on to the stack. See Figure 6.12(f).

j Operator × is read. This causes F × (D + E) to be formed and placed on the top of the stack. See Figure 6.12(g).

k Finally operator + is read. This causes the full result to be evaluated and placed in the top stack location as shown in Figure 6.12(h).

The machine code sequences to perform these operations thus consist of a string of MOV instructions to obtain data from the RAM, interspersed with PUSH and POP instructions to manipulate the stack and arithmetic orders to perform the required operations.

The way in which the stack functions is very suitable for this type of problem.

Q6.8

Questions

6.1 Write a short essay entitled 'Stacks and their applications'. The description should contain some reference to the use of stacks for each of the following:

(a) Saving and restoring registers.
(b) Parameter passing.
(c) Subroutine entry and exit.

6.2 Show how the last-in, first-out mode of operation of a stack is particularly appropriate to the operations involved in nested subroutine calls. What limits the depth to which nested calls can be made?

6.3 A main program contains calls to nine separate subroutines. Each of these is used six times during the program run. The subroutines are named subroutine A, subroutine B, subroutine C, etc., to subroutine I. If A itself requires to call C, B calls F, C calls G, D calls A, E calls both D and A and, finally, G calls H, draw the program structure, showing the main program, the subroutines and their interlinking. What size of stack is required to cope with this structure? Assume that each subroutine call needs to use three stack locations (two for processor register saving and one for program counter saving).

6.4 Describe how an area in the normal RAM of the microcomputer can be used as a stack and explain what happens to the contents of the stack pointer register when a PUSH and a POP instruction are executed by the processor.

6.5 A microcomputer possesses an 8-byte stack within the processor chip. The processor registers are each 8 bits wide and the program counter is 16 bits wide. Whenever a subroutine call is made the contents of three processor registers must be saved. Could the stack be used to exchange arguments with a multiply subroutine of the type outlined in Section 6.4? Explain the reasoning behind your answer. What would be the most suitable alternative method by which the arguments could be exchanged in this application?

6.6 In normal stack operation in which the stack pointer is decremented first during a PUSH instruction and incremented last during a POP instruction, the stack 'grows' towards the low-address end of the RAM. Is it possible, by alteration of the way in which the stack pointer works, to devise a method whereby a stack in RAM grows towards the high-address end of the memory? Explain your reasons by drawing diagrams showing a succession of PUSH and POP operations.

6.7 Write a short subroutine to evaluate the expression

$$A = (B + C) - (D - E) + F$$

Where the values of B, C, D, E and F are passed to the subroutine as arguments and the value of the result (A) is passed back from the subroutine to the calling program. Show how these arguments could be exchanged:

(a) using the processor registers and
(b) using the stack.

Assume the 8085 instruction set given in Appendix 1 and the PUSH and POP operations described in the last chapter.

6.8 Using a stack as described in this chapter, draw a flowchart for a program to evaluate the expressions:

1 $(A + B)$. Stored in RAM as AB+.
2 $(A + B) \times (C - D)$. Stored in RAM as AB + CD − ×.
3 $A(A + B) - C(B + D)$. Stored in RAM as AB + A × BD + C×−.
4 $A + (B \times ((C + D/E + F)/C)$. Stored in RAM as ABCDE/ + F + C/× +.

Assume that multiply and divide instructions are available.

Chapter 7 Subroutines

Objectives of this chapter *When you have completed studying this chapter you should be able to:*

1. *Appreciate the basic mechanisms of a subroutine.*
2. *Appreciate that a CALL instruction:*
   - *(a) Stores the contents of the program counter in a suitable way and then*
   - *(b) Loads the start address of the subroutine into the program counter.*
3. *Appreciate that a RETURN instruction reloads the program counter with the value stored when the subroutine was last entered.*
4. *Understand the detailed operation of the CALL and RETURN instructions in a practical microprocessor (Intel 8085) and realise that the CALL instruction in the system occupies three bytes of memory and the RETURN instruction one byte.*
5. *Appreciate that storage of the value in the program counter on entry to a subroutine may be achieved using:*
   - *(a) A register or registers in the microprocessor chip.*
   - *(b) Locations within the microcomputer store.*
6. *Understand the operation of the stack pointer and the use of the stack in subroutine calls.*
7. *Appreciate that the instructions responsible for saving and restoring the machine state on entry to and exit from a subroutine may be placed either:*
   - *(a) In the calling program or*
   - *(b) In the subroutine itself.*
8. *Provide a time delay operation in a microcomputer used for generating electrical waveforms.*
9. *Provide for the average of a set of positive numbers to be calculated.*

7.1 Introduction

This chapter will complete the study of subroutine facilities and usage in the microcomputer system. However, before embarking on the detail of this it is appropriate to briefly look back and review the topics considered so far.

Chapters 5 and 6 both contained introductory information on subroutines. Section 5.2, for example, outlined the need for special 'call' and 'return' instructions to allow entry to and exit from a subroutine.

Section 5.4 demonstrated that these instructions require the value in the program counter to be stored whenever a call is executed and to be reloaded when a return is met. Sections 5.5 and 6.1 suggested the role of a stack in such operations.

Let us briefly reconsider the steps involved in entering and leaving a subroutine. Figure 7.1 shows the situation. The main program, during its execution, requires to call subroutine A twice, once as shown by the solid arrow and once as shown by the dotted arrow. Return from the subroutine is to the instruction following the relevant call order, again as shown by the solid and dotted arrows.

Subroutine A itself calls subroutine B as illustrated by the solid arrow from the call instruction within A to the head of the instructions making up B. Return is as shown.

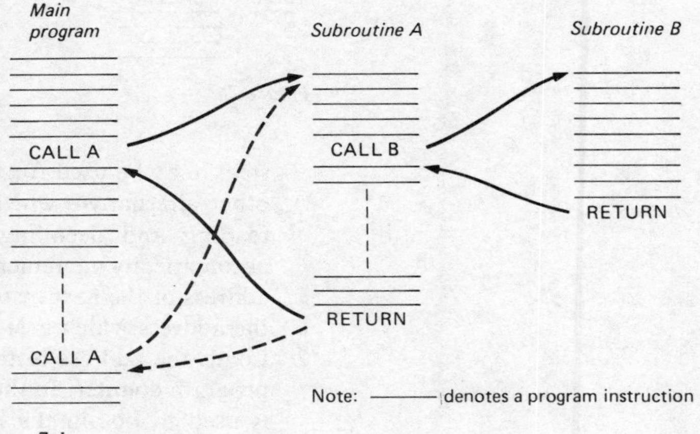

Figure 7.1

7.2 The CALL and RETURN instructions

The detailed operation of the CALL and RETURN instructions is best illustrated by the use of a specific example. Suppose that the main program and subroutines are stored at the addresses shown in Figure 7.2. The first instruction in the main program is at address 00B0, subroutine A starts at 0301 and subroutine B starts at 0401. These are just arbitrary addresses chosen to illustrate this example. The two CALL A instructions are at addresses 00E0 and 0230, respectively, and the CALL B instruction is at address 03A0 within the code of subroutine A.

The instructions CALL A, CALL B and RETURN function as follows. When the first CALL A is encountered, at address 00E0 in the main program, the computer:

1 Stores the contents of the program counter in a suitable way. The

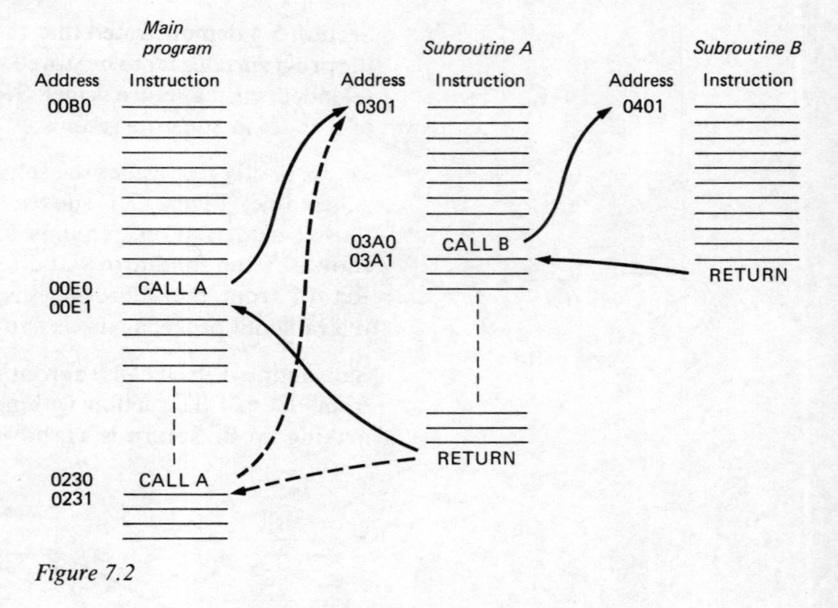

Figure 7.2

stack may be used for this, as has been indicated, but there are other alternatives which will be described later. Note that after reading and decoding the CALL instruction the computer automatically increments the program counter to contain the address of the next instruction (00E1 in this example) and this is the address which is stored.

2 Loads the address of the start of the subroutine (0301) into the program counter. In the next instruction–fetch cycle this address is used to obtain the instruction to be executed and program operation thus jumps to the first instruction in the subroutine.

When the RETURN instruction at the end of subroutine A is executed, the stored value (00E1) is reloaded into the program counter, thus causing instruction execution to transfer back to the main program.

These operations can be shown diagrammatically as in Figure 7.3. In this figure the subroutine has been shown as following on in the memory, as it does in reality, after the main program. Subroutine B has been omitted for clarity.

The second CALL A instruction in the main program causes the relevant return address (0231) to be stored and loads the program counter with the value 0301 as before. The RETURN subsequently executed at the end of subroutine A then causes the program counter contents to be restored to 0231.

The CALL B instruction in subroutine A causes the return address (03A1) to be stored and loads the program counter with the address

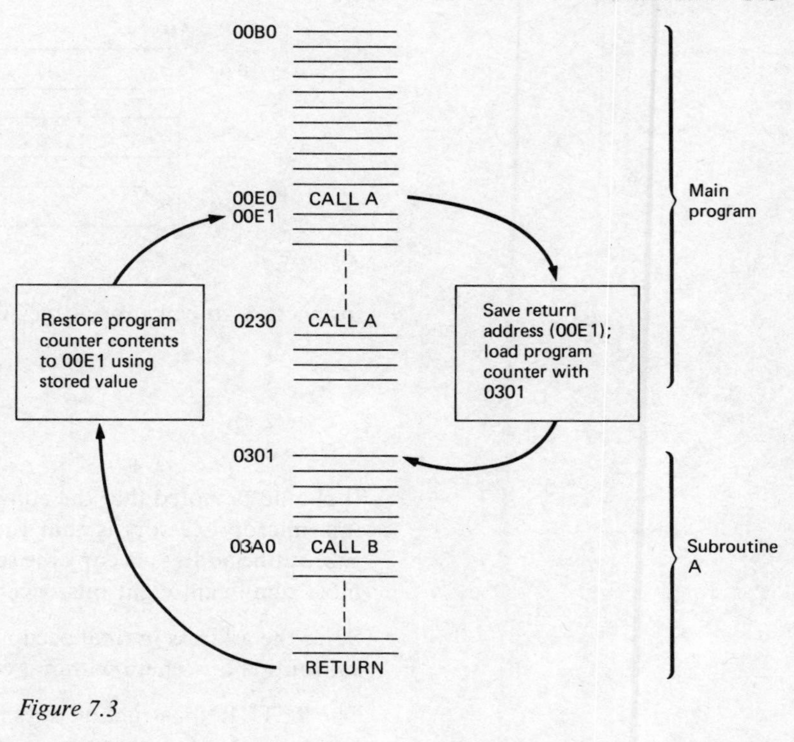

Figure 7.3

of the first instruction in subroutine B, namely (0401). And, finally, the RETURN instruction at the end of subroutine B causes the program counter contents to be restored to 03A1.

When subroutines are nested, as in this example, the way in which the return addresses are saved is important. This will be reconsidered shortly.

The Intel 8085 CALL and RETURN instructions

In the foregoing examples the CALL and RETURN instructions have been written in assembly language form. Thus the instruction has been represented by a mnemonic and the subroutine by its symbolic name.

The machine code instruction format of the CALL instruction in the Intel 8085 microcomputer is as illustrated in Figure 7.4. This is introduced here as a practical example of such an order. It is an instruction that occupies three bytes. The first byte holds the operation code, which in fact is CD (hex), i.e. 11001101 (binary). The second and third bytes hold the address of the first instruction of the subroutine being called. For instance the precise three-byte

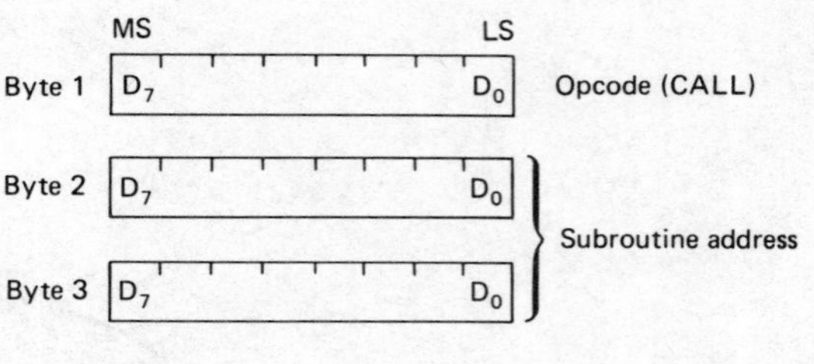

Figure 7.4

instruction to call subroutine A (Figures 7.2 and 7.3) is:

	Hex	*Binary*	
Byte 1	CD	11001101	CALL A
Byte 2	01	00000001	
Byte 3	03	00000011	

It should be noted that the convention (set by the manufacturers of this microprocessor) is that the least significant eight bits of the subroutine address occupy the second byte of the instruction and the most significant eight bits occupy the third byte.

Since the address in total occupies 16 bits, a CALL can be made to a subroutine anywhere within a 64K address range.

The RETURN instruction does not require any associated address (it simply causes the program counter contents to be restored) and is, therefore, a single-byte instruction. Its operation code in the 8085 is C9 (hex), i.e. 11001001 (binary).

One further detail should be clarified. In the examples given so far it has always been assumed that the program counter contents are incremented by *one* after an instruction is fetched from memory so as to point to the next instruction. In practice this is not always exactly the case.

The program counter *is* incremented so as to contain the address of the next instruction — that is always true. However the amount by which it is incremented may be one, or two or three. With a three-byte instruction such as the CALL, for example, the situation when it is stored in memory is as shown below:

Address	*Instruction*
0000	CD
0001	01
0002	03
0003	Next instruction

When the first part of the instruction, the operation code, is being fetched from memory the program counter contains the value 0000 (if the instruction is stored in the addresses shown above). Its contents are then incremented by one (to 0001) and the second byte of the instruction is fetched. Following this the program counter is again incremented by one (to 0002) and the third byte is fetched. Finally the program counter is incremented once more ready for the next instruction-fetch cycle.

Overall, therefore, during the execution of the CALL instruction the program counter is incremented by three. This does not alter any of the arguments presented previously except that the return address stored on entry to a subroutine is the address of the firt byte of the call order *plus three* rather than plus one. This address is, of course, still that of the next instruction following the CALL.

In a practical microprocessor such as the 8085 there are a number of variations of the straightforward CALL and RETURN instructions. Thus the processor contains *conditional call* orders such as:

CNZ address	Call on not zero
CZ address	Call on zero
CNC address	Call on no carry
CPO address	Call on odd parity
CP address	Call on plus
CM address	Call on minus

The exact interpretation of each of these is not important at this stage. It is sufficient to note that a subroutine can be called on condition that certain conditions are met.

There are corresponding *conditional return* instructions such as:

RNZ	Return on not zero
RZ	Return on zero
RNC	Return on no carry
RPO	Return on odd parity
RP	Return on plus
RM	Return on minus

These allow return to the main program from a subroutine as long as the specified conditions are met.

7.3 Program counter saving

There are a number of ways in which the return address from a subroutine can be stored. These may be broadly classified as:

1 Within a register or registers in the microprocessor chip.
2 Within the microcomputer store.

Registers on the processor chip

Some microprocessors contain a register or several registers on the processor chip specifically intended for storing subroutine return addresses. Example of these have been quoted in Section 6.3 and their limitations have been discussed.

In these systems the program counter contents are automatically placed in the register or registers whenever a subroutine call instruction is executed. It is not necessary for any access to be made to the main memory of the system during such a call.

Program counter saving in the microcomputer store

Saving of a subroutine return address within the microcomputer store can be achieved in one of two ways. First, a portion of the store can be organised in conjunction with a stack pointer register, as discussed in Chapter 6, as a last-in, first-out stack. Alternatively, the return address can be saved (stored) within the subroutine itself. This latter possibility will be considered first.

One technique used is to reserve the first memory location or first two locations in the subroutine to hold the return address. The program code of the subroutine then follows this in the second or third and subsequent locations.

The instruction causing entry to the subroutine then writes the value in the program counter into these reserved location(s) and transfers program execution to the first instruction of the subroutine proper. At the subroutine end the instruction restores the program counter contents using this stored value.

This technique allows nesting of subroutines, the return address for each level of subroutining being stored at that level. However, it does not permit the use of *recursive* subroutines. (A recursive subroutine is one that calls itself.)

Each time a subroutine is called the locations used to store the return address are filled. When the return instruction is executed these

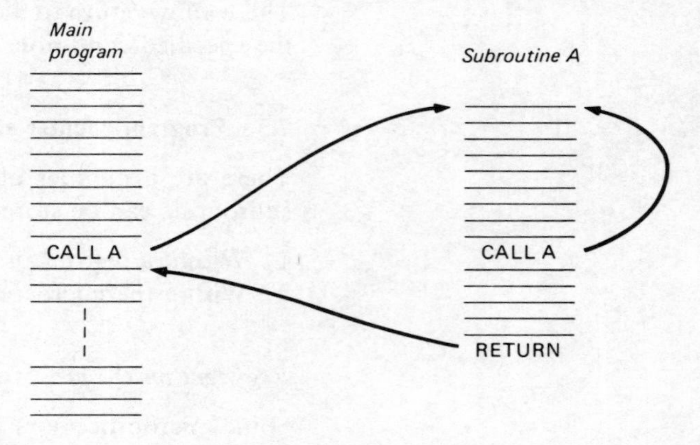

Figure 7.5

locations become free since the information in them is no longer required.

The recursive use of a subroutine, which at first appears an unlikely technique, is very useful in the solution of certain types of problem. However it involves execution of many calls to a subroutine without the execution of the corresponding return orders (Figure 7.5).

In this type of operation as many return addresses as there are calls to the subroutine must be stored. This is possible if a stack is used for holding return addresses, but it is not possible in the method just described.

Use of a stack

The use of a stack is much the most popular method of program counter saving in microcomputer systems, and its mode of operation in this application has been described in outline in Sections 5.5 and 6.1.

The 8085 is one microcomputer that uses a stack in this way.

The action of the CALL instruction can thus be defined as:

1 Push the contents of the program counter on to the stack.
2 Load the address specified in the call instruction into the program counter.

The action of the RETURN instruction is:

1 Pop the value off the top of the stack.
2 Load it into the program counter.

It is now possible to combine the description of the use of the stack pointer, the use of RAM as a stack and subroutine entry and exit. Again this is best achieved using an example.

Suppose that a main program stored in addresses 00B0, etc., as illustrated in Figure 7.6, calls a subroutine held in addresses 0301, etc. The CALL instruction occupies three bytes in addresses 00E0, 00E1 and 00E2 (hex).

Suppose, further, that the stack is in the RAM and that the address of the head of the stack, i.e. the address held in the stack pointer, is 0404 (hex).

Figure 7.7 shows the contents of the stack, the stack pointer and the program counter at various points during the execution of the program. All values are in hexadecimal notation.

Initially, when the instruction at address 00B0 is under execution the program counter contains the value 00B1 (the address of the next instruction), the stack pointer holds 0404 and the values in the stack

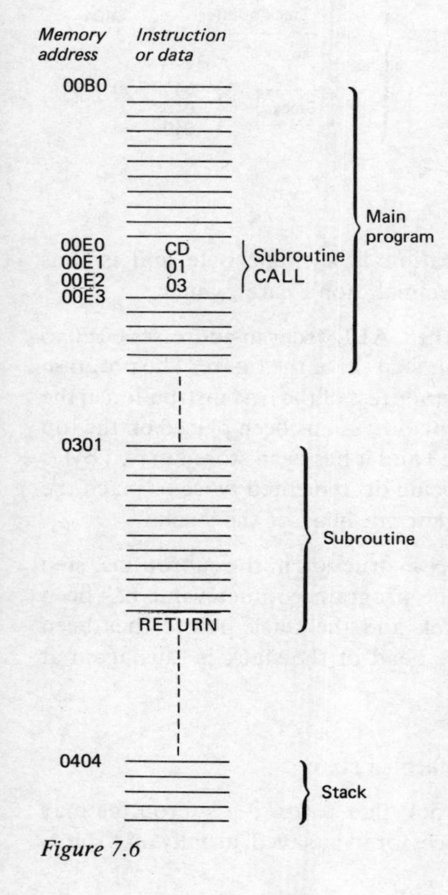

Figure 7.6

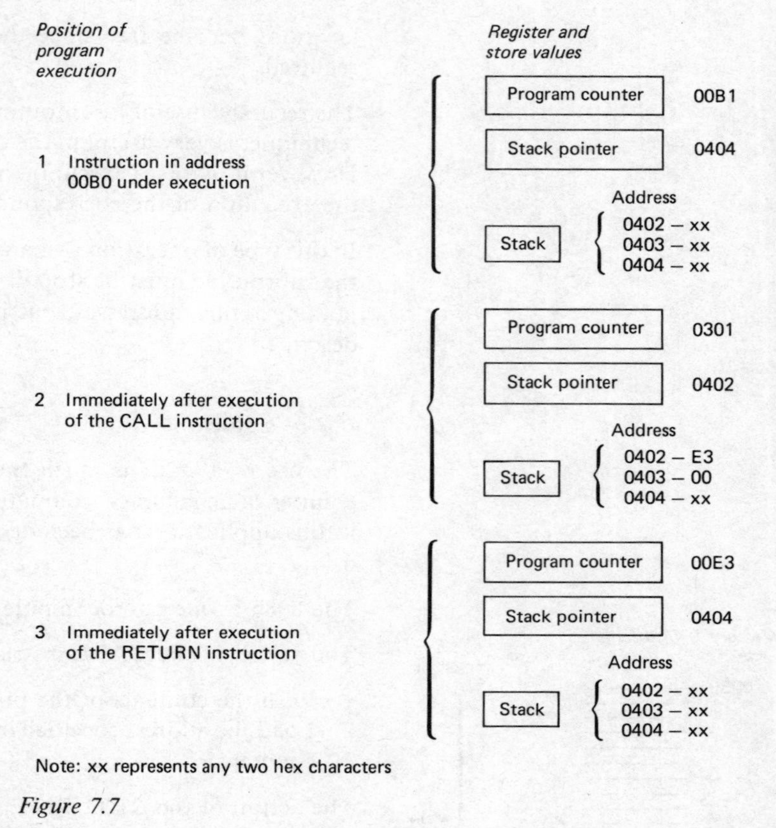

Figure 7.7

are irrelevant. Each stack location is a single byte and is thus represented by XX, two hexadecimal 'don't care' values.

Immediately after execution of the CALL order in addresses 00E0 to 00E2 the situation is as shown in step (2) of the figure. The program counter has been loaded with the address of the first instruction in the subroutine (0301) and the return address has been placed on the top of the stack. This address is 00E3 and it has been stored in two bytes of the stack, the stack pointer being decremented twice to reach the value 0402, i.e. to point to the current head of the stack.

After execution of the RETURN instruction in the subroutine, step (3) of Figure 7.7 is reached. The program counter value has been restored to 00E3 from the stack and the stack pointer has been incremented twice to 0404. The head of the stack is thus again at address 0404.

Q7.1, 7.2

7.4 Saving and restoring the machine state

We have already seen (Section 5.4) that entry to a subroutine may require the state of the microprocessor to be saved, usually on a stack, so that the calling program execution can resume following the RETURN instruction. Section 6.1 described one way in which this can be achieved. The instructions responsible for saving and restoring the machine state were positioned in the calling program. Thus instructions in this program push the contents of the processor registers onto the stack before entry to the subroutine and further instructions restore these registers after exit from the subroutine.

This is shown diagrammatically in Figure 7.8. The save orders are a sequence of PUSH operations and the restore orders a sequence of PULL operations. With this system the program counter value is the last piece of data to be placed on the stack and the first to be retrieved (see Section 6.1).

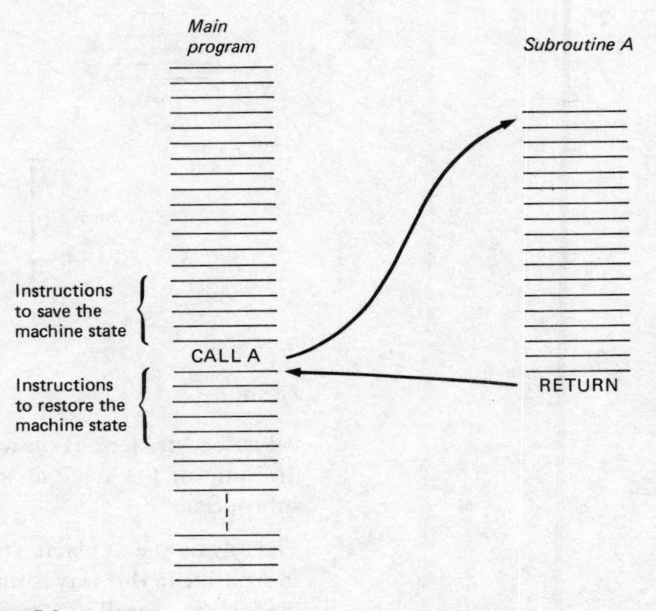

Figure 7.8

An alternative possibility is to place the save and restore instructions inside the subroutine itself. This is shown diagrammatically in Figure 7.9(a). The CALL A instruction in this figure causes the program counter value to be pushed onto the stack and program execution to transfer to the start of subroutine A. Instructions (PUSH operations) at the head of the subroutine then immediately save the processor register contents.

At the end of the subroutine the stored values are pulled from the stack and replaced in the registers. The RETURN instruction is then executed.

In this system the program counter value is held below the register

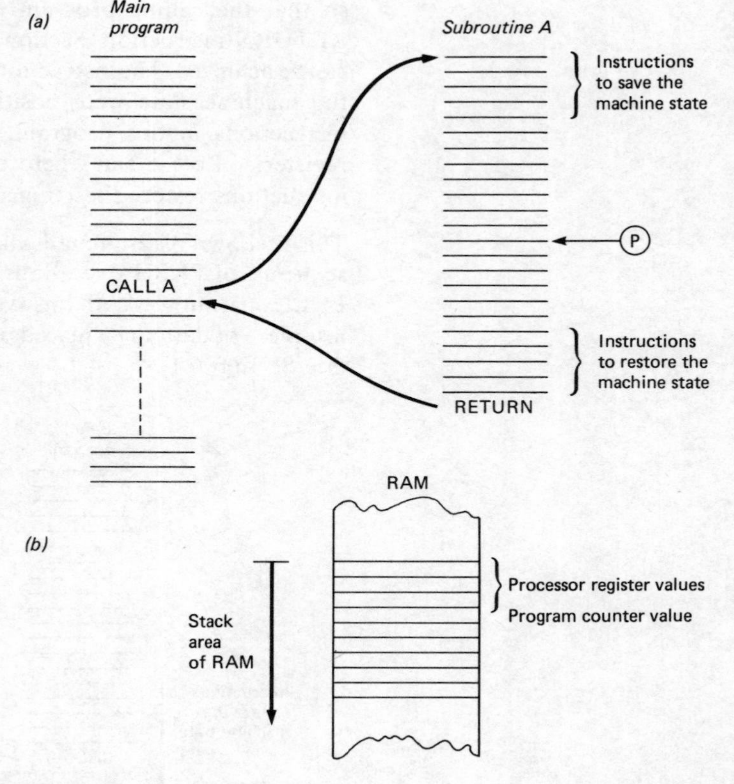

Figure 7.9

values on the stack as shown in Figure 7.9(b). The diagram represents the state of the stack at some point, say P, within the body of the subroutine.

The advantage of placing the save and restore instructions inside the subroutine in this way is that, although the subroutine itself becomes longer, the overall program length is reduced. With this arrangement there is only one set of save and restore instructions (those in the subroutine) in the whole program.

If, however, these instructions are placed in the main program they have to be included in it every time that the subroutine is called. There may well, therefore, be several copies of them. **Q7.3**

7.5 Examples of subroutines

A timing example

Let us suppose that a microcomputer is to be used to generate a square-wave signal. A possible system to do this is shown in Figure 7.10.

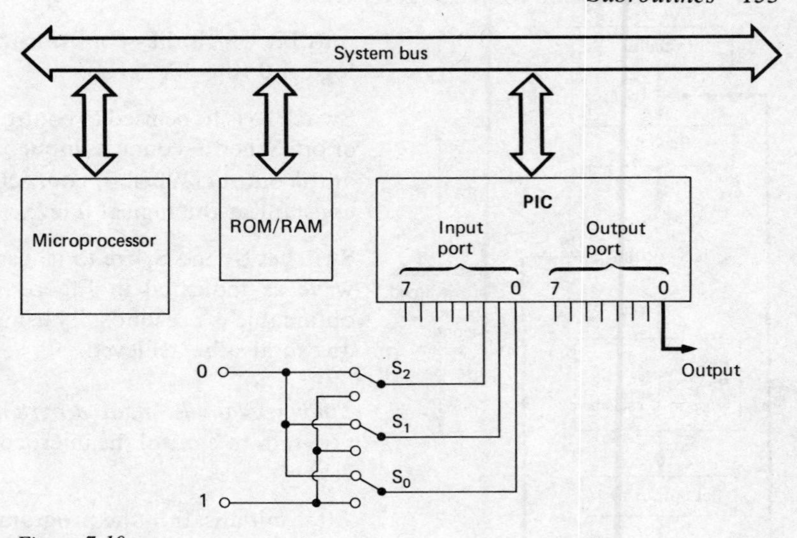

Figure 7.10

The microcomputer contains a processor, some ROM, some RAM and a peripheral interface circuit interconnected by the normal system highway.

Two of the ports of the peripheral interface circuit are used in this example, one of these being configured as an input and one as an output. Although both ports, as described earlier in Chapter 2, are capable of transferring parallel bytes of information, only one bit of the output port and three bits of the input port are required for this application.

The single output line is to be used to carry the output square-wave as shown in Figure 7.11(a). The three input lines are connected to switches S_0, S_1 and S_2. Each of these switches can connect the input

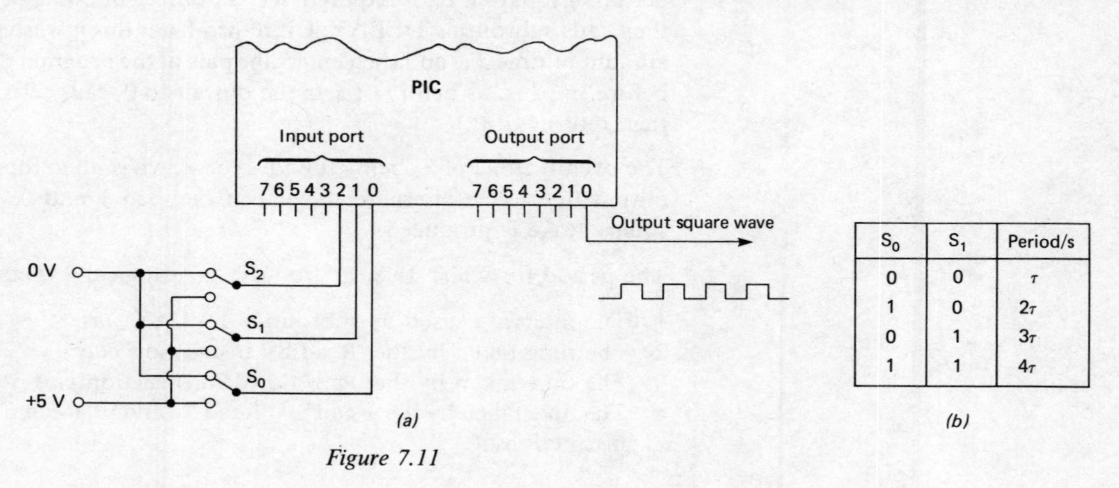

S_0	S_1	Period/s
0	0	τ
1	0	2τ
0	1	3τ
1	1	4τ

(b)

Figure 7.11

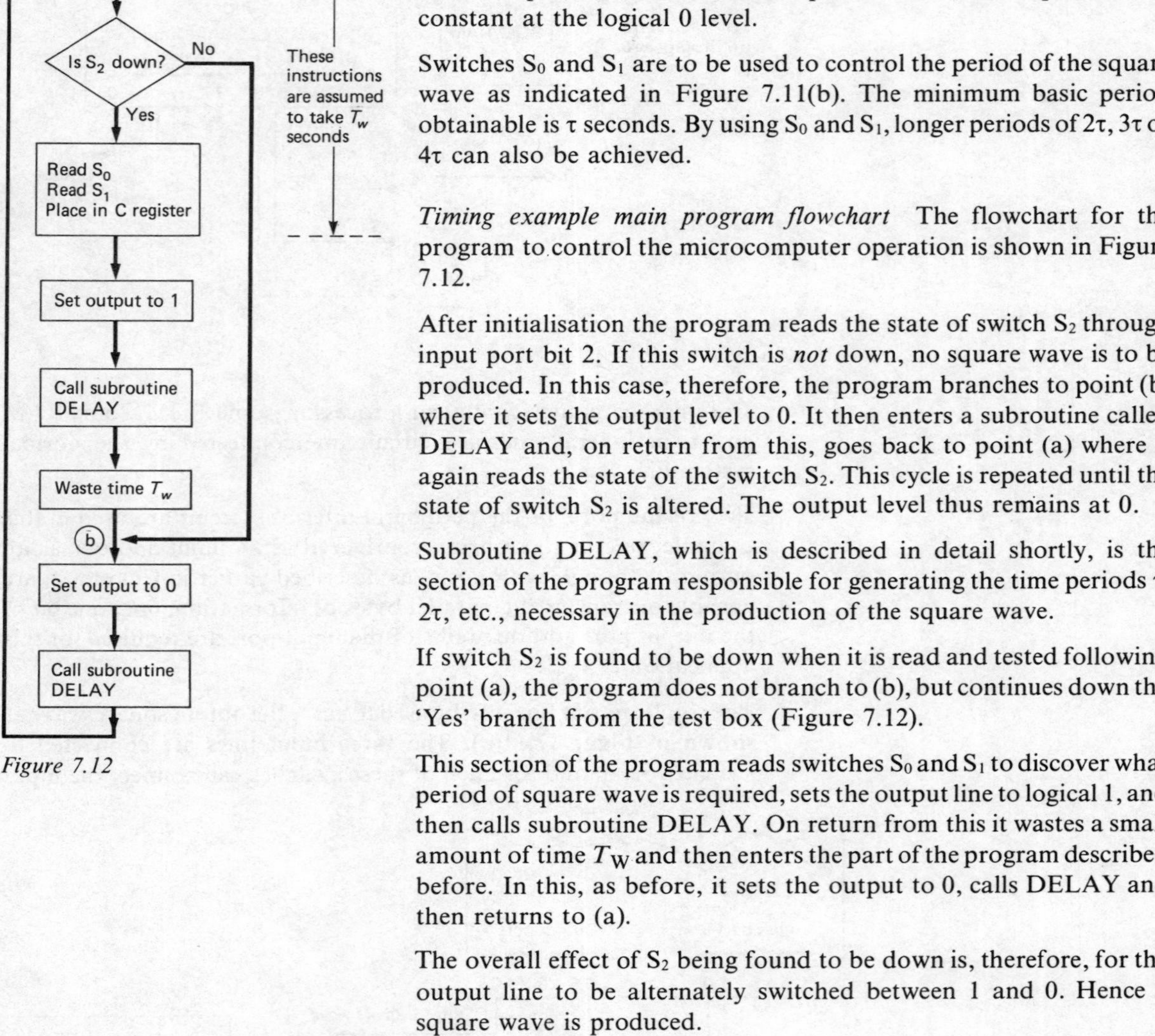

Figure 7.12

port bit which they control either to logical 1 (the +5 V level) or to logical 0 (the 0 V level).

Switch S_2 is to be used to control whether the square-wave shall be on or off. When S_2 connects input bit 2 to 1, the square wave must appear at the output. When S_2 connects input bit 2 to 0, the output must be constant at the logical 0 level.

Switches S_0 and S_1 are to be used to control the period of the square wave as indicated in Figure 7.11(b). The minimum basic period obtainable is τ seconds. By using S_0 and S_1, longer periods of 2τ, 3τ or 4τ can also be achieved.

Timing example main program flowchart The flowchart for the program to control the microcomputer operation is shown in Figure 7.12.

After initialisation the program reads the state of switch S_2 through input port bit 2. If this switch is *not* down, no square wave is to be produced. In this case, therefore, the program branches to point (b) where it sets the output level to 0. It then enters a subroutine called DELAY and, on return from this, goes back to point (a) where it again reads the state of the switch S_2. This cycle is repeated until the state of switch S_2 is altered. The output level thus remains at 0.

Subroutine DELAY, which is described in detail shortly, is the section of the program responsible for generating the time periods τ, 2τ, etc., necessary in the production of the square wave.

If switch S_2 is found to be down when it is read and tested following point (a), the program does not branch to (b), but continues down the 'Yes' branch from the test box (Figure 7.12).

This section of the program reads switches S_0 and S_1 to discover what period of square wave is required, sets the output line to logical 1, and then calls subroutine DELAY. On return from this it wastes a small amount of time T_W and then enters the part of the program described before. In this, as before, it sets the output to 0, calls DELAY and then returns to (a).

The overall effect of S_2 being found to be down is, therefore, for the output line to be alternately switched between 1 and 0. Hence a square wave is produced.

The period for which this square wave is at logical 0 is equal to:

1 The interval caused by subroutine DELAY *plus*
2 The time taken by the 'Read S_2' instruction *plus*
3 The time taken by the 'Is S_2 down?' instruction *plus*
4 The time taken by the 'Read S_0', 'Read S_1' and 'Place in C register' instructions.

The times listed under (2), (3) and (4) are assumed to sum to a total period of T_W, as shown in Figure 7.12.

If a true square wave is to be developed this period must also be added into the interval during which the output is held at logical 1. This is why the 'Waste time T_W' box is inserted into the flowchart immediately before point (b).

The square wave produced at the output is thus as illustrated in Figure 7.13.

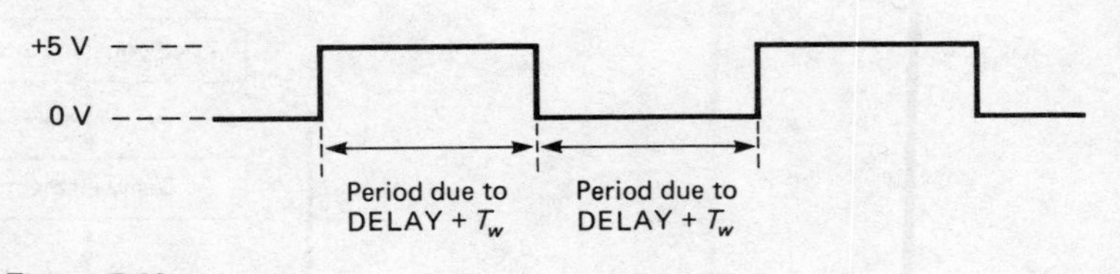

Figure 7.13

Subroutine DELAY Subroutine DELAY is a short section of program code which generates a time interval of either τ, 2τ, 3τ or 4τ s.

The interval required is, as has been explained, controlled by the value read from switches S_0 and S_1 in the main program. Thus this value must be passed to the subroutine as a parameter when it is called. The method which has been chosen for doing this is to place the value in register C of the processor (see Figure 7.12).

The flowchart for the subroutine is given in Figure 7.14. Since the D and E registers are used within the subroutine their contents are saved on the stack when it is entered and are restored when exit is made from it.

On entry to the subroutine, after the contents of the D and E registers have been pushed on the stack, the value in the C register is transferred into D. This allows the value in C to remain unaltered when the subroutine runs so that this value can be used again the next time that the subroutine is called. The value in D is the one used within the subroutine.

The required time delay is produced by two timing loops, one of which is nested within the other in the subroutine. The inner loop (Figure 7.14) contains a delay element, i.e. it includes instructions that simply use up time. The number of times this loop is cycled during program execution is controlled by the value placed in register E before the loop is executed.

The inner loop is itself within an outer loop and this latter is cycled according to the value in the D register, i.e. the number read from S_0 and S_1.

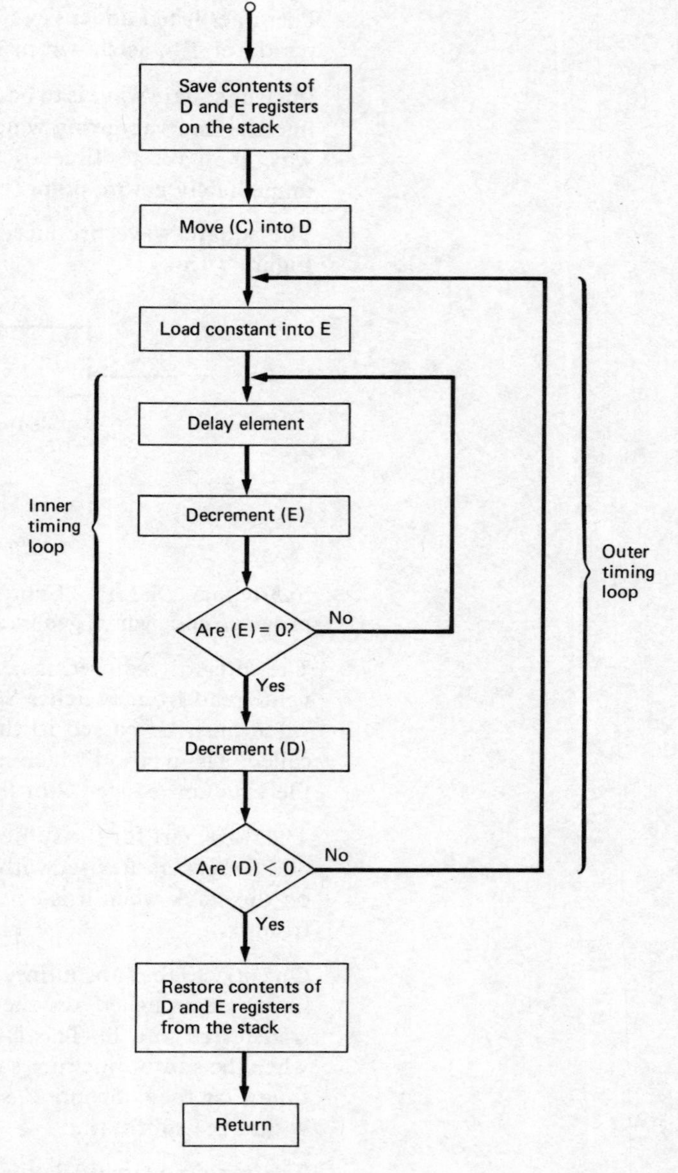

Figure 7.14

If the number in D is zero, the inner loop is cycled once, if it is one the loop is cycled twice, if it is two the loop is cycled three times and if it is three the loop is cycled four times. This is because of the way the outer loop is arranged.

Thus if the delay produced by the inner loop is τ s, the total delay introduced by the subroutine can be τ, 2τ, 3τ or 4τ s. These figures are not quite exact since the additional instructions in the subroutine outside the loops also add a small amount of delay and increase the period slightly.

On exit from the outer loop the subroutine code causes the stored values of the D and E registers to be popped from the stack and replaced in those registers before the RETURN instruction to the main program is executed.

The code for the time-delay subroutine is therefore as shown in Table 7.1. As in previous examples the subroutine code is assumed to be in memory starting at address 0301, and the head of the stack is assumed to be at address 0404.

Table 7.1

	Instruction		
Address	*Binary*	*Hex*	*Meaning*
0301	11010101	D5	Push (D) and (E) to stack
0302	01010001	51	Move (C) to (D)
0303	00011110	1E	Move immediate 0F to E
0304	00001111	0F	(decimal value 15)
0305	00000000	00	No operation orders
0306	00000000	00	(delay element)
0307	00011101	1D	Decrement (E)
0308	11000010	C2	
0309	00000101	05	If result ≠ 0, jump
030A	00000011	03	to address 0305
030B	00010101	15	Decrement (D)
030C	11110010	F2	
030D	00000011	03	If result ⩾ 0, jump
030E	00000011	03	to address 0303
030F	11010001	D1	Restore (D) AND (E)
0310	11001001	C9	RETURN

All addresses and constants are specified as hexadecimal numbers. The delay element in this subroutine consists of two NOP (no operation) instructions. These just occupy time. The constant loaded into E has been assumed to be 0F (hex), i.e. 15 (decimal).

Main program code Part of the program code for the main program is shown in Table 7.2. Only sections that relate to use of the stack and to calling the delay subroutine are included. The sections omitted, i.e. those for reading the state of the switches, for changing the output level, etc., are straightforward. Examples of routines like these appear in later chapters.

The main program code is taken to be in addresses 00B0 onwards as

Table 7.2

Address	Instruction: Binary	Instruction: Hex	Meaning
00B0	00110001	31	Initialise stack pointer
00B1	00000100	04	(load it with 0404 — the
00B2	00000100	04	address of the head of the stack)
00B3			
.	.	.	.
.	.	.	.
.	.	.	.
00E0	11001101	CD	Call DELAY (push 00E3 to stack
00E1	00000001	01	and place 0301 into program
00E2	00000011	03	counter)
00E3			Next instruction
.	.	.	.
.	.	.	.
.	.	.	.

before. The first instruction in the program sets the value in the stack pointer to be 0404 (hex) and thus sets the position of the head of the stack in the memory.

Subsequent PUSH, POP, CALL and RETURN instructions then manipulate the value in the pointer starting from this base position.

Q7.8

An arithmetic example

In the previous example it was only necessary to pass a single parameter to the subroutine from the main program. Moreover, since the subroutine effect was just to produce a time interval, no parameters were passed back from it to the main program.

Other subroutines may require to exchange large amounts of data with the main program. As has been indicated (Section 5.3), this is achieved by placing the data in the main memory and by passing a pointer to this data across to the subroutine.

Consider a main program which, periodically, needs to calculate the average value of a set of positive numbers. A subroutine AVERAGE is to be written to perform this function.

The set of numbers result, we will suppose, from calculations performed by the main program and are placed in memory. The number of numbers to be included in the average may be variable. Thus in one call to the subroutine there may be, say, 20 numbers to be included and in another 55.

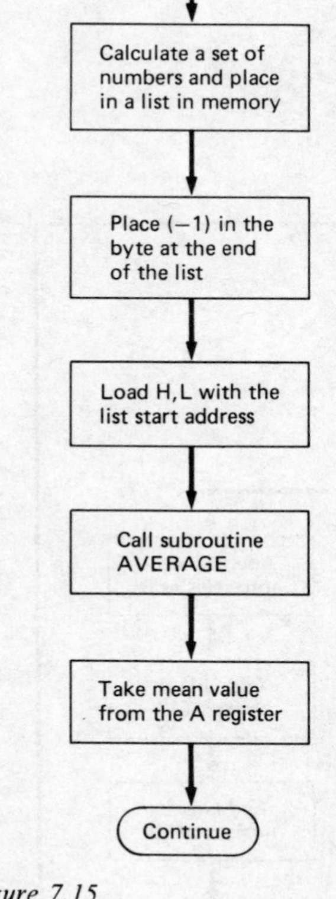

Figure 7.15

So that the subroutine can tell when it has reached the end of the list of numbers in memory the last number is made negative. This value acts as an indicator of the list end and must not be included in the average.

A part flowchart of the main program is thus as shown in Figure 7.15. The program calculates a set of values and places them in the main memory. It puts a negative number (of any value; but -1 is convenient) at the end of the list. The list can be positioned in any suitable unoccupied area of memory. To indicate its location the H,L register pair is loaded with the address of the first byte of the list immediately before the subroutine is entered.

The mean value calculated by the subroutine is passed back to the main program in the processor A register.

The main program then continues its operation, calling the subroutine whenever further average values need to be calculated.

Subroutine AVERAGE The flowchart of the subroutine for calculating the required average is illustrated in Figure 7.16. The way that this works is to retrieve the values to be included in the average from memory, one at a time, and to add them into register B. Thus B is used to accumulate the *sum* of the values. A count of the *number* of values added into B is kept in register C.

The main loop of the program therefore continually repeats the cycle of extracting a value from memory, adding this value into register B, adding one to register C (incrementing C that is), and incrementing registers H,L. This last operation ensures that the program steps through the memory, one byte at a time, retrieving successive values to be included in the mean.

The cycle described above continues as long as the values taken from the memory remain positive. When a negative value is encountered, however, the subroutine code exits from the test box (Figure 7.16) to point (b).

At this stage it is necessary to calculate the required mean by dividing the total in register B by the number of values as recorded in register C. To do this another subroutine, DIVIDE, is called.

Subroutine DIVIDE will not be described in detail here. It is sufficient that it takes two input parameters, passed to it in the B and C registers, and divides the contents of B by those of C. The result is placed in the A register and return is made to the calling program.

Thus at point (c) of Figure 7.16 the required average is in register A ready to be passed back from subroutine AVERAGE to the main program. Before this return is made, however, the contents of the B and C registers are restored to their original values.

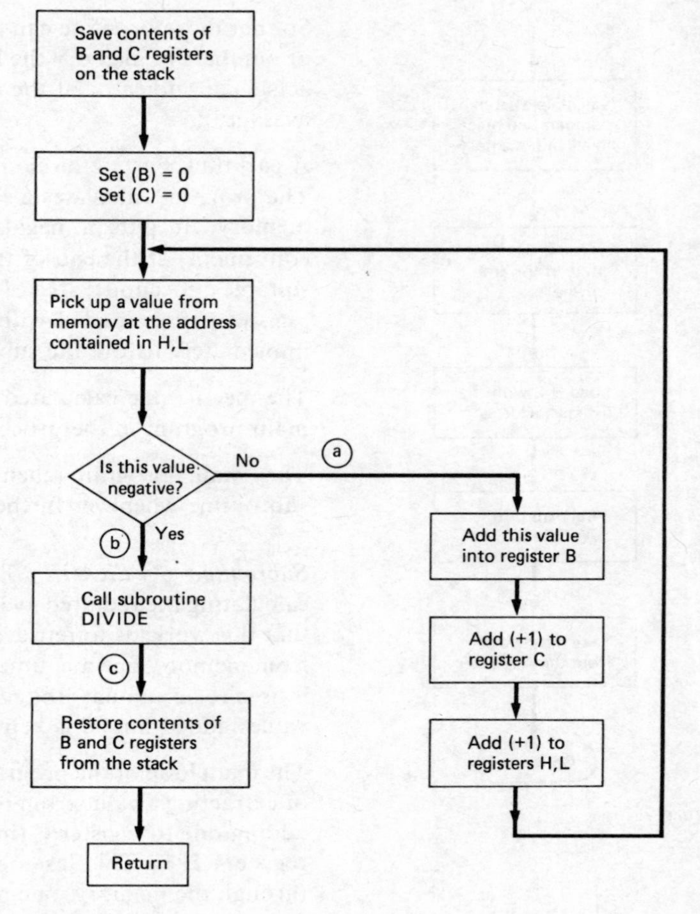

Figure 7.16

The code for subroutine AVERAGE is as presented in Table 7.3. For consistency the code is again shown as starting at address 0301 in memory and the head of the stack is taken to be at address 0404.

The parameter-passing area, i.e. the section of memory used to store the values to be included in the mean, is assumed to start at address 0501.

Several points should be elaborated a little:

1 The instructions used to set (B) and (C) to zero are 'Move immediate 0' orders. These just place the value zero in the appropriate register.
2 To test if the value moved from memory into the A register by the instruction in address 0306 is negative, a 'Jump on minus' instruction (the FA in address 0309 is employed). However this instruction works by testing the 'sign' status flag, and this flag is

Table 7.3

Address	Instruction: Binary	Instruction: Hex	Meaning
0301	11000101	C5	Push (B) and (C) to stack
0302	00000110	06	Set (B) = 0
0303	00000000	00	
0304	00001110	0E	Set (C) = 0
0305	00000000	00	
0306	01111110	7E	Move date from memory at address (H,L) into A
0307	11000110	C6	
0308	00000000	00	Test if value in A is negative.
0309	11111010	FA	If it is, jump to address 0313.
030A	00010011	13	
030B	00000011	03	
030C	10000000	80	Add (B) into A
030D	01000111	47	Move (A) into B
030E	00001100	0C	Increment (C)
030F	00100011	23	Increment (H,L)
0310	11000011	C3	
0311	00000110	06	Jump to address 0306
0312	00000011	03	
0313	11001101	CD	
0314	XX	XX	Call DIVIDE (address of DIVIDE
0315	YY	YY	is YYXX)
0316	11000001	C1	Restore (B) and (C)
0317	11001001	C9	RETURN

unaffected when a move instruction alone is performed. Thus an 'Add immediate 0' instruction has been added in addresses 0307 and 0308 before the jump. This instruction does not alter the value in the A register but does set the sign flag to the appropriate value as dictated by the result of the operation.

3 To add the value in A into B, two operations are performed. Firstly the value in B is added into A and secondly the result is moved from A into B. This is necessary because arithmetic can only be performed in the A register.

Main program code The parts of the main program code concerned with entry to the subroutine are shown in Table 7.4. As in the previous example the stack pointer must be initialised at the head of the program.

The instruction in address 00F6 transfers the value (–1), held in the accumulator, into the memory. The address in memory which is accessed is that contained in the H,L register pair. It is assumed,

Table 7.4

Address	Instruction: Binary	Instruction: Hex	Meaning
00B0	00110001	31	Initialise stack pointer
00B1	00000100	04	
00B2	00000100	04	
00B3			
.	.	.	
.	.	.	
.	.	.	
00F4	00111110	3E	Place (–1) in the A register
00F5	11111111	FF	
00F6	01110111	77	Write (–1) into memory
00F7	00100001	21	Load (H,L) with 0501 (the address of the parameter area)
00F8	00000001	01	
00F9	00000101	05	
00FA	11001101	CD	Call subroutine AVERAGE
00FB	00000001	01	
00FC	00000011	03	
00FD			Next instruction
.	.	.	
.	.	.	
.	.	.	

above, that this register pair has been used in the main program to hold the addresses necessary to fill the parameter area and that, as a result, it is set to point to the byte following the one holding the last parameter.

Assembly language version of subroutine AVERAGE The version of subroutine AVERAGE listed in the previous section is, of course, in machine language. This approach has been adopted so that the exact operation of the subroutine CALL and RETURN orders can be seen and so that the addresses used for the various parts of the program can be explicitly stated.

An assembly langue version of the subroutine is given below:

Assembly instructions *Meaning*

```
       PUSH  B      ;Save (B) and (C) on stack
       MVI   B,00   ;Set (B) = 0
       MVI   C,00   ;Set (C) = 0
NEXT:  MOV   A,M    ;Move data from memory into A
       ADI   00     ;Add immediate 0 to A
       JM    CALC   ;Jump on minus to CALC
       ADD   B      ;Add (B) into A
```

```
        MOV   B,A     ;Move (A) into B
        INR   C       ;Add (+1) to C
        INX   H       ;Add (+1) to the H,L
                      ;register pair
        JMP   NEXT    ;Jump to NEXT
CALC:   CALL  DIVIDE  ;Call subroutine DIVIDE
        POP   B       ;Restore the values in B and C
        RET           ;Return
```

As can be seen this version is much easier to read and understand than its machine code equivalent.

Q7.4–7.7

Questions

7.1 Describe the alternative ways in which the contents of the program counter may be stored on entry to a subroutine. Discuss the applicability of each method to:

(a) Nested subroutines
(b) Recursive subroutines

7.2 A main program calls a subroutine A which, in turn, calls a subroutine B. Subroutine B itself calls another subroutine C. Subroutine A is in memory starting at address 03A0, subroutine B starts at address 03D4 and subroutine C starts at address 0605.

If the CALL instruction to A from the main program is at address 00BE, the call instruction to B from A is at address 03B6 and the call instruction to C from B is at address 04E1, show the contents of the program counter, the stack pointer and the stack at the following points in the program:

(a) Just after entry has been made to subroutine A
(b) Just after entry has been made to subroutine B
(c) Just after entry has been made to subroutine C
(d) Just after return has been made from subroutine B to subroutine A.

Assume that the main program initially loads the stack pointer with the value 1000.

7.3 Show how the instructions to save the contents of the processor registers may be placed either in the program calling a subroutine or within the subroutine itself. Discuss the relative merits of each method.

7.4 The Intel 8085 microprocessor contains the instructions:

```
DAD  B
DAD  D
```

The first of these adds the contents of the register pair B and C to those of the register pair H,L. The second adds the contents of the register pair D,E to those of H,L. The result, in both cases, is placed in the H,L pair.

Using these instructions to perform the addition, write a subroutine which calculates the sum of the odd numbers between 0 and N. The value of N, which may lie anywhere in the range 0 to 100, is to be passed to the subroutine as a parameter.

7.5 Write a subroutine to calculate $N!$ [the value of $N!$ is $N \times (N-1) \times (N-2) \times (N-3) \times \ldots \times 2 \times 1$. Thus, for example, $4! = 4 \times 3 \times 2 \times 1 = 24$]. The value of N, which may lie between 0 and 7, is to be supplied to the subroutine in the D register. Assume that a subroutine MULTIPLY, capable of forming products up to +32,768, is available.

7.6 Write a subroutine to set all the memory locations between address N(hex) and address M(hex) to zero. Assume that both N and M lie in the range 0000 to FFFF and are supplied to the subroutine as parameters.

7.7 A set of numbers (X_n) is stored in addresses 0B00 to 0CFF. Thus X_0 is held in the byte at address 0B00, X_1 is at 0B01, X_2 is at 0B02 and so on. Write a subroutine to calculate the value of $1 + X_n + X_n^2$ for any value of n supplied to the subroutine.

7.8 A microcomputer system is to be used to generate a pulse train as shown in Figure 7.17. The length of the pulses in the train increases

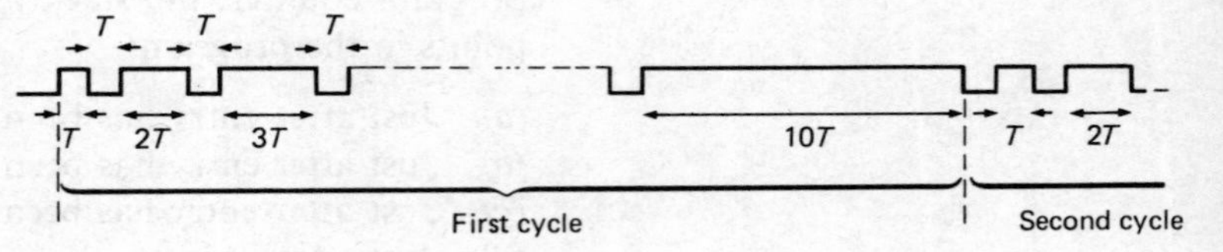

Figure 7.17

from T to $10T$ in ten steps. After this the cycle repeats starting again with a pulse of width T. The spaces between the pulses all have a constant duration of T.

Show how a main program and a subroutine which generates a time delay can be used to produce this pulse train.

Chapter 8 **Interrupts**

Objectives of this chapter *When you have completed studying this chapter you should be able to:*

1. *Appreciate that there can be a wide difference in the speeds at which a microcomputer and its peripheral devices operate.*
2. *Appreciate that because of this speed disparity problems can arise in the synchronisation of peripheral and processor operation. These problems can result in:*
   (a) *inefficient use of the processor with a waste of processing time, or*
   (b) *poor response to the peripheral.*
3. *Understand that interrupts are electrical signals sent by a peripheral device when it requires immediate attention from the processor.*
4. *Appreciate that the result of such a signal is to cause the processor to break off execution of its current program and to enter an interrupt servicing routine.*
5. *Appreciate that the interrupt servicing routine deals with the situation causing the interrupt and then returns control to the interrupted program.*
6. *Appreciate that the interrupted program continues with its processing exactly from the point at which it broke off, as though it had never been interrupted.*
7. *Appreciate that this process can be used to enable efficient transfer of data between a peripheral and a microcomputer in which each operates at its own rate with momentary synchronisation being provided by the interrupt whenever necessary.*
8. *Understand that a microcomputer system may contain many interrupt inputs and that, if this happens, priorities must be allocated to interrupt inputs to resolve possible clashes if simultaneous demands occur on two or more of them.*
9. *Appreciate the similarities that exist between subroutines and interrupt service routines, including the analogy between nested subroutines and interrupted interrupt service routines.*
10. *Understand that specific arrangements are usually made to save and restore the contents of registers used by the main program during interrupt servicing.*
11. *Appreciate that storage of such registers is normally performed using the microcomputer stack.*

12 *Appreciate that dangers exist in connection with interrupts, particularly in a real-time system, because each interrupt service routine requires time to operate.*
13 *Appreciate that the rate at which interrupts can be accepted may be limited by the total processing time needed to service them.*
14 *Use the facilities available for processing and controlling interrupts in a practical microcomputer system such as the Intel 8085.*
15 *Appreciate that other circuits such as programmable interrupt controllers are available to assist in developing comprehensive interrupt facilities in microcomputer systems.*

8.1 Introduction

Interrupts, as will be explained later in this chapter, are signals that are used to synchronise a microcomputer system with the peripheral devices attached to it. Mention was made in Chapter 1 of the speed disparity between the computer and its peripherals. It is largely to cope with this disparity that interrupts are required.

The exchange of data between a microcomputer and the external world is (as discussed in Chapters 2, 3 and 4) achieved by placing data transfer instructions in the program.

Such instructions may be special peripheral transfer orders, for instance IN and OUT as in the Intel 8085, or they may be normal data MOV instructions if memory-mapped I/O (Chapter 4) is employed. In either case a specific program instruction is responsible for sending each item of data to the peripheral device or for taking each item of data from it.

This straightforward system is inadequate on its own because of the slowness of the operation of many peripherals.

Speed of peripherals

Chapter 1 mentioned that the microcomputer can execute an instruction in, typically, a microsecond or two. Peripheral rates of operation are much slower. A paper tape reader takes about 1 ms to read an 8-bit character, for instance, and a teletype takes about 100 ms to print a character. Thus the tape reader works at only one-thousandth the rate of the computer and the teletype at one hundred-thousandth the rate.

Clearly it is important to have some means of synchronising the computer and peripheral operation.

8.2 The need for interrupts

Synchronising with peripheral devices

The need for interrupts is best explained by considering a practical example of microcomputer–peripheral communication.

Suppose that a paper-tape reader is to be connected to a microcomputer. This can supply information, as mentioned above, at a maximum rate of one 8-bit character every millisecond.

The way that the reader works is as follows:

1 It senses a character punched as a row of eight holes across a piece of half-inch wide paper tape.
2 It transfers the value of that character as an 8-bit binary number into a *buffer register* (a staticiser) in its control logic.
3 It initiates the mechanical operations needed to move the tape along one-tenth of an inch to the position of the next 8-bit character.
4 It returns to step (1) and repeats steps (1)–(3). This sequence is shown as a flow diagram in Figure 8.1.

As can be observed the first two steps (sensing the character and placing it in a buffer register) take only a few microseconds. It is the process of mechanically moving the tape through the reader to the next character position that is slow.

The character read from the tape is available to be taken into the computer from the instant when it is loaded into the buffer register until the commencement of reloading this register with the next character about 1 ms later.

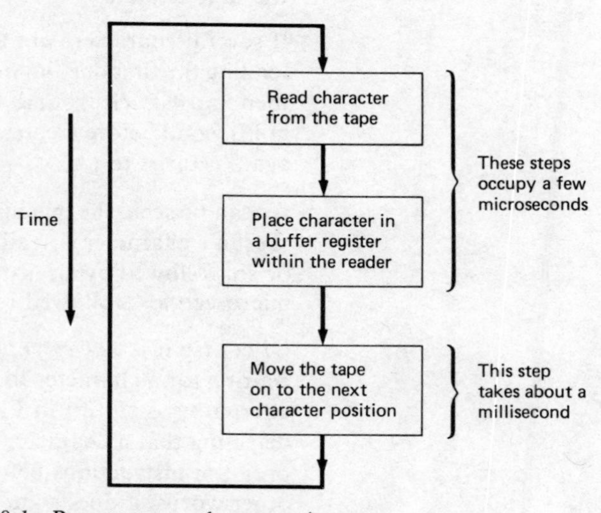

Figure 8.1 Paper tape reader operation

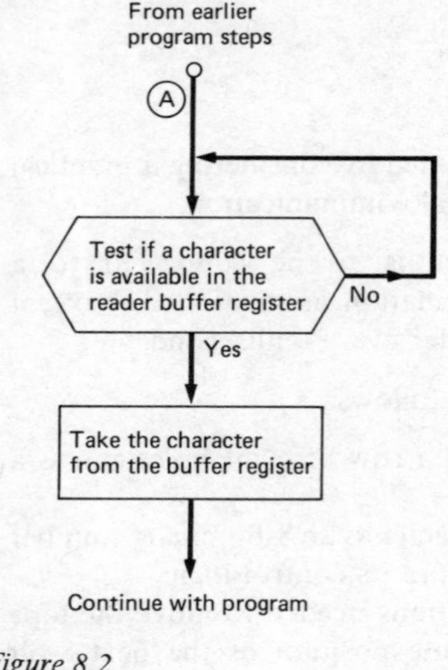

Figure 8.2

The computer can, with a program instruction, take the character from the buffer as soon as it becomes available. As has been indicated, this step occupies only a few microseconds. Thus, after taking the character the computer must wait a millisecond or so until the next character becomes available. To do this it requires to be able to sense when the waiting period is over and a new character is in the buffer.

This sensing is performed using a status signal from the reader or from the interface connecting the reader to the microcomputer highway. Section 2.4 mentioned the use of the registers in a programmable peripheral interface (PPI) to record the status of information transfers in this way.

Let us assume, then, that the computer, by using an IN instruction, is able to sense the status of the reader. A bit in the C port register of the PPI is, say, at 1 when a character can be read from the reader buffer and is 0 at all other times. Then the microcomputer operation will be as illustrated in Figure 8.2.

When a character is to be taken from the reader the program firstly examines the status bit. If this is a 1, the next instruction reads a character from the reader buffer and the program continues. If it is a 0, however, the program loops, waiting for the reader to finish its cycle of operation and for a character to become available. Each time it cycles around the wait loop the program tests the status of the reader.

This procedure ensures that the microcomputer only reads data from the reader at the correct times. It has one serious disadvantage, however; it reduces the microcomputer speed of operation to that of the tape reader.

If several characters are to be taken from tape the computer, after reading the first one, immediately returns to point (A) (Figure 8.2). It then must cycle round the 'Test if available' loop for about a millisecond before it can take the next character. After reading this it again returns to (A).

As can be seen, the machine operation consists of a long sequence of 'Test if a character is available' instructions, lasting for a millisecond or so, followed by an instruction taking the character, lasting a few microseconds, followed by a further 1 millisecond loop, and so on.

Of course it is not *essential* for the computer program just to cycle waiting for a character to be placed in the reader buffer register. An alternative is shown in Figure 8.3. In this the microcomputer, after detecting that a character is not yet available, executes some further program instructions before returning to the 'Test if . . .' order. In other words, it does some useful computation whilst waiting for the reader to fetch a character.

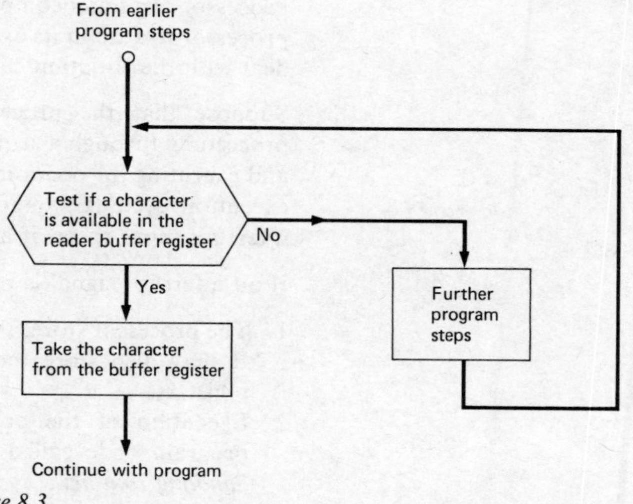

Figure 8.3

This situation is an improvement on the earlier possibility but even it has disadvantages. It is, for instance, difficult to establish how much useful work should be put in the 'Further program steps' box of Figure 8.3.

If only a small amount of processing is done here the computer will still waste a significant amount of time performing the 'Test if a character . . .' operations. On the other hand, if too much processing is done the computer will not get round to the 'Test if a character . . .' instruction very frequently and the response to the reader will be poor, i.e. the reader may have a character available to be taken for a significant time before the computer gets round to reading it.

Whatever balance of program length between useful computation and good response to the reader is chosen there must inevitably be some compromise involved. The use of interrupts removes this problem.

Real-time response

One further requirement that an interrupt system satisfies should be mentioned here. This is that it is often important for the computer to be able to respond rapidly to an externally generated demand. In some circumstances an event occurring outside the computer is of sufficient urgency for it to be necessary to cause the computer to deal with it immediately.

Q8.2

8.3 How interrupts work

An interrupt is an electrical signal which is fed directly into the processor of a microcomputer. The effect of this signal is to cause the processor to stop in its execution of a program and to take action to deal with the situation causing the interrupt.

Suppose that the processor is executing a program, i.e. it is proceeding through a sequence of instructions stored in the memory and executing the operations they specify. At the completion of each execution cycle (Chapter 1) the circuits of the processor test the interrupt input to see if a signal is present upon it.

If an interrupt signal is present the following operations occur:

1 The processor stores the value contained in the program counter. It may also store the values in some or all of the processor registers.
2 Execution of the program branches to a special section of program code called the *interrupt service routine* or *interrupt handling routine*.
3 The interrupt service routine performs whatever input or output operations are necessary to deal with the situation causing the interrupt.
4 The contents of the program counter and processor registers are restored to the values which existed before the interrupt.
5 Execution of the interrupted program is resumed from where it left off.

As an example of this consider the operation of the tape reader described earlier. If an interrupt method is used to link this to the computer the system operation is as shown in Figure 8.4. The operation of the reader, shown at the left of the figure, is substantially as before. The only addition compared to the block diagram of Figure 8.1 is that when the reader has placed a character in the buffer register it sends an interrupt to the processor. This is illustrated in the figure by the dotted arrow. The interrupt, in effect, informs the processor that a character is available for it.

Whilst the reader is operating, the processor is executing a program. This continues until the interrupt arrives from the reader, at which point the processor branches to the interrupt service routine. This routine, having been entered because of the interrupt coming from the reader, is specifically designed to deal with the reader. Thus it contains an IN instruction which takes the character from the reader buffer into the processor. When this has been done, a return is made to the main program. Providing that the register values on entry to the interrupt service routine can be restored, as described above, the main program operation can be resumed from *exactly* the point at which it was interrupted.

There is now no question of the processor needing to test the reader status before executing the IN instruction. A character must be ready

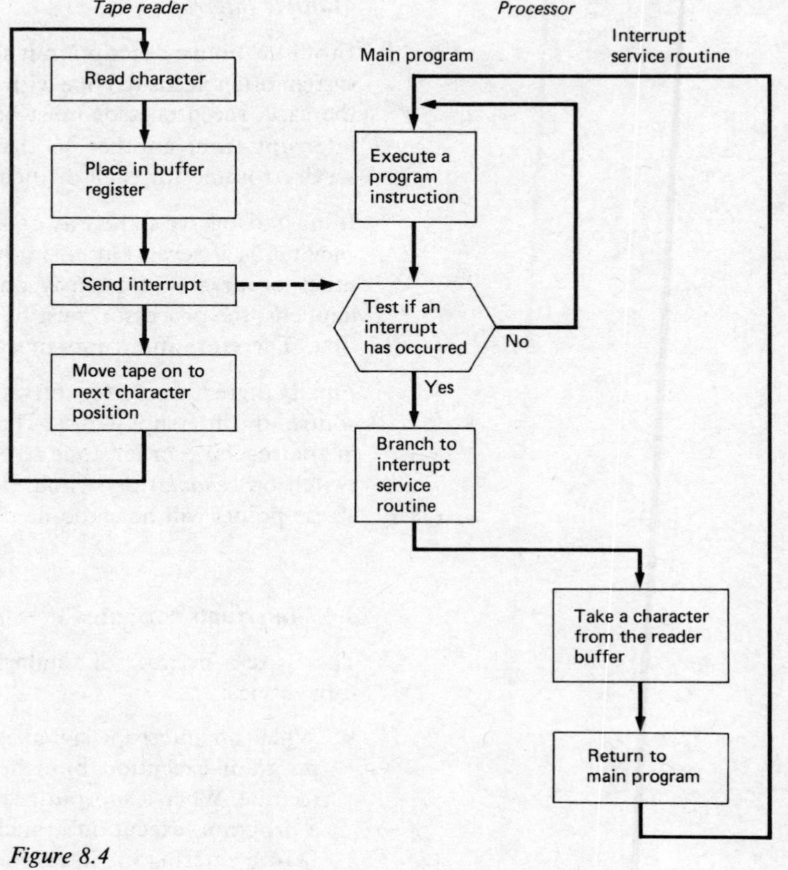

Figure 8.4

to be taken otherwise the interrupt would not have been generated and the interrupt service routine would not have been entered.

Thus the use of interrupts in this situation allows the reader to function at its speed, the processor simultaneously to operate at its speed and the two to be synchronised momentarily whenever it is necessary to exchange information between them.

Very little processor time is lost in such a system. Most of the time the processor just executes its program as if the reader were not there at all. It only needs to give up the few microseconds necessary to run the interrupt service routine at infrequent intervals of, in this case, about one millisecond.

The same mechanism can be used to make the microprocessor respond to external demands. If these demands are fed to the processor as interrupts, the associated service routines can be tailored to carry out the operations needed to deal with them.

Multiple interrupts

From the above description it should be clear that a microcomputer system often needs to cope with several interrupt inputs. When this is the case, the processor must have some way of distinguishing one interrupt from another so that it can branch to the appropriate service routine for each of them.

It must also have some way of allocating *priority* to interrupt inputs. Inevitably, if several interrupt lines are available, signals will sometimes occur simultaneously on two or more of them. When this happens, the processor must be able to choose which one to process first. Therefore interrupts must be ranked in order of importance.

Finally there is a need for software facilities to enable the processor to control the interrupt inputs. That is to say there must be instructions in the machine order code to allow it, under software control, to switch on (*enable*) or switch off (*disable*) any particular interrupt. These points will be elaborated later.

Q8.1

8.4 Interrupts compared to subroutines

There are a number of similarities between interrupt systems and subroutines:

1 When an interrupt signal is received from an external device, program execution branches to the relevant interrupt service routine. When a subroutine call instruction is encountered during a program, execution branches to the called subroutine.
2 Before entering the interrupt service routine the processor stores the contents of the program counter so that return from the routine can be correctly achieved. Before entering a subroutine the processor also stores the contents of the program counter.
3 Return from an interrupt service routine and from a subroutine are both achieved using an instruction, such as RET in the Intel 8085, which reloads the program counter using the value stored on entry.
4 The method used to save the value held in the program counter on entry to an interrupt service routine or on entry to a subroutine is the same. Typically the value is pushed on to the system stack.
5 It may be necessary to save the contents of the processor registers before executing an interrupt service routine, just as it is before executing a subroutine. If the registers are used within either type of routine, their contents must be restored before the interrupted (or calling) program can be resumed.

Thus it can be seen that an interrupt service routine is essentially a subroutine entered in response to an externally generated electrical signal rather than by the use of a CALL instruction in a program.

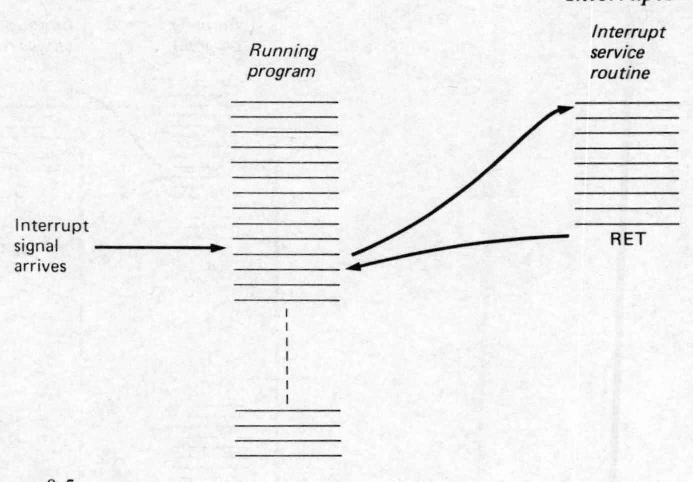

Figure 8.5

Because the interrupt signal can arise at any time or, to put it another way, at any point in the execution of a program, the entry to the service routine can happen after any instruction. In subroutine entry, by contrast, branching to the subroutine can only occur when the CALL instruction is executed. But, fortunately, the mechanism of storing and restoring the program counter value always works, no matter where the interrupt occurs.

Figure 8.5 shows diagrammatically the flow of control when an interrupt signal is received. The similarities to subroutine entry (Figure 5.2) are clear.

As has been explained, the arrival of an interrupt signal causes program execution to be transferred to the service routine for that particular interrupt. However, in practice, a further small complication arises.

There is no reason, in a system containing multiple interrupts, why several of them cannot occur in quick succession. And, if this does happen, the second interrupt may arrive whilst the interrupt handling routine of the first interrupt is still being executed, the third whilst the handling routine of the second is being executed, and so on.

The correct processor response to each of these interrupts should be to enter the service routine appropriate to a particular interrupt immediately after that interrupt occurs (there are some qualifications to be made to this statement but these are considered later). Thus the situation is as illustrated in Figure 8.6. The similarity of this process to nested subroutine calls is obvious.

When the main program (the running program, Figure 8.6) is interrupted by interrupt 'A' the service routine for A is entered. However whilst this is still running interrupt 'B' arrives. Thus

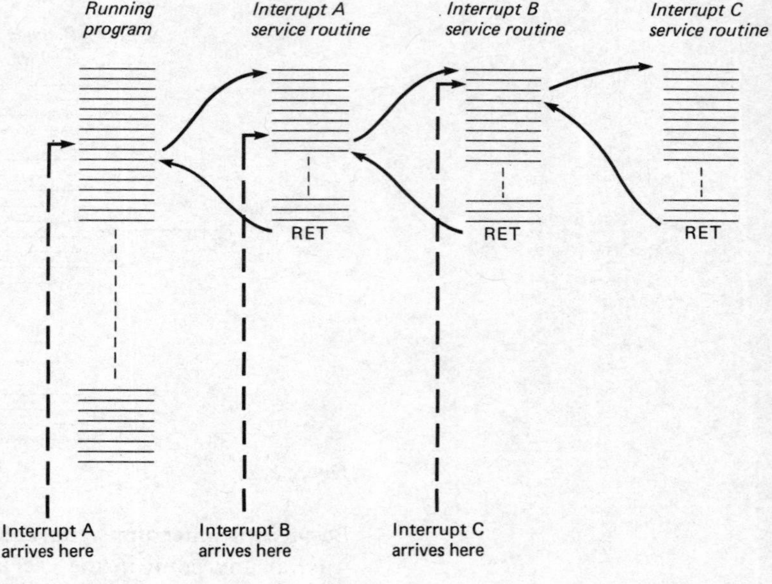

Figure 8.6

execution of service routine A is halted and service routine B is entered. A similar process subsequently causes entry to service routine C before the completion of B.

As long as the return address required to go back from C to B to A to the running program are stored on a stack, as they were for nested subroutines, the number of levels of interrupt that can be allowed is not limited by the software. It is generally limited by the number of interrupt inputs available to the processor. This topic is also considered later. **Q8.3**

8.5 Priorities

The topic of the priority of interrupt signals was introduced in Section 8.3. As stated in that section interrupt signals are normally given a ranking order, i.e. they are allocated priorities relative to each other. These priorities allow the processor to chose between two or more interrupts occurring together. In addition they may control the way in which interrupts and interrupt service routines interact.

The exact operation of priority interrupt systems varies from processor to processor. Some, for example the Intel 8085 discussed later in the chapter, automatically disable (switch off) all interrupts after an interrupt has been accepted. Others carry the use of priorities a little further.

Consider Figure 8.6. The assumption made in this, that the arrival of interrupt B causes execution of service routine A to be broken off and entry to service routine B to be made is, in some systems, only true if B is a higher priority interrupt than A. If it is not then the processor completes the instructions dealing with A before turning to B.

In this arrangement, then, an interrupt signal cannot interrupt the service routine of another interrupt signal which has a higher priority than it does. This is clearly a sensible arrangement. For instance the service routine of a high-priority interrupt, responsible for dealing with a critical fault condition in the microcomputer system, should not be interrupted by some less vital peripheral request.

8.6 The need to save and restore data

Although there are considerable similarities between interrupts and subroutine calls, as detailed earlier, an interrupt is, in a sense, a much less controlled event than a subroutine call. This is because of the random arrival times of interrupt signals.

A subroutine call is made at a specific point, set by the programmer, in a program. An interrupt may occur anywhere in the program. For this reason it is vital that all the data and parameters needed to return to the interrupted program should be stored before the interrupt service routine starts operation. Only if this is done can the interrupted program restart processing at exactly the point at which it was broken off.

Two possible methods for saving data and parameters have been discussed in connection with subroutine entry:

1 Data can be saved using orders placed in the main program before the CALL instruction is executed or
2 Data can be saved using instructions at the beginning of the subroutine itself. These are executed before the main subroutine processing starts.

Only the latter of these alternatives is suitable for use with interrupt handling routines. The arbitrary nature of the arrival of an interrupt means that it is not possible to save data or parameters prior to entry to the interrupt handling routine. Thus the interrupt handling routine itself must contain the necessary instructions to perform parameter and data saving.

A common arrangement, therefore, is for the arrival of the interrupt signal to cause storage of the program counter contents and branching to occur to the interrupt service routine. Instructions in that routine then immediately save the contents of the processor registers, data values, etc.

To allow for the flexibility of priority interrupts, and to allow the possibility of interruption of an interrupt service routine as shown in Figure 8.6, data and register values are normally stored using a stack. Thus the first few instructions at the start of the interrupt service routine are PUSH operations.

Similarly the last few instructions just before the 'return' order at the end of the service routine are POP operations. When the 'return' has been executed, therefore, the interrupted program can resume where it left off.

One further possibility should be mentioned here; as long as only one level of interrupt is permitted a double set of processor registers, such as those in the Z80 (Chapter 2), can be very useful. When the interrupt routine is entered the register exchange command (Section 2.2) is used to swop the registers currently in use from the main set to the alternative set. The interrupt service routine then uses this alternative set in its calculations, leaving the contents of the main set undisturbed. When the return from the interrupt service routine to the main program is executed the registers in use are swopped back to the main set and program execution is resumed.

The advantage of swopping the register set like this is that only a single instruction need be executed. There is no need to transfer data values from one place to another or to access the memory. Hence the operation is very fast.

Q8.4

8.7 The danger of interrupts

An interrupt is a signal that demands a response from the microcomputer. Very often there is an element of *time criticality* in this, i.e. the processor must respond within a limited period after the interrupt arrives. Should the response be too slow it may be too late to be useful when it does occur.

This urgency can give rise to problems. Perhaps the simplest way of considering it is to look at an example.

Interrupts can be particularly useful in a microcomputer system which is in a real-time environment. In this the microcomputer is responsible for controlling some real process connected to it. There are many such applications. One large class of them arises in the control of chemical processing plants. The microcomputer is able to monitor various measurements of the plant variables such as temperatures, flow rates and so on. It then operates valves, heaters, pumps and other control devices so as to keep the system working within specified operating limits.

Such an application requires the microcomputer system to cope with a lot of input/output traffic. In addition it must perform the calculations needed to establish what control variables should be changed and what values they should be given.

Thus it is convenient to allow the system to be *interrupt-driven*, i.e. the microcomputer contains a main program which it executes until an interrupt arrives. It then deals with the condition causing the interrupt and resumes the main program. Since there are many instruments and other devices connected to the processor there can be a number of interrupts. For instance, if a temperature sensor must be read into the processor at periodic intervals a sensible system is one in which regular interrupts generated by a timer chip (Chapter 2) cause entry to an interrupt handling routine. This, in turn, contains instructions to read the temperature value from the sensor.

The advantage of this method is that the responsibility for timing the intervals between the taking of readings from the sensor is removed from the microprocessor. It, therefore, is free to perform the necessary control computations.

Every interrupt response carries with it an *overhead* cost in processing time. When an interrupt arrives the processor must, as we have seen, branch to the interrupt routine. The program counter and processor registers must be saved. Thus, even before the interrupt routine does any useful processing, some processor time has been taken up.

Further processor time is consumed in the operation of returning from the interrupt to the main program. The processor register values must be restored and the program counter reloaded with the return address.

Each interrupt connected to the microcomputer system can, therefore, be seen (potentially at least) to reduce the time available for real processing. In a system carrying a heavy processing load this may be critical since it lessens the rate at which the system can get round to dealing with the various demands placed upon it.

It is important, in such a real-time system, to establish that the microcomputer is able to deal with the total processing required. The system must be able to take input readings and to update output control signals at the speed needed to ensure stable operation of the plant.

Furthermore, it must be possible to prevent an interrupt occurring. If the processor is engaged upon a calculation which has to be completed within a critical time period it is vital to ensure that it is not interrupted in the middle of it. The only way to make certain of this is for the processor to switch off (disable) all interrupts that could disturb the calculation. The disabling can be achieved by program instructions.

In the Intel 8085 processor the single-byte instruction DI, '*disable interrupts*' is available for this. Such an instruction prevents any interrupt from affecting processor operation until an '*enable interrupt*' (EI) instruction is subsequently reached.

Switching off all interrupts in this way may itself be a risky thing to do. After all, as has been explained, the function of an interrupt is to inform the processor of an external situation needing attention. To prevent the signal reaching the processor effectively shuts off its awareness of the outside world.

For these reasons it is good practice to keep interrupt service routines as short as possible. The section of such a routine during which interrupts are disabled must, in particular, be kept to a minimum in length.

In summary, then, there are various points which must be borne in mind in considering a microcomputer system containing interrupts:

1 The use of interrupts carries a time penalty. This is caused by the need to switch between routines when an interrupt occurs.
2 The time of arrival of any interrupt is generally unpredictable.
3 Some interrupts must be serviced within a critical time interval.
4 In a real-time system care must be exercised to ensure that the total time available is sufficient to permit all the necessary calculations to be performed. The overheads arising from interrupt handling must be included in this calculation.
5 The time during which interrupts are disabled should be kept to a minimum.
6 Interrupt service routines should be kept as short as possible. **Q8.6**

8.8 Examples of actual interrupt facilities

The interrupt facilities provided in practical microcomputer systems may be considered at two levels. First, there are facilities provided within the processor itself. Secondly, there are the facilities provided by the peripheral chips connected to the processor. The Intel 8255A programmable peripheral interface (see Chapter 2) is one such peripheral chip.

Processor interrupt facilities

It is convenient, at this point, to go back a little and consider what is required of a practical interrupt facility in a microprocessor.

The simplest possibility is for the processor chip to contain a single input pin upon which a peripheral can place an interrupt request signal. When this signal is received the processor:

1 Saves the contents of the program counter (usually on the system stack).

2 Branches to the interrupt service routine. Since there is, in this minimum system, only one interrupt, there need only be one service routine which can be in a fixed position in memory (or at least the first instruction of the routine can be in a fixed address – see later).
3 Runs the interrupt service routine. This may contain orders for saving and restoring the processor registers as described earlier.
4 Returns to the main program at the end of the interrupt service routine.

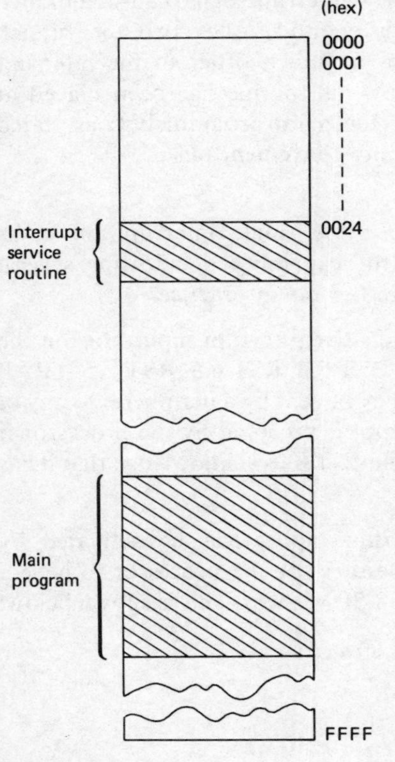

Figure 8.7

The organisation of the program memory for this arrangement could be as shown in Figure 8.7. In this the interrupt service routine has been assumed (arbitrarily) to be in RAM in the fixed locations shown. That is it starts at address 0024 (hex). The main (interrupted) program is placed in RAM at higher addresses.

Because the interrupt service routine always begins at address 0024 (we assume) the action of the processor on interrupt is simple. It:

1 Saves the program counter contents.
2 Branches to address 0024.
3 As above.
4 As above.

Since there is only one interrupt service routine it is important that no further interrupts be accepted whilst a previous one is being processed. Therefore another step must be added to the processor sequence of operations. It must disable the interrupt input whenever an interrupt is accepted. This is done automatically by the processor hardware.

So the steps on acceptance of an interrupt can be rewritten:

1 Disable the interrupt input.
2 Save the program counter contents.
3 Branch to address 0024.
4 As before.
5 As before.

Using this system, the interrupt service routine cannot be interrupted. However the interrupt input must be enabled again as soon as possible – immediately after the interrupt service routine has ended and return has been made to the interrupted program.

Whilst it is convenient for the interrupt to always cause a branch to a fixed address, 0024 (hex) in this example, it is inconvenient to always have to place the interrupt service routine at that position. This can easily be avoided by putting a branch instruction in the fixed position. This instruction causes the program to branch to the interrupt service routine which, now, may be anywhere in RAM.

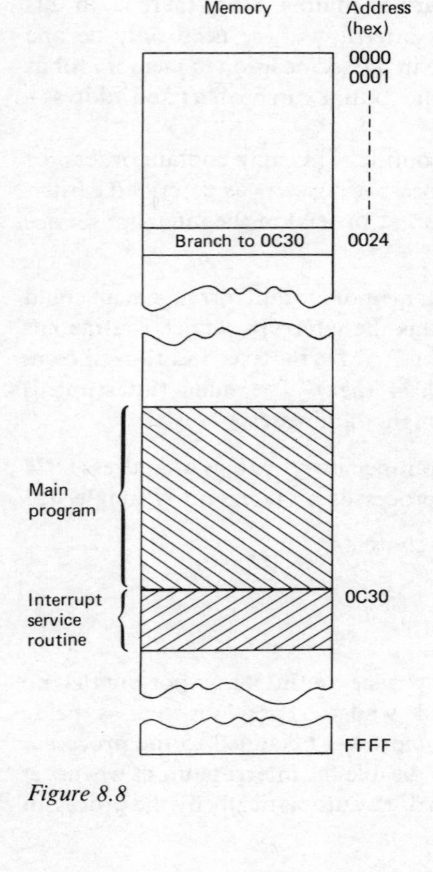

Figure 8.8

Figure 8.8 illustrates the point. The interrupt signal causes a branch to 0024 as before. This byte (or this byte and the next two since branch is a 3-byte instruction) contains a branch order to the interrupt service routine. For the example this routine has been placed at addresses 0C30, etc., following the main program but, as stated earlier, in practice it may be in any convenient place.

The Intel 8085 interrupt facilities A single interrupt input, as discussed above, is useful but the capability of allowing several different interrupts is much more flexible in practice.

The Intel 8085 microprocessor has five interrupt input pins on the processor chip. These are called RST 5.5, RST 6.5, RST 7.5, TRAP and INTR. An interrupt signal may be sent by a peripheral to any of these pins. When such an interrupt is accepted by the processor it sends a low signal on an output pin $\overline{\text{INTA}}$ to acknowledge that it has done so.

Because any of the five interrupt inputs can be activated by peripherals at any time it is necessary for the processor to have a priority system (Sections 8.3 and 8.5) for them. This is shown below:

Interrupt name	*Priority*
TRAP	1
RST 7.5	2
RST 6.5	3
RST 5.5	4
INTR	5

Thus the TRAP interrupt is a higher priority than RST 7.5 which itself is higher priority than RST 6.5 and so on.

The first four of these interrupts cause the processor to branch to individual addresses in memory. Thus:

TRAP causes branching to address 0024 (hex)
RST 7.5 causes branching to address 003C (hex)
RST 6.5 causes branching to address 0034 (hex)
RST 5.5 causes branching to address 002C (hex)

These locations are sometimes called *dedicated* locations, and are sometimes known as the *vector addresses* of the interrupts. Correspondingly this type of system, in which there are separate pins for the individual interrupts and in which a signal on a particular pin causes branching to a fixed address, is known as a *vectored* interrupt system.

To use the system it is necessary to place branch instructions at the vector addresses of the interrupts so as to cause program execution to transfer to the appropriate interrupt service routine (ISR). This is illustrated in Figure 8.9.

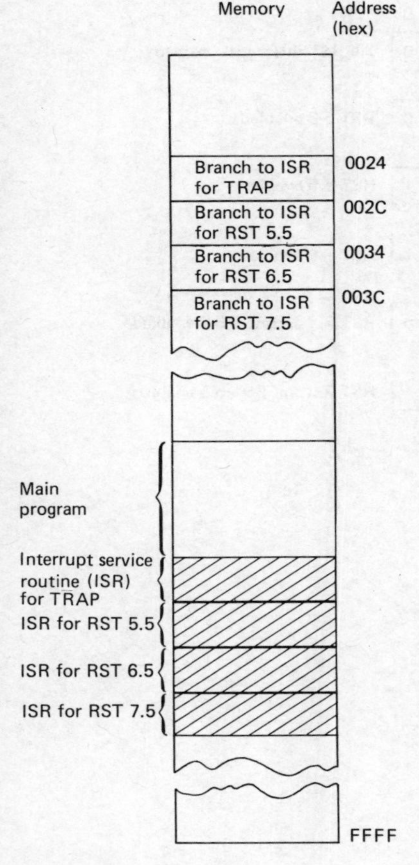

Figure 8.9

The fifth interrupt input, INTR, is a little different. When it is used it is necessary for the peripheral also to supply a program instruction to the processor. The peripheral must place this instruction on the data bus when the interrupt request is acknowledged. It is then used by the processor as the next order to be executed following the interrupt. Thus the use of INTR is more complex, in that the peripheral must supply extra information, but also more versatile.

The priority order of the interrupts is as has been shown. This order only affects the way in which the interrupt requests are accepted if several should arise together. It does not control the way in which the service routines operate.

The TRAP interrupt has the highest priority and cannot be disabled. Hence, whenever it occurs, it is immediately accepted. It is therefore most suitable for notifying the processor of critical conditions (power failure, alarms, etc.).

Apart from their different priorities the three RST interrupts all operate identically:

1 They are individually *maskable*.
2 They are all disabled by the 'disable interrupt' (DI) instruction.
3 When any interrupt is accepted by the processor (including TRAP and INTR) they are all disabled.

Each RST interrupt is controlled by an associated *mask* bit. These three bits and the overall interrupt enable bit are held in the *interrupt-mask register* in the processor (see Figure 8.10).

When the mask bit for a particular interrupt is 0, that interrupt is enabled (as long as the interrupt enable flag is set to 1). If the mask bit for a particular interrupt is 1, that interrupt is disabled. Figure 8.11 shows some possible patterns.

The mask bits may be set and reset by using a special instruction:

```
SIM (set interrupt mask)
```

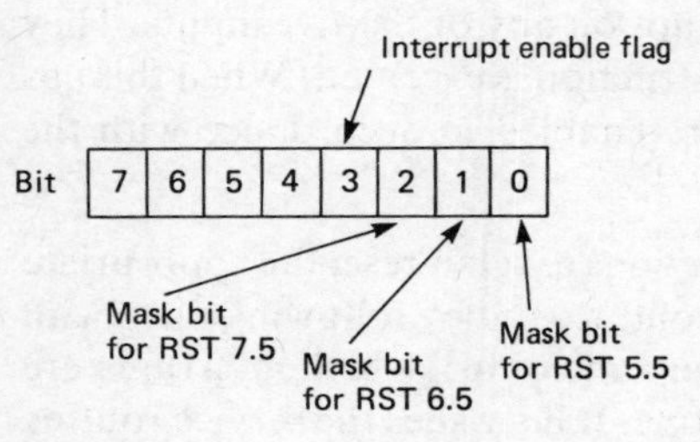

Figure 8.10

This transfers the contents of the A register into the mask register. Thus to enable all the RST interrupts the instruction sequence

```
MVI  A,08
SIM
```

can be used, setting the bottom four interrupt mask positions to

```
1000
```

To enable interrupt RST 5.5 the sequence is:

Bit 7	6	5	4	3	2	1	0	
				1	0	0	0	All RST interrupts enabled
				1	1	1	0	RST 5.5 enabled
				1	1	0	1	RST 6.5 enabled
				1	0	1	1	RST 7.5 enabled
				1	0	1	0	RST 7.5 and RST 5.5 enabled
				1	0	0	1	RST 7.5 and RST 6.5 enabled

Figure 8.11

```
MVI  A,0E
SIM
```

To enable interrupt RST 6.5 it is:

```
MVI  A,0D
SIM
```

To enable interrupt RST 7.5 it is:

```
MVI  A,0B
SIM
```

and so on.

The mask bits may be examined by using a special instruction

```
RIM (read interrupt mask)
```

This transfers the contents of the interrupt mask register into the A register.

Using these facilities the system response to the various interrupts can be flexibly controlled.

As we have seen all RST interrupts are disabled automatically following acceptance of an interrupt on any of the five inputs. They remain in this state until an EI instruction is executed. When this has been done the RST interrupts are enabled in accordance with the setting of the mask bits.

Thus by placing the correct instructions to set or reset the appropriate mask bits in an interrupt service routine, and by following these with an EI instruction, the programmer can control which interrupts are able to interrupt that service routine. If he wishes the service routine to complete execution without interruption, for example, he does not insert an EI instruction until after it has finished. In this connection it is worth recalling, though, that the TRAP interrupt cannot be disabled.

If he wishes, the programmer can also allow any interrupt service routine to be interrupted by another interrupt. This may be of either higher or lower priority than the interrupt which caused entry to the service routine.

Q8.7, 8.10

Zilog Z80 interrupt facilities The Zilog Z80 processor has two interrupt input pins. There can, therefore be two separate interrupts. One of these is (like TRAP) not maskable by the programmer and is thus accepted whenever it occurs. The other is maskable using an interrupt disable order (DI as before).

There is a single interrupt mask bit which can be set or reset under program control.

When the non-maskable interrupt is accepted, the vector address used is fixed and is 0066 (hex). When the maskable interrupt is accepted the vector address used can be either:

1 Fixed at 0038 (hex) or
2 Supplied by the peripheral device causing the interrupt.

Which of these possibilities is used depends on the *mode* of the interrupt response. This latter can be changed under program control.

Q8.5, 8.8, 8.9

Peripheral chip facilities

The properties of the Intel 8255A programmable peripheral interface have been outlined in Section 2.4. As explained there, the PPI can operate in any of three *modes* known as mode 0, mode 1 and mode 2:

Mode 0 is the basic I/O mode.
Mode 1 is a 'handshaking' I/O mode.
Mode 2 is a 'handshaking', bidirectional bus mode.

In any of these modes the PPI exchanges data with peripheral devices using its three ports: A, B and C. In mode 0 all the ports are used for data transfer. In modes 1 and 2 ports A and B are used for data transfer whilst port C provides certain control functions.

The registers in port C in these latter modes are used to generate handshaking signals for synchronising with peripheral devices and to hold interrupt requests and interrupt mask bits. Thus, in mode 1, for example, the port C register holds two interrupt mask bits and generates two interrupt signals. The latter may be taken to the processor interrupt inputs.

The mask bits may be set or reset by normal write operations to port

C (OUT instructions) and the status of the interrupt and mask bits may be read using an IN instruction to read the port C register.

Programmable interrupt controllers

The interrupt facilities in the processor chip may be expanded to allow more inputs by the use of special circuits known as Programmable Interrupt Controllers. One such device is the Intel 8259A PIC. This circuit contains eight input lines upon which interrupt requests from peripheral devices can be placed. It has one output which is connected to the interrupt input, say INTR, of the processor. It can thus be represented as in Figure 8.12.

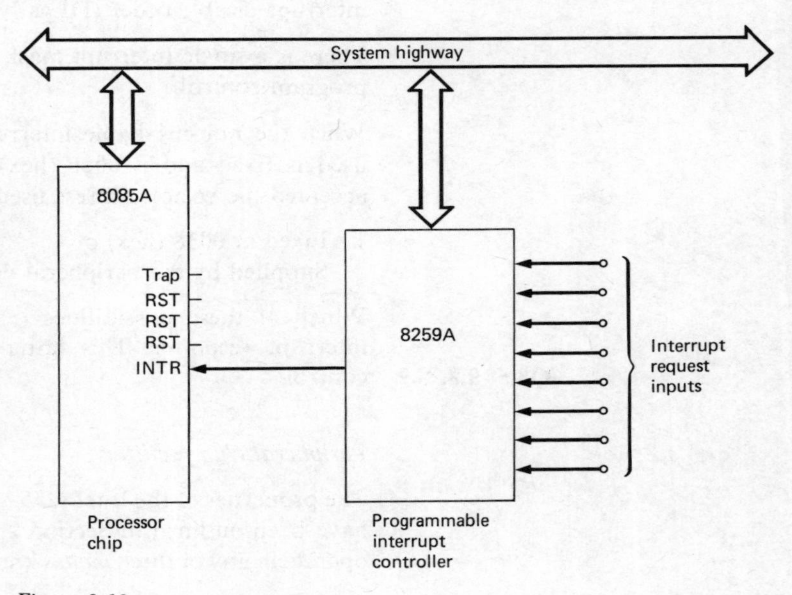

Figure 8.12

In practice a number of 8259A chips can be interconnected to give up to 64 input request lines.

The device places the requests on its inputs in priority order, using built-in priority-resolving circuits and passes the highest priority one on to the processor.

The circuit also generates the information which must be sent on the processor data bus to identify the interrupt. It will be recalled that this information consists of an instruction which is executed by the processor as the next instruction following the interrupt request. That is, the processor, following an interrupt request on INTR, takes the next instruction to be executed from the data bus (and hence from the peripheral) rather than from memory.

The 8259A generates a CALL instruction for this information. The address with this instruction is that of the service routine appropriate to the particular interrupt being serviced. Execution of this CALL thus causes storage of the contents of the program counter and entry to the appropriate routine.

The 8259A provides other facilities such as interrupt masking, recording of interrupt status and so on. These are too detailed to discuss here.

Q8.11, 8.12

Questions

8.1 Describe what is meant by an interrupt in a microcomputer system. Discuss the operations that occur when an interrupt is received by the processor and explain the reasons for each of them.

8.2 Outline the reasons why interrupt facilities are important in microcomputer systems. Illustrate your answer by discussing the way in which the processor responds to demands from external devices and by describing the way in which it communicates with slowly operating peripherals.

8.3 Make a comparison of the microcomputer response to an interrupt demand and to a subroutine call. Highlight the similarities and the differences in these operations.

8.4 Explain why it is often necessary to save the contents of the processor registers during interrupt servicing. Describe how this is done in practical microcomputer systems.

8.5 Show, in detail, how interrupts can be used to transfer information between a microprocessor and a peripheral device. Assume that interrupt line RST 5.5 is to be used, that the interrupt service routine begins at address 00B0 (hex), that the stack pointer contains 0100 and that the main program begins at address 01FF. In particular show the instructions needed in the main program and in the interrupt service routine to ensure correct flow of control in program execution and correct management of the interrupt input.

8.6 What problems can arise in a microcomputer system because of the use of interrupts? Illustrate the answer with examples.

8.7 Describe why a microcomputer system may need several interrupt input lines. Explain the additional facilities which must be present in such a multiple interrupt system when compared to a single interrupt input. Give reasons why these facilities are required.

8.8 What instructions does a practical microcomputer system possess to allow it to control its interrupt facilities? Explain the use of interrupt masks and the special orders EI and DI.

8.9 A chemical processing plant is to be controlled by an Intel 8085 microcomputer. The plant uses four of the interrupt lines to the 8085, namely TRAP, RST 7.5, RST 6.5 and RST 5.5. It is desired to arrange the interrupts so that:

(a) Interrupt RST 7.5 can interrupt the interrupt service routine of RST 6.5 and of RST 5.5.
(b) Interrupt RST 6.5 can interrupt the service routine of RST 5.5 but not that of RST 7.5.
(c) Interrupt RST 5.5 can interrupt the service routine of RST 7.5 but not that of RST 6.5.
(d) TRAP can interrupt the service routine of any other interrupt. Its own service routine cannot be interrupted by any of the others.

Explain how this can be achieved, listing the instructions for controlling the interrupts which must be placed in each service routine and in the main program.

8.10 Explain the concept of a *vectored* interrupt system and describe how it works. Illustrate your answer with examples from a practical microcomputer.

8.11 How can specialised interrupt-handling peripheral chips be used to expand the interrupt capabilities of a microprocessor? If data is available upon it use the Intel 8259A programmable interrupt controller chip as an example.

8.12 A microcomputer system using an Intel 8085 processor is to be connected to three interrupt signals. These are:

(a) An interrupt from a counter-timer chip.
(b) An interrupt from a voltage-sensing circuit signifying a power failure.
(c) An interrupt from a tape reader signifying that a character is ready to be taken by the processor.

Suggest a suitable priority ranking for these signals and hence state which inputs of the 8085 processor they should each use. Propose how the interrupts can be controlled and list the orders in the three interrupt service routines which are responsible for achieving this control.

Chapter 9 Interfacing and synchronising with the outside world

Objectives of this chapter *When you have completed studying this chapter you should be able to:*

1 *Appreciate that the device which initiates a peripheral transfer operation is normally known as the master device for that transfer and that the other device involved is the slave.*
2 *Understand that polling of peripherals is a method of communication between the processor and its peripherals in which the processor is the master device.*
3 *Understand the way in which a polling system operates and the manner in which priorities are allocated in such a system, together with the advantages and disadvantages of polling.*
4 *Use subroutines for input/output.*
5 *Understand the way in which the processor, using a peripheral interface circuit, can:*
   (a) *Control a number of two-state indicators such as light-emitting diodes.*
   (b) *Use an input subroutine which reads the settings of a number of two-state switching devices together with an output subroutine which operates two-state indicators so as to allow the indicators to display the state of the switching devices.*
6 *Appreciate the need for closely interrelated hardware and software in peripheral transfer operations.*
7 *Distinguish between parallel and serial data transfer in a microcomputer system.*
8 *Understand the principles of asynchronous serial data transmission.*
9 *Explain:*
   (a) *Duplex transmission.*
   (b) *Half duplex transmission.*
   (c) *Simplex transmission.*
10 *Understand the use of a shift register in communicating with a peripheral device which employs serial data and the operation of the shift register in this application.*
11 *Appreciate that various LSI chips are available for use in interfacing microcomputers to serial data transmission lines.*
12 *Appreciate that interval timers find applications in:*
   (a) *Devices in which a precise interval measurement is required (such as a washing machine).*

(b) Systems which require operations to occur at exact times (such as a household in which an immersion heater, for example, must be switched on and off at preset times of the day).

13 Understand the operation and interaction of the microcomputer hardware, the microcomputer software and the interval timer in applications such as those listed in (12), above.

9.1 Introduction

The question of how the microcomputer communicates with external devices and systems has been considered in several sections of this book. For example, Section 1.4 discussed the speed difference between the processor and many of the peripheral devices connected to it. Section 1.5 outlined how handshaking is used to synchronise the processor and the peripheral during the transfer of a single item of information (one byte of data for instance) between them. That section also mentioned that the two techniques used to establish when such a data item can be transferred are:

1 Polling of peripherals by the processor.
2 Interrupts.

The latter has been described in detail in Chapter 8. In this the peripheral can be considered to act as the *master* device.

Master and slave devices

The master device in a peripheral transfer is the device that initiates the transfer. Thus a peripheral having information ready to give to the processor sends an interrupt. As has been seen, this interrupt initiates a sequence of events that cause data to be exchanged. The actual exchange is synchronised using handshaking.

The time at which the exchange begins, or at least at which the sequence of events making up the exchange begins, is fixed by the occurrence of the interrupt signal. The processor in such an interrupt-driven system only performs I/O transfers when an interrupt is received. It is thus the *slave* in such transfers.

An alternative method of data transfer, in which the processor is always the *master*, is to use a polling technique.

9.2 Polling of peripherals

Chapter 8 described the need for the processor to test whether a peripheral device is ready to perform an information transfer before it attempts to execute that transfer. The description was given in

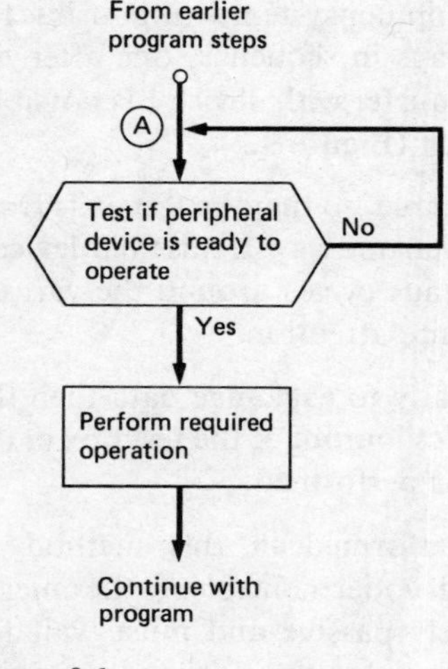

Figure 9.1

terms of the operation of one particular device – a paper-tape reader – but is, of course, applicable to a wider range of peripherals.

Thus Figure 8.2, which showed a possible (but not very good) way of synchronising the reader and the microprocessor, can be generalised as illustrated in Figure 9.1.

When the computer requires to communicate with the peripheral device it first tests whether communication is possible, i.e. whether the device is ready to give or take data. If it is, the required exchange is made and the program continues. If it is not, the processor returns to point A and tests the device again.

In this method, as can be seen, the processor loops continually on the 'Test if peripheral device is ready to operate' instruction. This looping is not essential and is often very wasteful of processor time.

A system in which the processor *polls* a number of peripherals is an extension of this. As implied in the previous sentence polling is only applicable when the processor is communicating with several peripherals. However, if this is the case, it can form a convenient and appropriate mode of operation.

A polling system operates in the manner shown in Figure 9.2. Any peripheral which is able to communicate with the processor, i.e. any which either has information to send, which requires information, or which requires attention for any other reason, sets a status flag (a one-bit status indicator as described in earlier chapters).

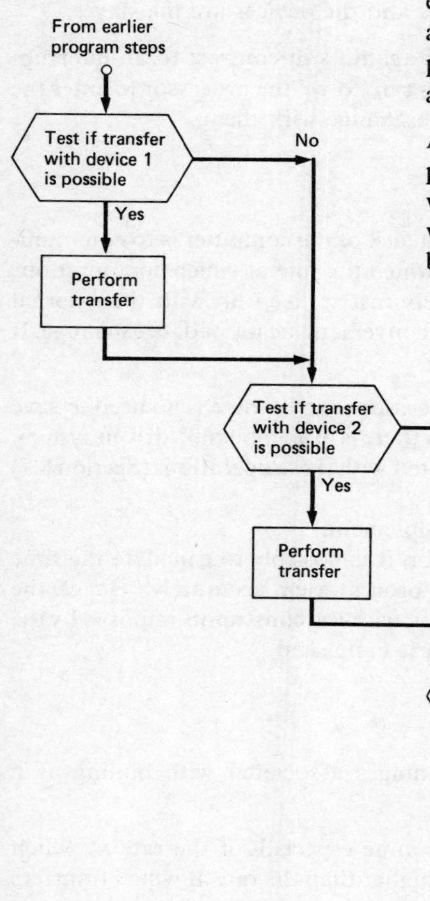

Figure 9.2 Polling of peripherals

The program running in the microcomputer system is responsible for testing the state of the peripheral flags in sequence, one after the other. Thus it performs the 'Test if transfer with device 1 is possible' instruction at the top of the flowchart (Figure 9.2).

If a transfer using device 1 is not possible, so that the test exits from the 'No' output, device 2 is tested in the same way. If this fails device 3 is tested and so on. The processor thus cycles around the various devices examining whether they require attention.

If any device, when it is tested, is ready to exchange data then the processor operation exits from the 'Yes' output of the test box in the flowchart and the required transfer is performed.

As can be seen all operations performed in this method of communication are initiated by, and under control of, the microprocessor. The peripherals are purely passive and must wait for attention until the polling cycle gets round to them. The processor is thus the master in any transfer and the devices are the slaves.

This, it should be emphasised again, is in contrast to an interrupt system in which the peripherals can 'force' the processor to enter the program controlling the data exchange with them.

Q9.1

Advantages of polling

In applications in which a main task of the computer is to communicate with peripherals, and in which the rate at which computations can be performed is adequately fast to keep up with the external system, polling provides a very convenient means of data exchange. It possesses the advantages that:

1 Since it is wholly under processor control there is no need to save data or register contents, as there is in an interrupt-driven system. Thus the overheads associated with these operations (Section 8.7) are largely avoided.
2 It is a simple method to implement.
3 In any particular application it is possible to calculate the time consumed by the polling process very accurately. Hence the system can be 'tuned' to fit in with the constraints imposed by the external system to which it is connected.

Disadvantages of polling

Of course, there are disadvantages associated with polling as a method of data transfer:

1 It is wasteful of processor time especially if the rate at which devices are tested is much higher than the rate at which transfers occur.

2 Since devices must wait for attention until the polling cycle reaches them they need to contain logic to enable this to happen. For instance if a device produces data to be read into the microcomputer it must have some way of storing this data until the processor gets round to taking it. In other words, peripherals in a polling system cannot request immediate processor attention like they can in an interrupt system.

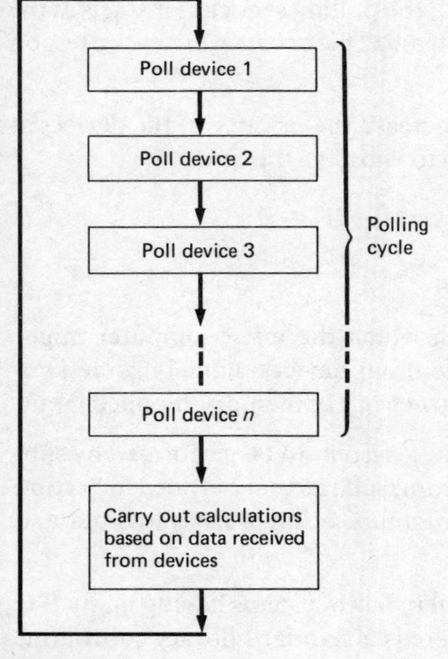

Figure 9.3

Priority in polling systems

The priority of a peripheral device, in a polling system, is determined simply by the order in which the processor polling is arranged. Figure 9.3 shows the flow diagram of the software of a typical system in which the processor scans the peripheral devices then carries out various computations required by the system, then scans the peripheral devices again and so on.

In this figure the boxes 'Poll device 1', 'Poll device 2', etc., are assumed to include the steps of testing the device and, if applicable, exchanging data with it.

The scheme shown is a 'round robin' scan. The priority of a device is just its position in the polling list. Hence device 1 has highest priority, device 2 next highest and so on. Many variations of this scheme are possible. For instance, it is possible, every time that data is exchanged with a device, to return to the top of the polling sequence. Figure 9.4 illustrates this. If the test on device 1 is unsuccessful the polling sequence moves on to device 2. However, if the test on device 1 is

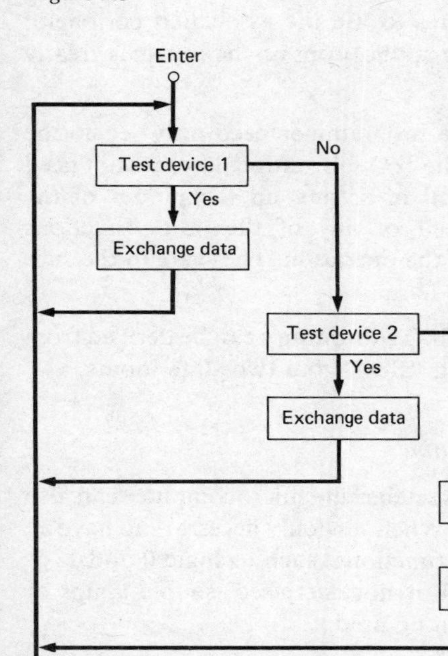

Figure 9.4

successful, and data is exchanged, the polling sequence restarts at the beginning and device 1 is polled again. This occurs whenever a test on a device is successful.

The effect of this strategy is to increase the priority of the devices at the head of the list with respect to those at the bottom.

Q9.2, 9.3

9.3 Subroutines for input/output

Section 4.8 discussed the way in which the microcomputer might examine the state of some simple input devices, namely some two-state switches, using either IN instructions or memory-mapped input.

It is common for I/O functions in a system to be performed by subroutines. Thus the part of a program, such as that outlined in Section 4.8, that deals with peripheral communication is separated out and written as a subroutine.

This concept is particularly useful in large systems having many I/O functions. If, in such systems, there is a standard library subroutine with well defined input or output parameters which can be called whenever a programmer requires to use the associated peripheral device, the ease of programming applications on the system is greatly increased.

To perform I/O operations the programmer need only set up the necessary parameters and call the I/O subroutine. He does not need to be concerned with the detail of setting up the modes of the peripheral interface circuit used or any of the other functions associated with the minutaie of the operation. These are in the subroutine.

A simple example of the use of I/O subroutines can be derived from the previous example of reading values from two-state inputs.

An example of I/O using subroutines

As well as taking in data from switches the microcomputer can also output data to various devices. When it is only necessary to have an output indication of two-state functions, such as logic 0 and 1, or whether an output is energised or not energised, simple lamps or *light-emitting diodes* (LEDs) can be used.

A light-emitting diode is just a diode which, when current is passed through it, glows in one of a selection of colours. The current through the diode is set to a suitable value using a resistor. Thus if an output line from the computer switches between 0 V (for logical 0) and +5 V (for logical 1), a light-emitting diode and resistor form a very economical and convenient indication of the state of the line.

The light-emitting diode does not, of course, contain any memory. When current is applied to it it glows and when the current is removed it goes off. To maintain a diode in the 'lit' state it must be connected to a latch (a one-bit memory, see Sections 2.2 and 3.6). The latch 'remembers' the last state of the output line and causes the diode to be switched on or off accordingly. As discussed in Chapter 2, the output ports of peripheral interface circuits contain latches for holding output data.

Thus a microcomputer system could be connected to a number of switches and a number of light-emitting diodes as shown in Figure 9.5. This figure is an extension of Figure 4.17.

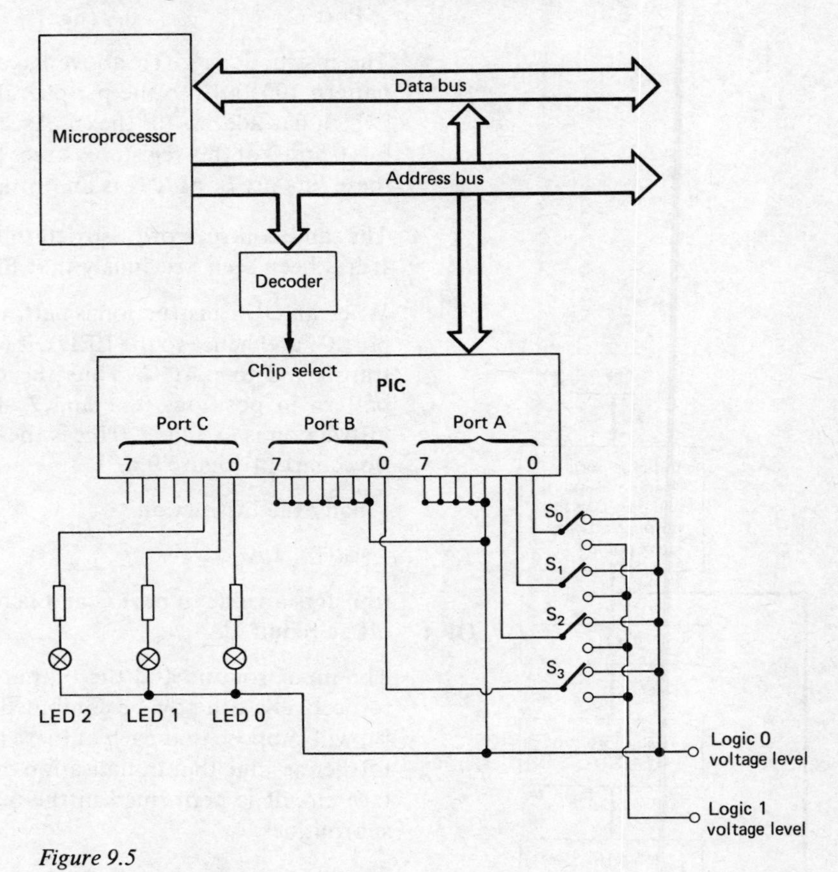

Figure 9.5

Four input switches S_0, S_1, S_2 and S_3, are connected to ports A and B of the peripheral interface circuit. Three light-emitting diodes LED 0, LED 1 and LED 2 are connected to port C. As mentioned above it is assumed that the output section of port C contains latches.

The flowchart for a program to output values to port C, and hence to switch the LEDs on and off, is shown in Figure 9.6.

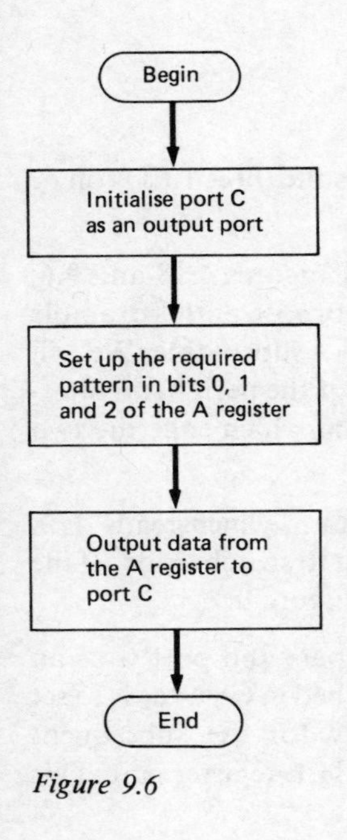

Figure 9.6

The program must begin by initialising port C to be an output. As described in Section 4.8 this can be achieved by the instructions:

```
MVI  A,92
OUT  0B
```

Note that these instructions, and those to be used later, assume the same addresses for the peripheral interface circuit and for its ports as those which were used in Chapter 4. For reference these are:

PIC	08 (hex)
Port A	08 (hex)
Port B	09 (hex)
Port C	0A (hex)

The instructions given above have the effect of sending the binary pattern 10010010 to the peripheral interface circuit control register [which has address 0B (hex)]. As shown in Figure 2.13, the effect of bits 0 and 3 of this register is to set the function of port C. When both these bits are 0, port C is an output.

The same control word also determines the function of ports A and B. It has been seen previously that these are both set to input mode.

When an OUT instruction is performed to pass data to the register in port C, and hence to the LEDs, it is the value in the A register that is transferred to port C. Thus the output program must set the bit pattern in positions 0, 1 and 2 of the A register before the OUT instruction is executed. This is the function of the second box of the flowchart of Figure 9.6.

Finally the instruction

```
OUT  0A
```

transfers a value to port C and hence switches the three LEDs on or off as required.

Q9.4

The input routine and the output routine of Figures 4.18 and 9.6, respectively, can now be combined. For the purpose of this example we will suppose that each of these is written as a subroutine. We will further assume that initialisation of the ports of the peripheral interface circuit is performed in the main program which calls the two subroutines.

The block diagram of a complete I/O program, which reads data from the switches attached to port A and uses it to switch on or off the LEDs connected to port C, is illustrated in Figure 9.7.

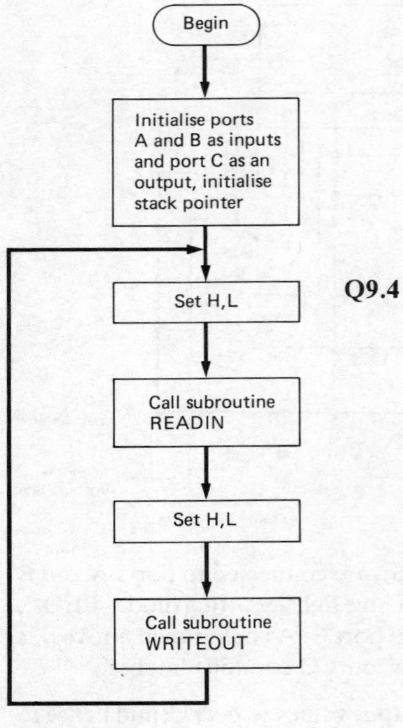

Figure 9.7

The program initialises ports A and B as inputs and port C as an output. It initialises the stack pointer, as described in Chapter 7, to set the position of the stack in memory ready for the subsequent subroutine calls. It then places a value in the H,L register pair. This value is the address in memory to be used to hold the byte read from port A. The byte read from port B is placed in the address following it.

After the initialisation procedure the program calls subroutine, READIN. It then again sets a value into H and L and calls subroutine WRITEOUT.

The block diagram of subroutine READIN is shown in Figure 9.8. Data read from port A is placed in memory at the address passed to the subroutine by the main program using the H,L register pair. Data read from port B is placed in memory in the next address.

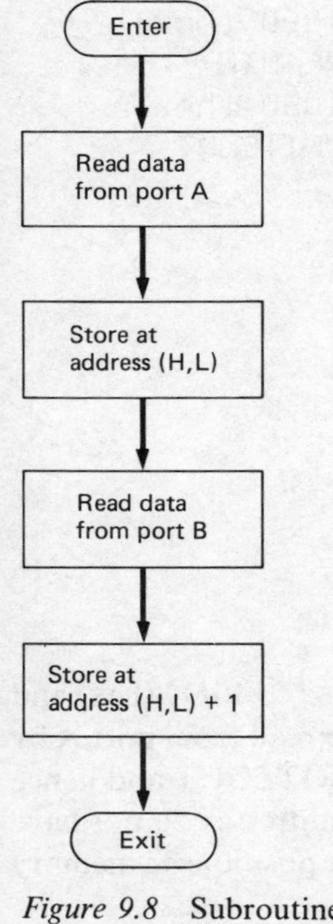

Figure 9.8 Subroutine READIN

The block diagram of subroutine WRITEOUT is shown in Figure 9.9. The action of this subroutine is very simple. It takes a byte of data from memory at the address held in H,L and sends it to port C of the PIC. The bottom three bits of the byte are thus displayed on the LEDs.

If the address loaded into H,L before entry is made to READIN and the address placed in H,L immediately before entry to WRITEOUT are the same, the states of the three switches S_0, S_1 and S_2 are displayed on the LEDs.

If the address placed in H,L immediately before entry to WRITEOUT is one greater than that used before READIN, the state of switch S_3 is displayed on LED 0. LEDs 1 and 2 are always off in this case.

Because the main program cycles continuously (Figure 9.7), the effect (assuming the data read from port A to be displayed) is to allow the LEDs to be controlled by the switches. This is a simple-looking result but, as should now be apparent, there is some complexity underlying it.

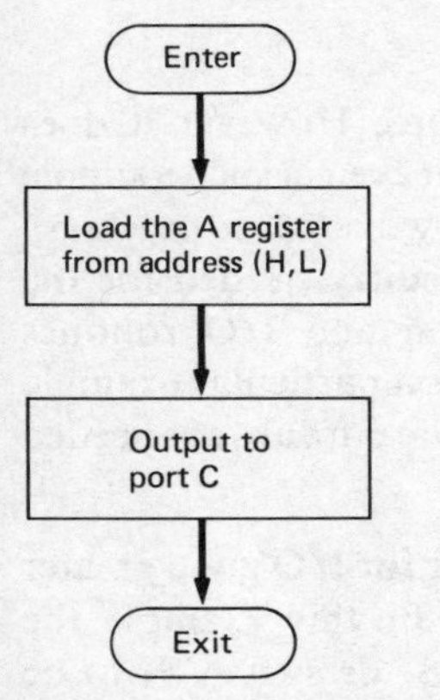

Figure 9.9 Subroutine WRITEOUT

One further point should be mentioned for clarity. The original flow diagram of the input routine given in Figure 4.22 assumes that the state of the switches needs to be individually determined. Thus at stage 3 of that flow diagram the switch values are said to be stored *separately*.

In the application just discussed, where a byte of data is effectively passed straight from the input subroutine to the output subroutine, it is not necessary to separate out the states of the switches.

I/O program

An assembly language version of the I/O program is as follows:

```
BEGIN:      MVI   A,92      ;Initialise ports A, B and C
            OUT   0B
            LXI   SP,10D4   ;Initialise stack pointer
```

(Continued)

```
START:     LXI  H,1090    ;Set (H,L) to be 1090 (hex)
           CALL READIN    ;Call subroutine READIN
           LXI  H,1090    ;Set (H,L) to be 1090 (hex)
           CALL WRITEOUT  ;Call subroutine WRITEOUT
           JMP  START     ;Go back to start
READIN:    IN   08        ;Read port A
           MOV  M,A       ;Store in memory
           IN   09        ;Read port B
           INX  H         ;Add (+1) to (H,L)
           MOV  M,A       ;Store in memory
           RET            ;Return
WRITEOUT:  MOV  A,M       ;Set value into A
           OUT  0A        ;Output to port C
           RET            ;Return
```

Subroutine READIN (READIN: … RET)

Subroutine WRITEOUT (WRITEOUT: … RET)

This assumes that the stack pointer is initialised to 10D4 (hex) and that address 1090 (hex) is used to pass the byte read from port A by subroutine READIN to output subroutine WRITEOUT and hence to the indicators connected to port C. These addresses do not have any special significance; they are just reasonable positions in memory to use for these purposes.

The need for hardware and software

The preceding example is very straightforward. However it does bring out two important points. The first is that even in such a simple system hardware and software are closely interwoven. It is necessary to have in the system both the interface circuitry needed for the indicators and switches and the initialisation and I/O routines required to transfer data between them. This is a particular example of a general situation; both hardware and software are always needed in a complete system.

The second point is that the use of subroutines for I/O gives greater flexibility than a straightforward program. In this example the flexibility gained allows switches S_0, S_1 and S_2 or switch S_3 to be displayed by a very simple modification of the main program. In general the display subroutine WRITEOUT can be used to show the state of the three least significant bits of any byte in memory simply by setting the address of the required byte into H,L before entering the subroutine.

The restriction that only the three least significant bits can be displayed is not, of course, a software limitation. If LEDs were connected to all the bits of port C the whole of any byte in memory could be shown. Again hardware and software must be combined to achieve the desired result.

9.4 Serial input/output

Chapter 1 contained a very brief reference to the distinction between parallel and serial I/O. As was mentioned there, serial I/O, in which information is output or input one bit at a time, minimises the number of wires needed to connect the microcomputer to the device with which it is exchanging data.

Serial and parallel data transfer are compared in Figure 9.10. Part (a) of the figure shows two bytes of data being sent from the computer via

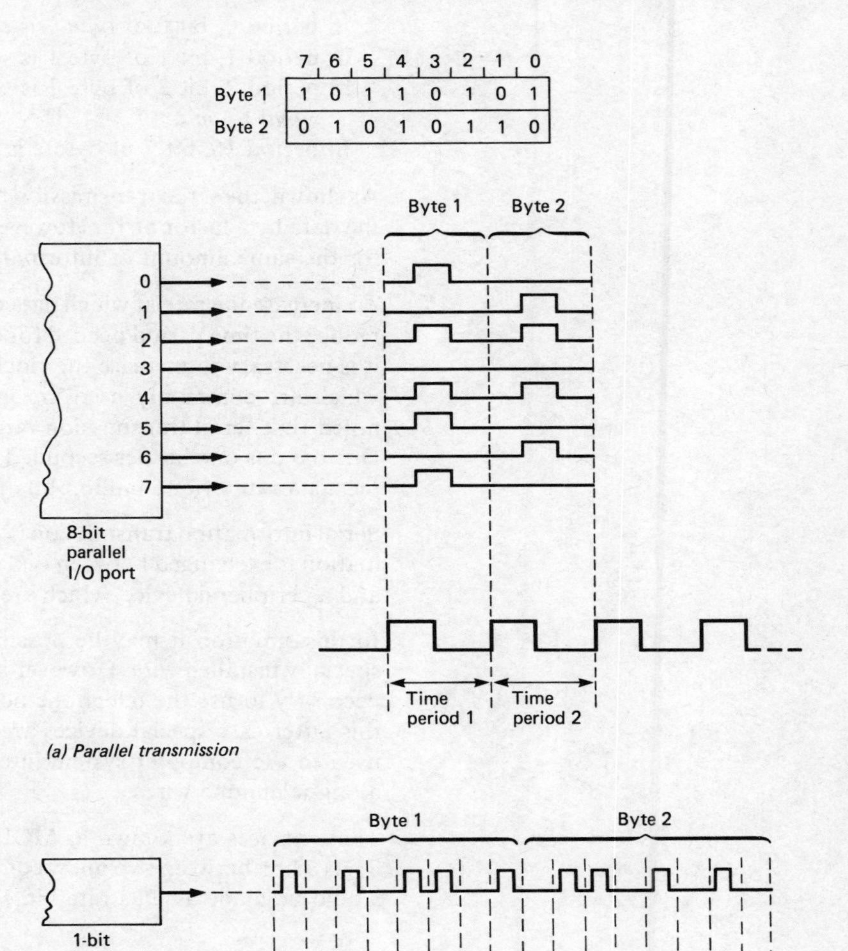

(a) Parallel transmission

(b) Serial transmission

Figure 9.10

an 8-bit parallel I/O port of the type already discussed in some detail. Transmission of these takes two time periods. In period 1 the first byte (byte 1) is sent and in period 2 byte 2 is sent. The pulses on the 8 port-output wires are as shown. the timing signal below them is for reference. Part (b) of the figure illustrates the same two bytes being transmitted along a single output wire from a serial port. Transmission of these takes sixteen time periods. The representations of these periods is compressed in the figure only so that sixteen of them fit in the space available.

In period 0, bit 0 of byte 1 is sent.
In period 1, bit 1 of byte 1 is sent
In period 2, bit 2 of byte 1 is sent
and so on until
In period 16, bit 7 of byte 2 is sent.

As shown, the serial transmission reduces the number of wires to send the data by a factor of 16. However, it also increases the time needed for the same amount of information by the same factor.

To increase the rate at which data can be sent serially it is necessary to reduce the time period needed for each bit. Or, to put it another way, it is necessary to increase the clock rate. Some examples of the rates which are commonly used are given later. However, it should be noted that serial transmission rates are normally measured in *baud.* One baud is one bit per second. Thus a *megabaud* transmission rate means a rate of one million bits per second.

Serial information transmission is particularly applicable when information is exchanged between two computers, or between a computer and a peripheral device, which are a long way away from each other.

In this situation it may be possible to interconnect the two with a specially installed wire. However if the distance is too great it may be necessary to use the telephone network to make the connection. In this latter case special devices are used to change the binary signals used in the computer system into a form suitable for transmission along telephone wires.

These devices are known as MODEMS (*mod*ulator–*dem*odulators). Thus a link between two microcomputers over the telephone network would be made as illustrated in Figure 9.11.

Peripheral devices

Serial communication links have been used in connecting computers to their peripheral devices for many years. Of course, not all peripherals can use serial links. Devices having a high data transfer rate, e.g. magnetic disk backing stores, must use parallel paths to

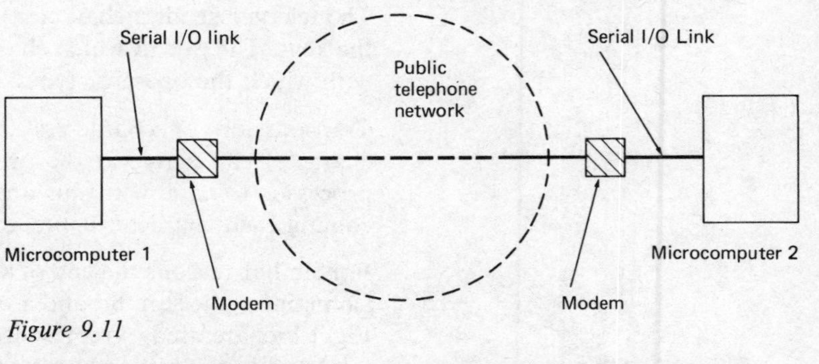

Figure 9.11

obtain the necessary speed. But there are many devices which can and do use serial links.

Perhaps the commonest of these is the teletype. In modern microcomputer systems it is becoming surpassed by the visual display unit (VDU) – a keyboard and television-type cathode-ray-tube display – but it is still very widely used especially in situations where hard copy is required, i.e. when a printed record of the communication with the microcomputer, rather than just a screen display is needed.

Because teletypes have been used for so long, various standards have been adopted which specify how they communicate with the processor. The most common of these are the so-called EIA RS 232 standard and the 20 milliampere current loop. These define the electrical signals exchanged between the processor and the peripheral.

When a key is pressed on a teletype (or indeed on the keyboard of a visual display unit) a character, often in ASCII code, is sent to the computer. ASCII, the initial letters of American Standard Code for Information Interchange, is the standard code. This code has been defined to allow standard binary patterns for representing

1 The upper-case or capital letters.
2 The lower-case letters.
3 The numerals.
4 A wide range of special characters such as commas, full stops and control patterns for use in various types of system.

Each ASCII character is sent to the computer serially, and is made up of eight bits, as shown in Figure 9.12.

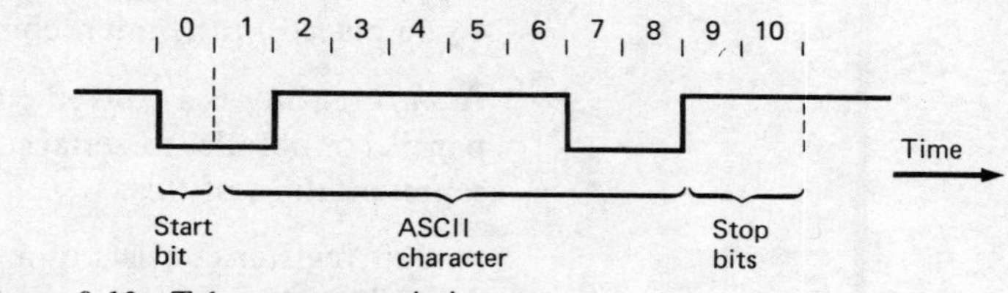

Figure 9.12 Teletype transmission

The teletype sends a character whenever an operator presses one of the keys. The rate at which characters are sent depends on the speed with which the operator types.

Transmission of characters is, therefore, *asynchronous* since a character can arrive at the processor at any time. To enable the processor to cope with this and to allow it to detect when data is coming each character is preceded by a *start bit*.

For similar reasons the end of a character is marked by two *stop bits* (sometimes one stop bit and a parity bit is used, but that is a detail). Eight bits are used to represent which character is being sent so the total number of bits transmitted per character is eleven. Figure 9.12 shows the eleven bits used to send the character 'A'.

Serial transmission between a teletype and the microcomputer or, indeed, between any two communicating devices may be *duplex*, *half-duplex* or *simplex*.

A *duplex system* can transmit information in both directions simultaneously. Thus the teletype, for example, can send a character to the microprocessor at the same time as a character for printing is being sent from the microprocessor to it. In such a system there must be separate wires for each direction of transmission.

A *half-duplex system* can also send data in both directions, but only one direction can be used at any time.

A *simplex system* is unidirectional.

Many other peripherals also use serial communication of the same sort as has been described. Hence there is a requirement for the computer system to be able to send and receive data in this form.

Serial-to-parallel and parallel-to-serial conversion

Microcomputer systems nearly always operate on data in parallel form. As has been seen they commonly handle 8- or 16-bit 'chunks' of information. The tendency in later generations of devices is to increase their parallelism (the newest processors are 32 bits wide). Because of this it is necessary to perform a transformation from parallel to serial form in order to send data out from a microcomputer to a serially driven peripheral. Conversely it is necessary to perform a serial-to-parallel conversion when data received from a serial link is to be placed in the microcomputer memory.

A *shift register* is a convenient device to employ for either serial-to-parallel or parallel-to-serial conversion. Figure 9.13 gives a schematic representation of this.

A shift register consists of a number of one bit stores or *flip-flops*. These have been mentioned earlier as components of staticisers. The

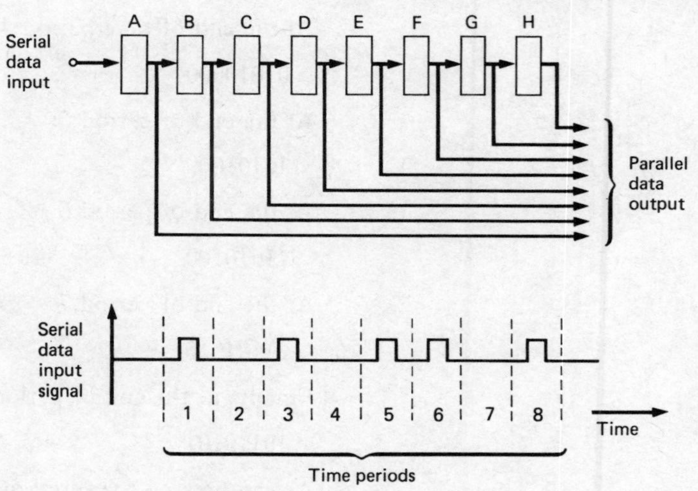

Figure 9.13 Serial-to-parallel conversion

figure shows eight flip-flops, labelled A, B, C, . . . , H, connected so that the output of A goes to the input of B, the output of B goes to the input of C, and so on.

Data arrives at the input flip-flop A on the 'serial data input' line. Suppose that a pattern of eight bits, as shown at the bottom of the figure, appears on this input. During time period 2 it is a 0, during period 3 it is a 1, etc.

During time period 1 the input signal then present at the input of flip-flop A (*stage* A of the shift register) is taken into stage A and stored. At the end of time period 1, therefore, stage A contains a 1.

Also during period 1 the signal present at the input to stage B (that is the output of stage A) is taken into stage B and stored. The same process happens all along the register. Thus stage C stores the output of stage B, stage D stores the output of stage C, and so on.

If, initially, before period 1 all the stages of the register held zeros, then at the end of period 1 the pattern in the register must be

10000000

During period 2 the same thing happens again. The signal on the data input line, in this case a 0, is taken into stage A, the output of A (a 1) is taken into B, etc. At the end of time period 2, therefore, the pattern in the register is

01000000

At the end of time period 3 it is

10100000

At the end of time period 4:

01010000

At the end of period 5:

10101000

At the end of period 6:

11010100

At the end of period 7:

01101010

Finally, at the end of period 8:

10110101

As can be seen the serial data on the input line is 'shifted into' the register.

After period 8 is finished the input pattern, now stored in the register, can be read out in parallel using the eight data output lines shown in the figure. This takes a single time period. Thus the shift register acts as a *serial-to-parallel converter*.

So that the instants at which data is placed in stage A of the shift register and at which the information in one stage is shifted to the next can be precisely defined, the register normally possesses a clock input (not shown in the figure) upon which timing pulses are placed.

A *parallel-to-serial converter* is shown in Figure 9.14. The principle is essentially the same as that of the serial-to-parallel converter just described. However, in this case data is placed individually, in parallel during a single time period, into every stage of the register using the 'parallel data input' lines. It is then shifted out of the register serially during eight time periods onto the 'serial data output' line.

To communicate with a serial peripheral device, such as a teletype or a visual display unit, the processor can output parallel data into a parallel-to-serial converter using a shift register. The serial data is

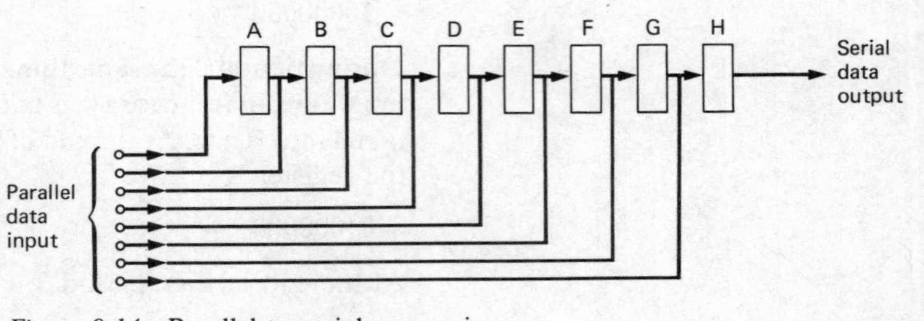

Figure 9.14 Parallel-to-serial conversion

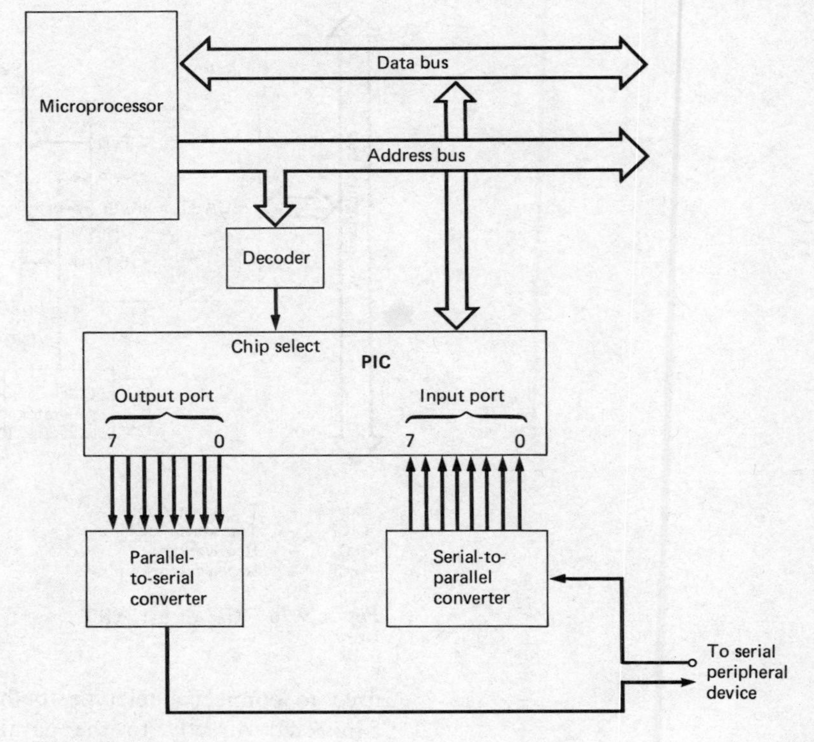

Figure 9.15

then obtained by applying eight clock pulses to the register so as to shift the data out of it.

Similarly serial data arriving from a teletype is shifted into the register within a serial-to-parallel converter. It is then read, in parallel, into the processor.

A complete system for communication between the processor and a serial peripheral is shown in Figure 9.15. One part of a peripheral interface circuit is used to send parallel 8-bit data to a parallel-to serial converter and thence, in serial form, to the device.

Another port of the PIC, configured as an input, reads data from a serial-to parallel converter.

LSI chips for serial transmission

As mentioned in Chapter 1, a number of large-scale integrated circuits are available for use in interfacing microcomputer systems to serial data transmission lines.

One class of such chips is known as UART (Universal Asynchronous Receiver and Transmitter). Figure 9.16 illustrates how such a chip is

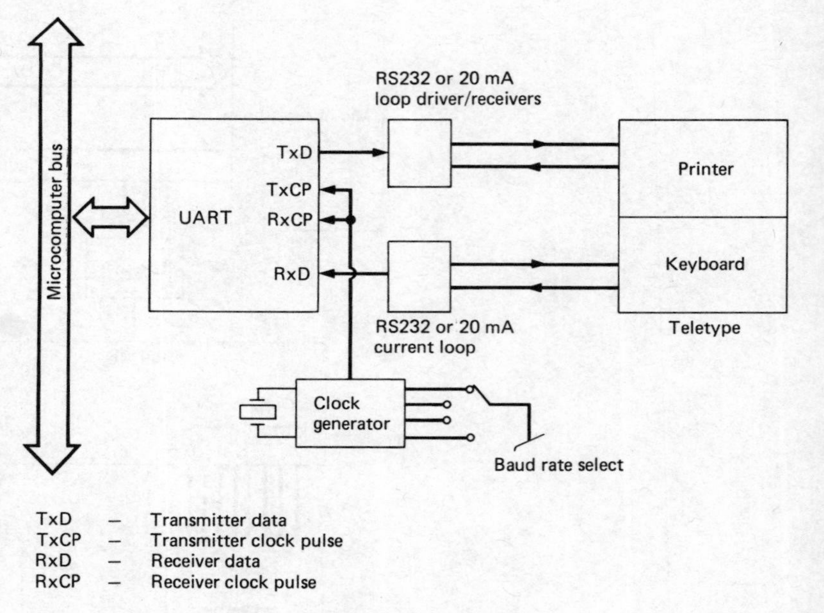

Figure 9.16 Use of a UART

used to connect a teletype to the microcomputer. The UART is connected directly to the parallel microcomputer data bus. It contains the necessary tri-state drivers and receivers required to utilise this bus correctly.

Asynchronous serial transmission is only suitable for relatively low-speed links (up to 9,600 baud). Below this limit a range of transmission rates upwards from 110 baud, the teletype speed, are used. Hence the frequency of operation of the UART is determined by a crystal-controlled oscillator. In some systems the rate of the clock pulses applied to the UART is switch-selectable, as shown in the figure, allowing the receive and transmit baud rates to be adjusted as required.

The receiver in the UART synchronises itself on the start bit transmitted by the teletype and then samples the succeeding data bits. When a complete character has been received it is checked (using the parity bit in the ASCII code) and is sent to the processor along the data highway. The UART performs the necessary serial-to-parallel conversion on received data.

The transmitter section of the UART converts parallel data from the microcomputer bus to serial form, adds the start, stop and parity bits, and sends the data over the link.

The UART possesses control inputs and outputs to enable synchronisation of transfers between it and the microcomputer bus.

It thus incorporates all the necessary functions for convenient interfacing to serial devices.

Q9.11

Synchronous serial data transmission

Asynchronous serial transmission (and reception), as outlined above, is only suitable for relatively low-speed links. For higher-speed links, such as those involved in the interconnection of multiple microcomputers in a network, *synchronous* transmission is to be preferred.

Asynchronous transmission is sometimes described as *start–stop* transmission because of its intermittent mode of operation. In synchronous transmission, on the other hand, characters are sent along the transmission line continuously, without breaks.

When there is no data to be sent along a line a stream of 'synchronisation characters' are transmitted to ensure that the sending and receiving devices remain locked together in synchronisation. This removes the need to add start and stop bits to characters so line usage becomes more efficient.

The sequence of characters in a transmission is divided into blocks and error-checking is carried out at the end of each block. The block length is variable, depending on the sending and receiving devices and upon the nature of the data being sent. For instance, if data from punched cards is being sent over a link it is sensible to use blocks containing 80 characters each. Because the card contains 80 columns, each capable of representing a single character, this means that each block transmitted represents a single card.

Various international standards committees have been set up over the past few years. These have defined '*protocols*' for data transmission networks which include specifications of block and message formats for synchronous transmission.

Large-scale integrated circuits for use in synchronous serial data transmission have been available for some years. One such circuit is the USART (Universal Synchronous/Asynchronous Receiver Transmitter). These devices connect to the microcomputer address and data highways in the usual way and can be programmed to operate in asynchronous or synchronous mode.

Transmission speeds for synchronous operation range up to 56 kbaud (Intel 8251 programmable communication interface).

Q9.9, 9.12

9.5 Interfacing to peripheral timing circuits

Interval timers

The hardware of interval timers and the way in which they can be interfaced to the microcomputer highway was introduced in Section 2.5. It will be recalled that an interval timer is a device containing a number of counters each of which can be loaded with a value from the microcomputer using a normal OUT instruction. The counters can then be made to count down from this value by applying pulses from an external source to their 'clock' input lines.

For reference the block diagram of such a timer is shown in Figure 9.17. Application of clock pulses to the 'clock 0' line causes counter (0) to count down. When its contents reach zero a signal is generated on OUT (0). Counters (1) and (2) operate similarly.

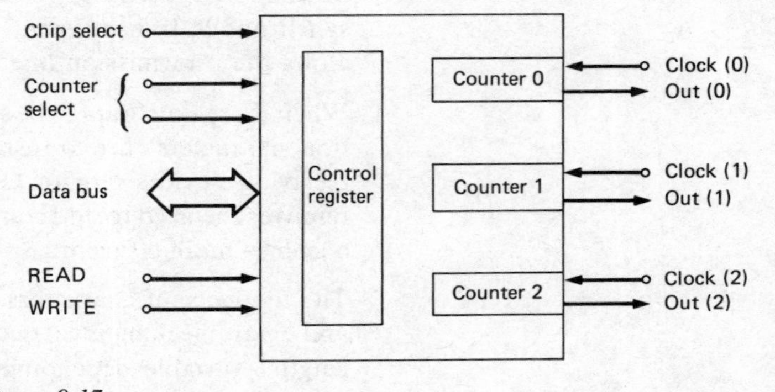

Figure 9.17

Many applications of microcomputers involve the accurate measurement of time intervals. These intervals can vary, according to the application, from a few microseconds to many minutes. Thus it is important that the timer chip be as flexible as possible.

Each counter typically contains 16 bits. Thus a number up to 65,535 ($2^{16}-1$) can be stored in it. Suppose that the input clock frequency is 50 Hz. The maximum interval that can be measured is:

65,535/50s
= 1,310.7 s
= 21 min 50.7 s

This period can be varied either by

1 altering the value placed in the counter or
2 altering the clock frequency.

If a longer interval is required the clock input frequency must be decreased. If a shorter interval is needed the number placed in the counter can be reduced. For instance, a clock frequency of 10 Hz would allow measurement of periods up to about 100 min. Alternatively a value of 10,000 placed in the counter, using the original clock frequency of 50 Hz, would give a period of 200 s.

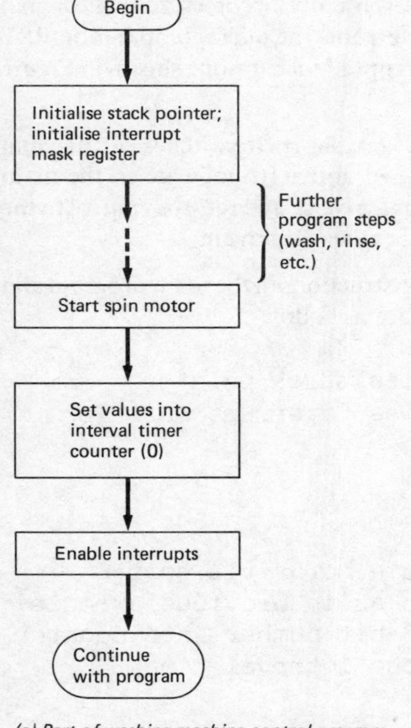

(a) Part of washing machine control program

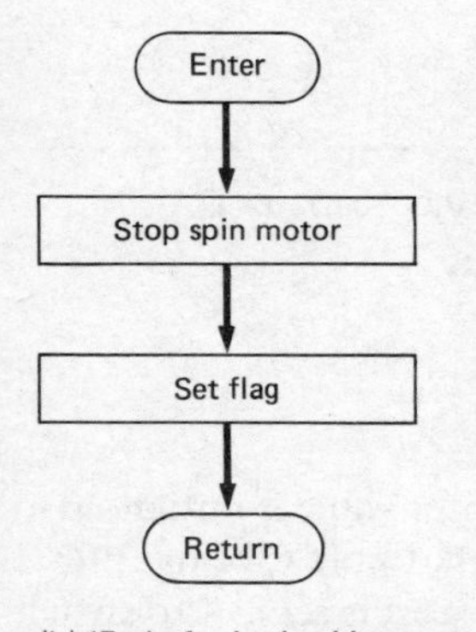

(b) 'End of spin time' interrupt service routine

Figure 9.18

When the value in the counter reaches zero the signal generated on the OUT line is usually used to interrupt the microcomputer.

One example of the use of an interval timer is a domestic washing machine. Such devices require the setting of several intervals:

1 The wash time.
2 The rinse time.
3 The spin time.

Thus a microcomputer used as a controller in a washing machine must generate suitable length time periods for these operations.

Suppose that the microcomputer contains an interval timer chip and that counter (0), say, is to be used to control the spin time of the machine. Counter (2) could be used for the rinse time and counter (3) for the wash time. A flowchart for the program controlling the washing machine must then contain sections as shown in the diagram of Figure 9.18(a).

At the start of the program the stack pointer is initialised, to set the position of the stack in memory. The stack is then ready to accept the program counter and register values (if required) when interrupts arrive.

The interrupt mask register is set, as outlined in Chapter 8, to permit selected interrupts to occur. If, for this example, we suppose that the signal OUT(0) is used to cause an interrupt on the RST 5.5 input, the mask must be set to allow this, at least, to reach the processor.

The program continues controlling the various functions of the washing machine until the point in the wash cycle is reached where spinning is required. It then switches on the spin motor, using an OUT instruction to a peripheral port which controls that motor, loads a number into the interval timer register [counter (0)] controlling the spin duration and enables interrupts with an EI instruction.

It then continues with any other operations which are necessary. If there is nothing more to do until the spin operation has finished, the program can simply loop waiting for the 'End of spin time' interrupt to arrive.

So that the program can tell when this interrupt has occurred it examines a 'flag' (a one-bit indicator) each time it cycles round the waiting loop. This flag is normally reset (at 0), but is set to 1 by the interrupt service routine as will be seen.

Once a number has been placed in counter (0) of the interval timer it starts counting down at the rate of the input clock. For this application we will assume that the clock rate is 50 Hz since a signal of this frequency is easily derived from the a.c. mains.

When the value in counter (0) eventually becomes zero the signal generated on the OUT(0) line interrupts the microcomputer on RST 5.5. This causes entry to the interrupt service routine shown in Figure 9.18(b).

The interrupt service routine is very short. It switches off the spin motor, sets the 'flag' as mentioned above (to indicate to the main program that a timer interrupt has arrived), and returns control to the main program at the point where it was interrupted.

Some of the assembly language instructions in the main program and in the interrupt service routine are as follows:

Main program

```
      LXI  SP,10D4  ;Initialise stack pointer
      MVI  A,0E     ;Initialise interrupt mask for
      SIM           ;RST 5.5
      .
      .
      .
      MVI  A,01     ;Start spin motor via port C
      OUT  0A       ;(address as in previous example)
      MVI  A,30     ;Set a 16-bit number into counter
      OUT  13       ;(0) of the interval timer
      MVI  A,30
      OUT  10
      MVI  A,75
      OUT  10
      EI
      continue
-------------------------------------------------------
INT:  MVI  A,00     ;Stop spin motor via port C
      OUT  0A
      MVI  B,01     ;Set (B) to 1
      RET           ;Return
```

Interrupt service routine

In the above it is assumed that the stack pointer value is initialised to 10D4 (hex) as in the previous example and that port C of the PIC is used to control the spin motor. Bit 0 of this port is set to 1 to switch the motor on and to 0 to switch it off.

When interrupt RST 5.5 arrives the processor transfers control of program execution to the instruction in the address 002C (hex). This location must, therefore, contain the instruction JMP INT so as to cause entry to the interrupt service routine above.

Three steps are needed to transfer a 16-bit number into counter (0). The interval timer contains a control register (Figure 9.17) and, firstly, a control word must be placed in this. Secondly the least significant 8 bits of the number are sent to counter (0) and, finally, the most significant 8 bits are sent to counter (0).

If the address of the interval timer on the microcomputer bus is 10 (hex) the addresses of the control register and counters (0), (1) and (2) are:

Counter 0	10 (hex) (= 10 + 00)
Counter 1	11 (hex) (= 10 + 01)
Counter 2	12 (hex) (= 10 + 02)
Control Register	13 (hex) (= 10 + 03)

Thus firstly the control word is sent by the instructions:

```
MVI  A,30
OUT  13
```

Secondly the least significant byte of the counter value is sent:

```
MVI  A,30
OUT  10
```

Finally the most significant byte is sent:

```
MVI  A,75
OUT  10
```

A spin time of 10 min has been assumed. Hence, with a 50 Hz clock rate applied to Clock (0), the number placed in counter (0) must be 30,000 (decimal), i.e. 7530 (hex). The least significant byte is thus 30 (hex) and the most significant 75 (hex).

Q9.13

Real-time clocks

Chapter 2 has mentioned the use of interval timer chips as real-time clocks. These, too, are important in many applications.

Consider the use of a microcomputer to control the operation of a house. In such a system it is important for the microcomputer to keep a record of the time of day. It needs this so that it can control functions of the house that are time-dependent. For example it may switch on the central heating at preset times or switch on an immersion heater each night just before the children's bathtime. It may, perhaps, be responsible for waking up the household in the morning, and for a number of other similar time-dependent operations.

The use of an interval timer can assist the microcomputer in such applications. The microcomputer system keeps a record, in memory, of the current time of day. The interval timer interrupts it at exact intervals of, say, one minute.

Each time that an interrupt arrives the service routine associated with it updates the minutes time by adding one to it. If the resulting value should reach sixty the hours time is increased by one and the minutes time is set to zero.

These operations only represent a small overhead in terms of processor time since they involve the processor in executing just a few instructions every minute.

The microcomputer must contain switches or push buttons which can be used to set the correct time into it. However once this has been done only the accuracy of the clock frequency applied to the interval timer limits the accuracy of the stored time values.

Since the microcomputer, using this method, always contains an accurate record of the 'real' time it can be used for applications of the type outlined above.

Handling of the interrupts generated by the timer is very much the same as in the previous example.

Questions

9.1 Explain, in the context of transfer of information between a microcomputer and its peripheral devices, what is meant by master and slave devices. Explain how interrupt-driven and polling systems differ in this respect.

9.2 How does a system which uses polling of peripheral devices work? Discuss:

(a) Priority allocation in polling systems.
(b) Advantages of polling.
(c) Disadvantages of polling.

9.3 A microcomputer system used in a travel agency is connected to eight visual display units which operators can use to interrogate information stored in the system memory. Discuss how a polling system might be used to control these devices.

9.4 A block of data is stored in a microcomputer memory in the bytes between addresses 10,000 (decimal) and 10,255 (decimal). Show how eight light-emitting diodes can be connected to the microcomputer using a peripheral interface circuit and be used to examine the data bytes one after the other. Each byte should be displayed on the LEDs for about 5 s.

9.5 Would it be possible, in the system described in Question 9.4, to connect a push-button to an input port so that, at each push of the button, a new byte is displayed? Such a system could cycle through the memory, as in the previous question, but with each byte displayed until the next push of the button. Suggest hardware and software to permit this.

9.6 Write a short section of code to initialise ports A and B of a PIC (such as the Intel 8255A) to be inputs. Use the control register format shown in Figure 2.13. Continue the program to allow two bytes of data to be read from these ports and placed in the B and C registers of the 8085 processor.

9.7 Write a short section of code to initialise ports A and B as inputs and port C as an output. Read a data item in through port A, then another through port B, add the two and output the result to port C.

9.8 Show how a light-emitting diode can be connected to an output port of a microcomputer system and used, in conjunction with a suitable program to generate 500-ms long flashes of light at one second intervals. Use a time-delay subroutine, as outlined in Chapter 7, to generate the necessary time intervals and assume that each instruction takes 2 μs.

9.9 Why are input and output of data such important operations in a microcomputer system? Distinguish between serial and parallel I/O and discuss the circuits available to assist with each of them.

9.10 What is meant by each of the following terms?
(a) Interrupt-driven system.
(b) Polling system.
(c) Full duplex.
(d) Half duplex.
(e) Synchronous.

9.11 *(a)* Explain how a shift register can be used to assist the microprocessor with input and output of data in serial form.
(b) Outline the facilities provided by a UART and show how it can be used for serial I/O.

9.12 Distinguish between
(a) Asynchronous and
(b) Synchronous serial data transmission.
Highlight the differences between these and discuss their areas of application.

9.13 An interval timer chip is to be used to assist the microprocessor in the task of generating a square wave pulse train. The period of the square wave is to be variable from 500 μs to 100 ms. Discuss suitable frequencies for the clock input to the interval timer and suggest appropriate values to be placed in the counter. Outline the program for this application.

9.14 Four switches (A, B, C and D) and four light-emitting diodes (L, M, N and O) are connected to the peripheral interface circuits of a microcomputer. The system must sense the states of the switches and activate the LEDs in accordance with the following rules:
(a) L is on when C is down and off when C is up.

(*b*) M is on when C and B are down and D is up. The state of A does not matter.

(*c*) N is on when A is down and M is on.

(*d*) O is on when B or A are down and C and D are up.

Write a program to perform these operations.

Chapter 10 **Programming**

Objectives of this chapter *When you have completed studying this chapter you should be able to:*

1. *Appreciate that the design of a microcomputer-based system involves the development of both hardware and software.*
2. *Appreciate that an important stage in this development is that in which the hardware and software are combined and errors in them are detected and corrected.*
3. *Understand that software development involves a number of stages in the progression from system specification to machine code program.*
4. *Appreciate that a number of software development aids are available to assist the programmer (including editors, loaders, assemblers, high-level language compilers, cross products, monitors, utility routines, libraries and debugging routines) and have a general idea of the purpose of each of these.*
5. *Understand the format of assembly language statements and use pseudo-instructions in assembly language.*
6. *Appreciate the structure of a complete program including*
   - (a) *The use of I/O routines.*
   - (b) *The use of subroutines.*
   - (c) *The use of interrupt service routines.*

10.1 Introduction

The need for both hardware and software in a microcomputer system has been emphasised several times in earlier chapters. Hardware aspects of the microcomputer system – the processor, the memories, peripheral I/O chips, interval timers, and so on, have been discussed in some detail, and their interaction with the program has been outlined where appropriate. The main purpose of this chapter is to consider the software of the microcomputer in a little more detail and to look at an example of a complete application of a microcomputer in a digital stopwatch.

10.2 Microcomputer system design

The design of a complete engineering system that incorporates a programmable device such as a microcomputer necessarily involves

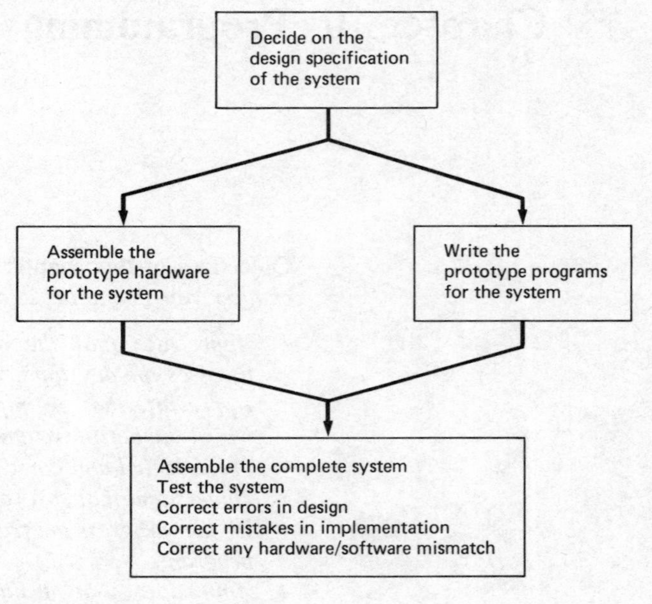

Figure 10.1

the development of both hardware and software. A typical sequence of events is as shown in Figure 10.1.

If a new system (perhaps a new product) is to be designed with a microcomputer contained in it, the initial step must be to produce a system specification. This covers the technical aims which the system must meet.

Once this is available the development of system hardware and software can proceed in parallel to a large extent. Thus one team of engineers can put together the components which make up the physical system whilst another group can set about writing the programs to go in that system and control its operation.

Finally the complete system is assembled and the hardware and software are tested together. At this stage it is inevitable that errors will become apparent in a number of areas. Although the hardware and software development groups keep in close contact during their separate phases of work there will be cases where small misunderstandings or omissions cause mismatches between hardware and software.

The hardware team will make errors in their part as will the software group in theirs. The design specification of the system may be inadequate or incorrect. Problems caused by all these factors have to be detected and corrected during the system-testing phase.

Q10.1

Software development

As mentioned above, this chapter is mainly concerned with the development of the software part of the system. This, itself, involves a sequence of stages.

The complete system specification contains sections covering both the hardware and software objectives. The software design starts with this specification and ends with the production of machine code instructions in the microcomputer program memory. This is shown in Figure 10.2. Clearly there is a big step to be taken between these two points; a step which, in general, is too difficult to complete in one operation. In other words it is necessary to have intermediate stages between the specification and the machine code program so as to assist the orderly progression from the one to the other.

The first step is to break down the problem to be programmed into a sequence of very simple operations. This is known as forming an *algorithm* for the task. The algorithm can be written as a list of operations or can be drawn as a flowchart of the type used in earlier examples.

Following this the steps in the algorithm must be written as program instructions. That is, the algorithm must be *coded*. There are several ways in which this can be achieved.

In a very simple microcomputer system it may be necessary to code the algorithm directly into machine code instructions. If this is to be

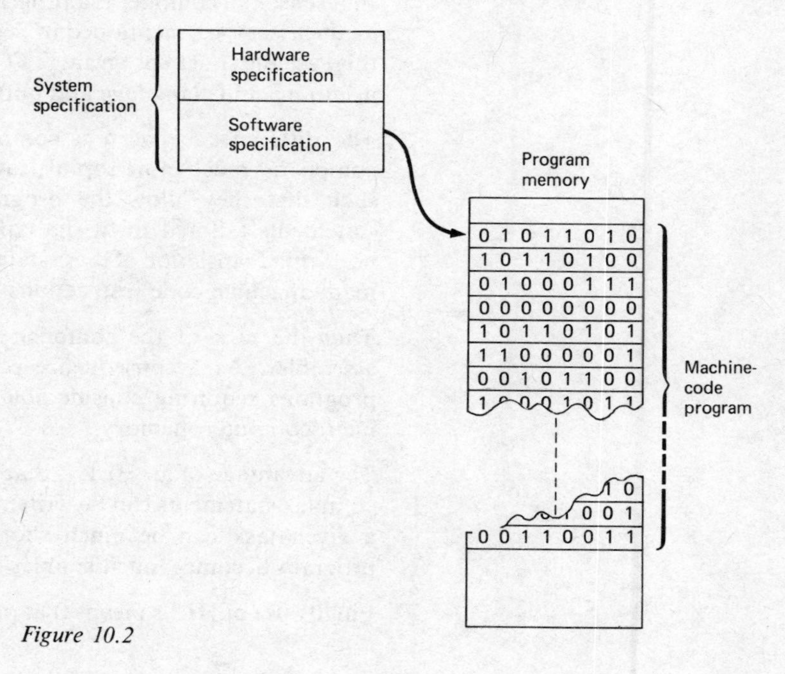

Figure 10.2

done the algorithm itself must be very detailed and considerable effort is required in its preparation. Moreover, as has been suggested, the use of machine code, either in binary or hexadecimal form, is neither a quick nor an easy way of writing a program.

A much better way of performing the coding operation is to employ a *higher-level* language than machine code. Assembly language, as introduced in Chapter 1 and as used in several earlier examples, is one step up from machine code.

As will be recalled, it allows the programmer to use mnemonics to represent the operation code part of an instruction together with labels and names for addresses and data. However, one assembly language instruction produces only one machine code instruction when it is passed through the assembler program. Thus programming in assembly language still requires a very detailed algorithm to be used.

High-level languages (HLLs) represent a better solution still since they are designed to reduce the gap between the language in which the task is specified and the implementation language in which the program is written.

When a program is written in an HLL such as FORTRAN, PASCAL, BASIC, ALGOL or COBOL, that program has to be translated into machine code before it can be placed in the microcomputer memory. This task is performed by a *compiler*.

In a sense the compiler is a program which operates in the same way as the assembler mentioned in Section 1.7. It takes in input data, in this case the source program in FORTRAN, ALGOL, etc., translates it into machine language and puts it in the microcomputer memory.

The difference between a compiler and an assembler is that a compiler is much more sophisticated. HLLs are application-oriented such that they allow the programmer to write his program in statements tailored to fit the types of operations that he needs to perform. Translation of these statements into machine code produces many machine code instructions for each statement.

Thus the task of the compiler is more difficult than that of the assembler. As a consequence of this compilers tend to be large programs requiring considerable amounts of storage space in the microcomputer memory.

The advantage of an HLL is that it is so much easier to use. Because complex statements can be written using it the algorithm required for a given task can be much shortened and simplified. The source program becomes much simpler to read.

Finally use of HLLs means that programs become portable from one type of microcomputer to another. This happens because the compiler can be tailored to a particular machine whereas the source program can be machine-independent. For instance:

1 The compiler for FORTRAN for a Z80 microcomputer system translates FORTRAN source programs into Z80 machine code.
2 The compiler for FORTRAN for an 8085 microcomputer system translates FORTRAN source programs into 8085 machine code.
3 The compiler for FORTRAN for a Motorola 6809 microcomputer translates FORTRAN source programs into 6809 machine code, and so on.

Steps involved in software development

After a task has been formulated as an algorithm, and a program has been written to perform the required functions, there are still a number of steps to be undertaken before the program is completed.

1 The program has to be entered into the microcomputer system.
2 The program has to be edited.
3 The program has to be converted to machine code by the assembler or compiler.
4 The program has to be *linked* with any library subroutines which it requires (see Section 5.2). Linking involves extracting the subroutine from the library, inserting it into the program and making appropriate arrangements for data and parameters to be exchanged with it.

Entry of the program into the microcomputer is normally achieved using a keyboard and visual display unit. Program statements are typed into memory using this device in conjunction with a program in the machine.

The editor program allows a programmer to alter the program statements, either to correct errors within them or to change the function which they perform should the program not behave as desired.

Software development aids

A number of aids are available to assist the programmer in converting the system specification to machine language program code. These include editors, loaders, assemblers, HLL compilers, cross products, monitors, utility routines, libraries and debugging programs.

Editors, as implied above, are programs that are available to help a user type in his program, correct it and alter it if necessary.

Loaders are used to read programs on some suitable input medium (paper tape, magnetic tape, floppy disk) into the computer and to place them in the memory in a convenient position. Quite often a program is made up of a number of separate sections. The loading process then consists of reading these into the computer, allocating storage space to them in an appropriate way and making such adjustments to addresses, etc., as are necessary to fit the separate sections (modules) together.

Assemblers and HLL compilers have been discussed earlier.

Cross products are programs which can be run on one microcomputer and which produce programs for another. We have seen, for example, that an assembly language program is read, as input data, by an assembler program. The assembler translates the assembly language instructions into machine code. In this process there is no need for the assembler to be run on the same type of microprocessor as that which will eventually run the machine code program being produced. The assembly process could, for instance, be performed on a PDP 11 computer system and could produce machine code programs for a Z80 microcomputer. All that this requires is:

(a) that the assembler itself be written in PDP 11 code and,
(b) that some method is available for transferring the Z80 code produced by the assembler into the Z80 microcomputer which is to run it.

A program of this type, which is run on one machine and produces software code for another, is called a *cross product*. If it is a program which translates assembly language to machine code it is a cross-assembler. If it translates an HLL to machine code it is a cross-compiler.

There are various ways in which the program code produced by a cross-assembler can be transferred to the microcomputer system which is to use that code (the latter system is often called the *target* system). It can, for example, be written on to a floppy disk by the machine performing the cross-assembly, or be stored on magnetic tape. The target machine then needs to have a floppy disk handler or tape reader which is compatible so that it can take the program in.

An alternative is to use *down-line loading*. A comparison of this method with that of using floppy disk or magnetic tape is shown in Figure 10.3.

In down-line loading the computer system performing the cross-assembly is directly connected, by wires, to the target system. The connection is usually a serial asynchronous link of the type discussed in Chapter 9.

Program code is sent down this link directly into the target system memory. It is a fast, convenient method.

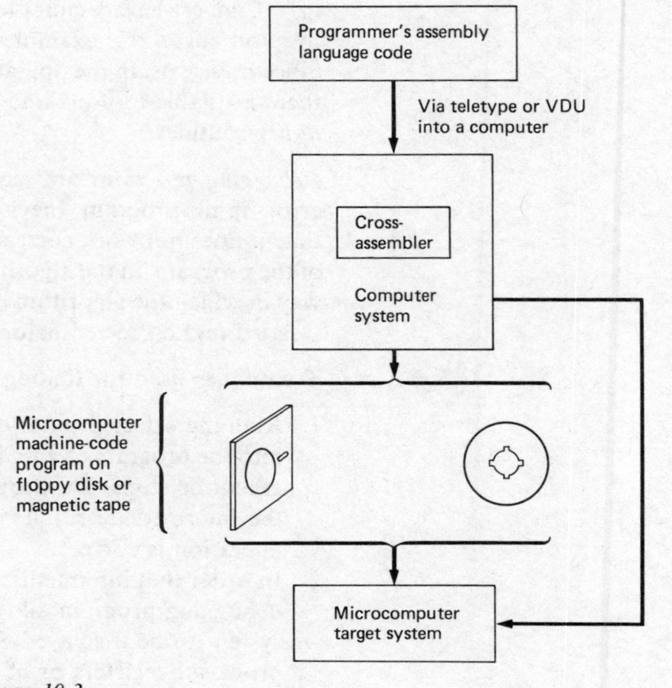

Figure 10.3

Monitor programs were mentioned briefly in Chapter 1. A monitor is the program that normally resides in a microcomputer in order to control the basic machine functions. In a simple system the monitor is also quite small and simple and contains only functions which are fundamental to the system operation such as facilities for input and output of programs and data, a way of starting execution of a program, and so on.

In larger microcomputers, with disk storage, the monitor becomes larger and more complex and is known as an *operating system*. In such systems there is a need for a file-handling section in the operating system which organises the allocation of storage space on the disk(s).

Utility routines Monitor programs, or operating systems, often contain sections of program code which are required for their own operation but which are also useful for incorporation into programs written by users of the system. Sections of program that

(a) Read in characters in ASCII code
(b) Output characters in ASCII code
(c) Convert ASCII code into binary form
(d) Convert a binary number into ASCII characters
(e) Print a string of text
(f) Convert decimal to hexadecimal code

(*g*) Convert hexadecimal to decimal code

to quote just a few examples, are often required within a program. Since these exist in the operating system it is straightforward to make them available to users and this is often done. They are then called *utility* routines.

Debugging programs are made available to assist the user to find errors in his program. Inevitably when a program is run for the first time it does not work correctly. There are errors both in the concept of the program, in the algorithm derived from this concept and in the way in which the algorithm has been coded. These must be detected, isolated and corrected before the program can run properly.

Techniques used for finding errors include:

1 Running selected parts of the program, i.e. setting *breakpoints* into the program. A breakpoint is a point in the program at which execution stops. The program can thus be run up to this point and the intermediate results obtained can be examined to see if its operation is correct.
2 In order that intermediate program results can be examined, the debugging program allows the contents of selected parts of the system to be displayed. These may include the contents of the processor registers or of locations in memory.
3 So that the program can be run using known test data the contents of selected memory locations or of the processor registers can be modified using the debugging program.
4 Execution of the user program can be started from a specified address.

There are many other possibilities too numerous to include here. Together they provide powerful ways of correcting programs.

Summary

As can be seen from the very brief outline given in the preceding sections there are comprehensive tools available to the programmer to assist him in bridging the gap between the system software specification and the machine code program in the memory of the final working prototype. Each of these tools has been considered only in the broadest sense. Further detail is left to texts specialising in such topics.

In the same way that software development tools are available to assist the programmer there are also hardware aids to assist the engineer in assembling the circuits of the system. Again space does not permit discussion of these but it is useful to note that the use of a manufacturer's microcomputer development system, in conjunction with test instruments such as a logic state analyser, provides the most comprehensive and convenient method of approach.

Q10.2

10.3 Assembly language

The programming examples in this book have been written in machine language or in assembly language and an outline of the latter of these has been given in Section 1.7. Before going on to a further example of the use of the microcomputer it is convenient to add a little formality to the description of assembly language.

To recapitulate what has been stated earlier, assembly language allows

1 Instructions to be labelled.
2 The order-code part of the instruction to be written as a mnemonic.
3 Variables to be specified as names.

In general, the format of an assembly language statement, i.e. the *syntax* of assembly language, is:

A label field	*An instruction (or opcode) field*	*An operand field*	*A comment field*

For example, an instruction might be:

```
START:  MOV          D,C          ;Move data from
                                   C to D
```

The first field contains the label which is used to refer to the instruction. Thus, in the example, to transfer control to this instruction would require a 'JMP START' or similar order.

The second and third fields of the instruction contains the instruction specification – what the instruction is to do (the opcode) – plus the specification of the operand or operands to be used. The example given causes the byte held in the C register to be placed in the D register.

The fourth field allows the programmer to insert a comment which, usually, describes what the instruction does, or rather is intended to do. It is not strictly necessary for the comment field to be used (it can be left blank) but it is desirable to use it if the program is to be easily understood, especially by programmers other than those who wrote it.

Assembler directives

In addition to allowing instructions to be written in the format described above, assembly languages also contain facilities for passing information to the assembler program itself. These are called *assembler directives* or, sometimes, *pseudo-instructions*.

Information that the assembler may require includes:

1 The address in memory at which the program, when translated

into machine code, is to begin.

2 The values to be placed in certain data items in the program at the time at which the assembly process is performed.

For example, the assembly language for the Intel 8080 or 8085 processors contains the assembler directives:

ORG – Used to set the program start address.
EQU – Used to assign a value to a variable name.
DB – define byte. Used to assign a value to the next available byte.
DW – define word. Used to assign a value to the next available two bytes.

It should be noted that these directives, although they appear in an assembly language program, do not produce any instructions in the final machine code program. They are simply instructions to the assembler program itself. This is why they are sometimes called pseudo-instructions.

10.4 Programming example: a stopwatch

Introduction

Suppose that a microcomputer system is to be used to develop an electronic stopwatch. Devices of this type have been available on the market for some time and provide a number of facilities.

Basically a stopwatch must allow accurate measurement of the time taken by a particular event. The event may be a race in an athletics meeting, the operation of a hydraulic press producing a component in a factory, the length of a lecture or one of many other possibilities.

In each of these the fundamental requirement is for the operator to be able to start the stopwatch at the beginning of the event and to stop it at the end. Between these actions the watch measures the time that has elapsed.

There are, of course, a number of possible variations of the basic scheme. For instance it is often necessary to measure a number of events one after the other. Initially the stopwatch starts from zero. After the first event has finished it contains (and displays) the time taken by that event. It can then operate in one of two ways.

1 When the 'start' button is pressed to begin timing the second event it can start from zero as before.
2 Alternatively, when the 'start' button is pressed for the second time it can begin from the reading it had at the end of the first event.

The former of these possibilities allows a sequence of events to be separately timed whilst the latter gives a cumulative time for the sequence. In either case, of course, a little arithmetic performed on the readings produces the information presented directly by the other possibility. Nevertheless it is convenient if the stopwatch can work in both modes.

Yet a further degree of complexity is introduced by the idea of a 'lap time' facility. As implied by the name this allows the laps of a long race to be separately timed. With it the display of the stopwatch can be 'frozen' at the end of a lap but the watch continues timing. The operator can thus write down the time for each lap without interfering with the timing of the next lap.

We shall consider a stopwatch which does not have a lap time facility but which can either:

1 Be reset to zero at the end of each timing interval, or
2 Continue timing from the previous reading.

Hardware

A block diagram of a possible microcomputer system is shown in Figure 10.4. The similarity of this to the system shown in Figure 7.10 for generating a square-wave pulse train is clear, although there are several important differences.

A peripheral interface circuit is used to provide the connection between the microprocessor and a liquid-crystal display which shows the readout of the stopwatch. Inputs to the stopwatch come from two spring-loaded push-buttons and are taken directly into the interrupt inputs RST 5.5 and RST 6.5 of the processor.

It is worth mentioning at this point that, if an Intel 8085 micro-

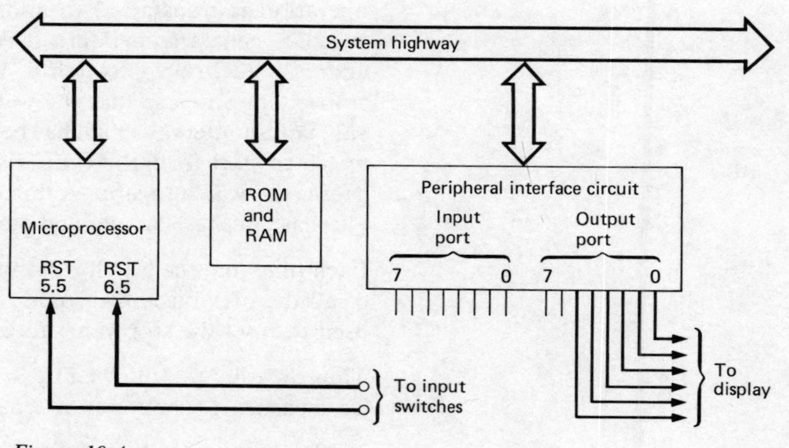

Figure 10.4

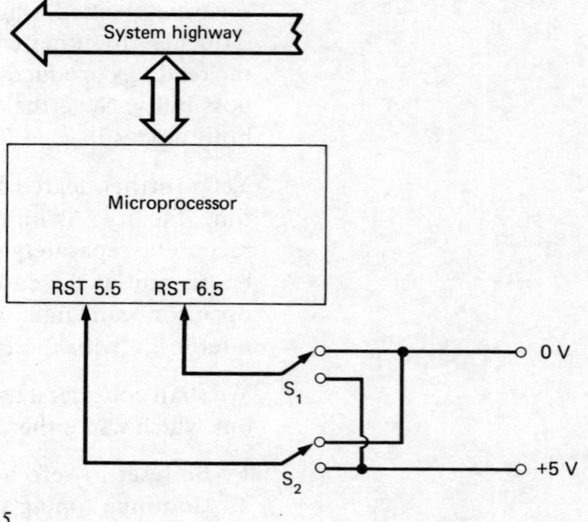

Figure 10.5

computer were to be used for this application in practice, it would not be necessary to use a separate peripheral interface circuit. The basic 8085 consists of three chips. These are, broadly speaking, the processor, a ROM chip and a RAM chip.

However each of the memory chips contains other facilities as well as storage. Both contain I/O ports for example, and these could be used to drive the display outputs rather than the extra peripheral interface circuit illustrated.

Figure 10.5 shows the input circuits of the microcomputer. Two switches, labelled S_1 and S_2, are connected to RST 5.5 and RST 6.5. These interrupts are triggered by a high (+5 V) level. Thus if switch S_1 is pressed, connecting RST 6.5 to +5 V, and if the interrupt mask levels are correctly set and interrupts are enabled, control of program operation is transferred to address 0034 (hex). Similarly pressing switch S_2 generates an interrupt from RST 5.5, transferring control to address 002C (hex). Switch S_1 is to be used to start and stop the stopwatch. Suppose that the watch is stopped and is displaying the value of an interval which has been measured. Pressing S_1 causes the watch to start from the value displayed. Pressing S_1 again after this causes the watch to stop. A third press causes it to restart and so on, alternate pushes starting and stopping the timing function.

Each time that the watch is stopped it displays the accumulated time of all the previously measured intervals. However switch S_2 can be used to reset the stopwatch to zero.

Thus pressing S_2, followed by S_1, starts the stopwatch from scratch. To measure a succession of separate intervals:

1 S_2 is pressed, followed by S_1, to start timing.

2 S_1 is pressed to end timing. The duration of the first interval is then displayed and can be noted down. Following this:
3 S_2 is pressed again, again followed by S_1. Timing of interval 2 then begins. At the end of this time S_1 is pressed again and the value of interval 2 is noted.
4 This process can be repeated as often as necessary.

The stopwatch measures elapsed time in minutes and seconds. It will be assumed that any interval of duration up to 99 min and 59 s can be accommodated. This limit is set because the output display to be used can present only four decimal characters. Two of these are used for the minutes and two for the seconds.

When the time measured exceeds the maximum period given above the stopwatch simply overflows and starts again from zero, i.e. the displayed time shown one second after 99 min 59 s is 00 min 00 s.

Figure 10.6 shows how the displays are connected to the microcomputer. As will be seen from Figure 10.4, six lines of the output port are used.

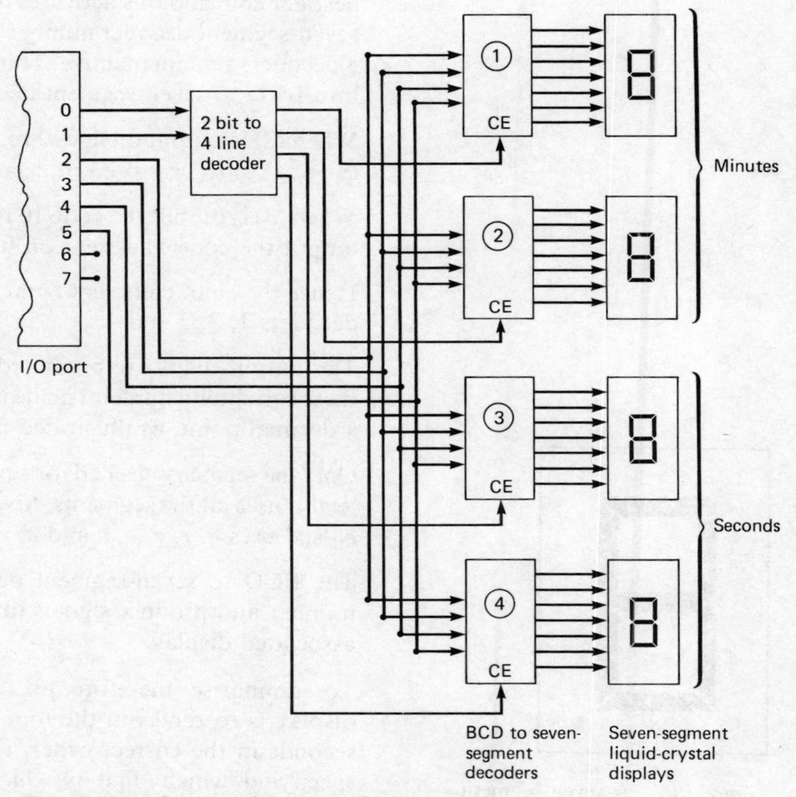

Figure 10.6 Stopwatch output display

Table 10.1

Decimal number	*BCD representation*
0	0000
1	0001
2	0010
3	0011
4	0100
5	0101
6	0110
7	0111
8	1000
9	1001

The numbers to be displayed are output from the computer as binary-coded-decimal (BCD) characters. Each character is thus composed of four bits. For reference, Table 10.1 gives the BCD equivalents of the decimal numbers 0 to 9.

Four of the six lines from the output port are used to send the BCD code of the number being output to the display. The other two lines are used to send a code specifying which digit of the display is being transmitted. The four digits are:

1 The most significant digit of the minutes.
2 The least significant digit of the minutes.
3 The most significant digit of the seconds.
4 The least significant digit of the seconds.

These are output, on the four lines numbered 2 to 5 inclusive of the port, in the sequence (1) then (2) then (3) then (4).

The BCD codes sent out go in parallel to all four BCD to seven-segment decoder chips. However, only one of these takes in each digit. When (1) is output from the port the code 00 is also sent on port outputs 0 and 1. These two bits are decoded by the 2-bit-to-four-line decoder chip and this activates the chip enable (CE) input of BCD to seven-segment decoder number 1. The chip enable input of the other 3 decoders remain inactive. Thus the code on lines 2 to 5 is only read into BCD to seven-segment decoder number 1.

When (2) is output on lines 2 to 5 the code 01 is sent on lines 0 and 1, causing (2) to be stored in decoder 2.

When (3) is output the code 10 is sent on lines 0 and 1 and when (4) is output the code 11 is sent on lines 0 and 1.

Hence the characters sent from the port are placed, in succession, in decoders 1, 2, 3 and 4.

The output digits are presented on liquid-crystal displays. Each of these can show a numeral made up from seven segments together with a decimal point, as illustrated in Figure 10.7.

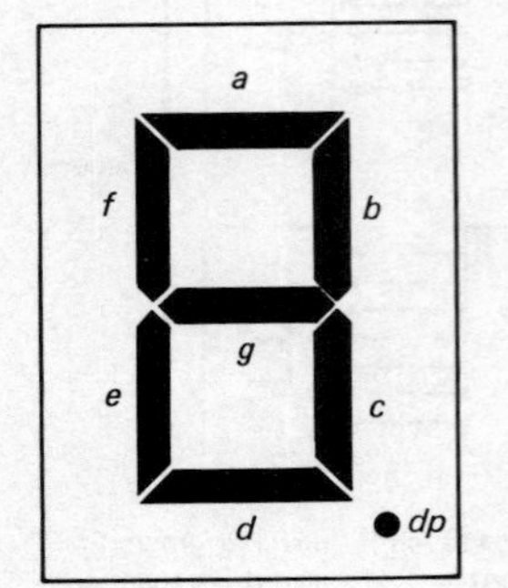

Figure 10.7 A seven-segment liquid-crystal display

Only the segments needed for a particular number are activated. Thus 'eight' uses all the segments, 'five' uses *a*, *f*, *g*, *c* and *d*, 'one' uses *b* and *c*, 'six' uses *a*, *f*, *g*, *e*, *c* and *d*, and so on.

The BCD to seven-segment decoders just decode the BCD input number and produce signals to activate the required sections of the associated display.

To summarise, therefore, all the computer need do to update the display is to send out the four digits representing the minutes and seconds in the correct order, together with the correct 2-bit codes specifying which digit is which. Four OUT operations are thus required.

The hardware and the modes of operation of the stopwatch have now been defined. The remaining task is to write the software (the programs) that control this hardware.

Software

As will become clear the software involves several separate sections. There must be, for example:

1. A main program responsible for determining the overall operation of the stopwatch and for coordinating the other routines.
2. A subroutine DELAY which performs the basic time-keeping function.
3. An interrupt handling routine to deal with the interrupt occurring when S_1 is pressed.
4. An interrupt handling routine to deal with the interrupt occurring when S_2 is pressed.
5. An output subroutine to manage and update the display.
6. A routine for converting values stored in binary form in the microcomputer into BCD form for output to the display.

The main program

Figure 10.8 illustrates the flowchart for the stopwatch main program. The operation of the watch is controlled by a parameter, shown in this diagram, called GO. When GO is set to unity the stopwatch runs. When GO is reset to zero the watch stops timing and simply cycles, displaying the time value which it has reached.

Thus, following the flowchart through from the top, the stopwatch is first initialised and GO is set to zero. The initialisation section sets the interrupt mask register and the stack pointer to their correct values, sets the status of the peripheral interface circuit ports and establishes the value of the delay parameter to be used later. It also resets GO to zero so that when the watch is first switched on it is initially in the stopped state.

Following initialisation, the program enters the loop in which the minutes and seconds readings are output but no other function is performed.

As soon as GO is set to 1 (and this is done by the interrupt service routine entered when S_1 is pressed), the stopwatch goes into the main timing mode.

Thus, as shown in Figure 10.8, it calls a delay subroutine which causes it to wait for a precisely defined period. Following this it increments the SECS by one.

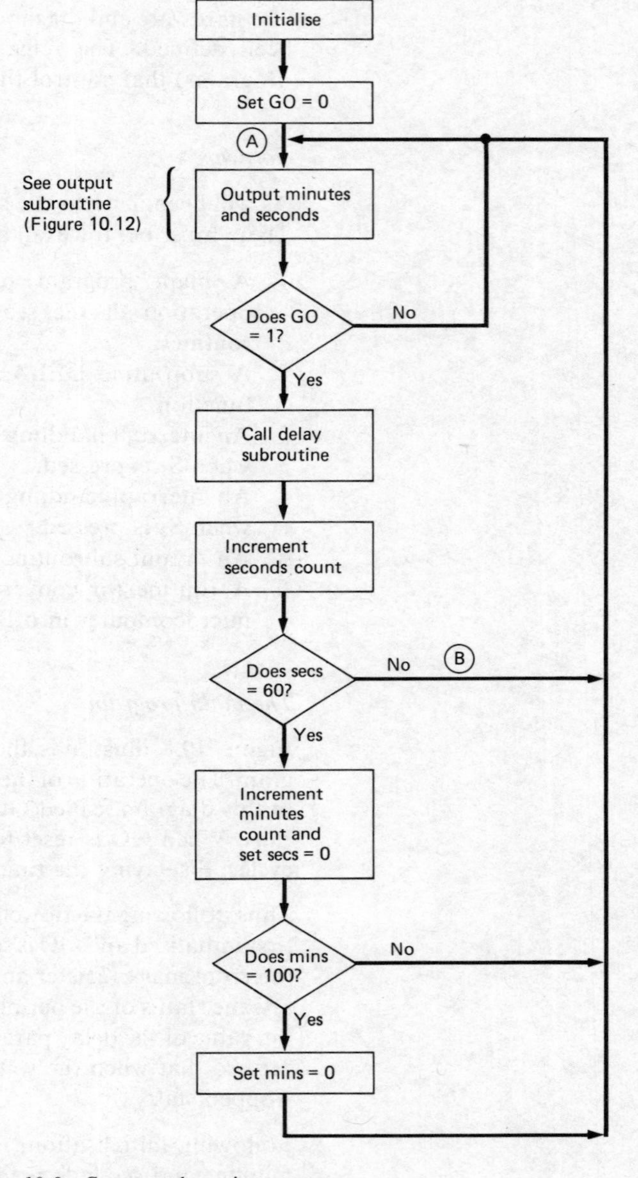

Figure 10.8 Stopwatch main program

The value of the interval being timed by the stopwatch is held in two variables called SECS (which holds the seconds value) and (not surprisingly) MINS (which holds the minutes value).

Whenever SECS is incremented it must be tested to see if it has reached 60. If it has, a minute has elapsed and the MINS count is incremented by one. At the same time SECS is reset to zero.

In a similar manner MINS is tested each time that it is incremented to ensure that it does not exceed the maximum value described earlier. If it should reach 100, both MINS and SECS are reset to zero.

The timing precision of the stopwatch depends critically on the exact time that the loop going from (A) to (B) and back to (A) takes. This should be precisely one second, and the delay introduced by subroutine DELAY must be adjusted until this is the case.

When the delay has been set, so that this loop takes one second to execute, the SECS count is incremented once per second and, correspondingly, the MINS count once per minute. The stopwatch therefore keeps an accurate measurement of elapsed time.

The stopwatch continues to increment SECS and MINS, and to update the display accordingly until GO is reset to 0. This operation is also performed by the interrupt service routine invoked when S_1 is pressed. Thus, if the watch is stopped, pressing S_1 causes it to start by setting GO to 1. If the watch is running, pressing S_1 causes it to stop by setting GO to 0.

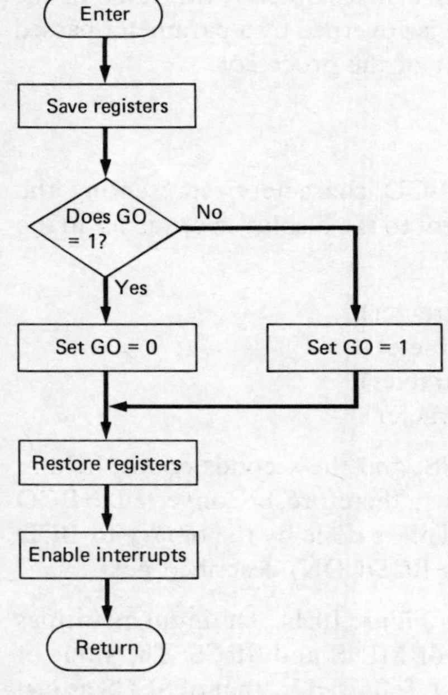

Figure 10.9 Interrupt service routine for switch S_1 interrupt

The interrupt service routines

The interrupt service routine for S_1 is represented as a flowchart in Figure 10.9. The operation of this routine is very simple. If GO is 1 on entry, it resets it to 0 and, if GO is '0' on entry, it sets it to 1.

In accordance with the usual practice on entry to an interrupt service routine, Figure 10.9 shows the processor registers being saved at the start of the routine and being restored before exit is made from it. In practice, as we shall see later, a careful choice of how these registers are used in the program removes the necessity to save any of them on entry to this routine. The step has nevertheless been included in the flowchart to emphasise that register saving is normally required.

The service routine for the interrupt arising when switch S_2 is pressed is shown in Figure 10.10. This routine first checks whether GO is in the 'zero' state. If it is not it must be at 'one' and the clock must, accordingly, be running. In this situation pressing S_2 has no effect since the routine simply returns straight to the main program without performing any other function.

When, however, GO is found to be zero the clock must be in the stopped state. In this case the service routine for the S_2 interrupt causes SECS and MINS to be set to zero. The clock is therefore reset and when S_1 is next pressed the time measurement begins from the value of zero.

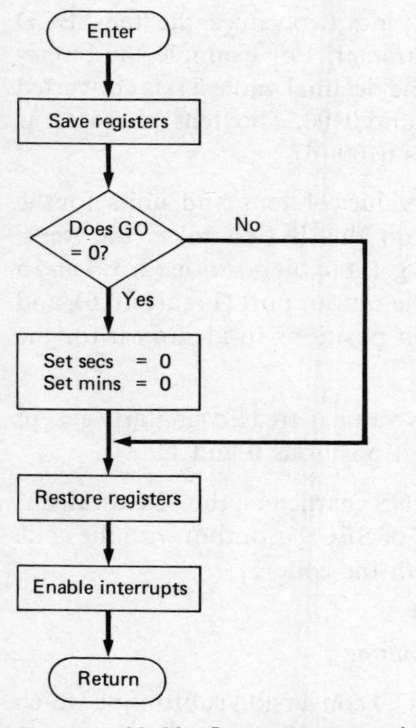

Figure 10.10 Interrupt service routine for switch S_2 interrupt

The delay subroutine

The delay subroutine mentioned in the previous section is similar to

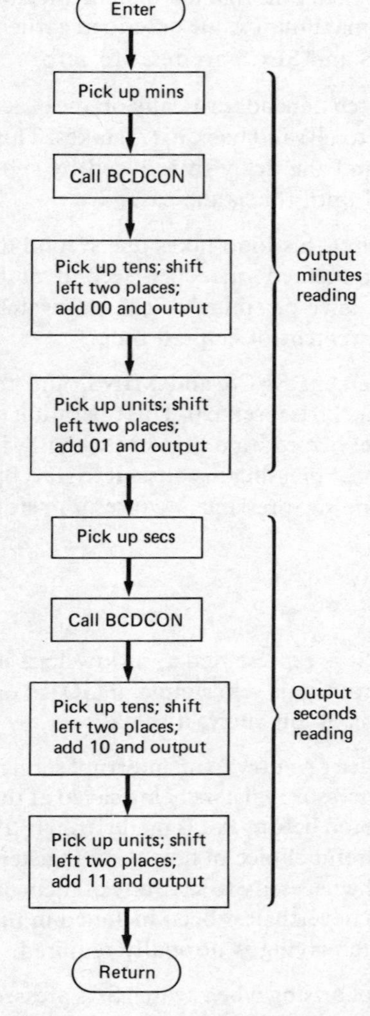

Figure 10.11 Output subroutine

that which has been explained in detail in Section 7.5 and which is shown in Figure 7.14. As discussed in Chapter 7, the value of the delay produced by the subroutine is governed by a parameter passed to it on entry using the C register of the processor.

The output subroutine

As explained earlier, the four BCD characters representing the minutes and seconds values are sent to the display in sequence in the order

1 Minutes (most significant character).
2 Minutes (least significant character).
3 Seconds (most significant character).
4 Seconds (least significant character).

The minutes count, held in MINS, and the seconds count, held in SECS, are in binary form. They must, therefore, be converted to BCD code before they can be output. This is done by the binary-to-BCD conversion subroutine (known as BCDCON) described next.

The output subroutine is shown in Figure 10.11. The input quantities to this subroutine are the values of MINS and SECS. The value of MINS is output to the display first, followed by that of SECS as just described.

The subroutine first calls BCDCON and passes the binary value of MINS to it. BCDCON converts this into two values, the 'tens' BCD character and the 'units' BCD character. For example the binary value 00110110 (which represents the decimal value 54) is converted into the two BCD characters 0101 and 0100. The 'tens' character is 0101 (5) and the 'units' character is 0100 (4).

Once the output subroutine has the values of 'tens' and 'units' for the minutes it can output them. To do this it first takes the 'tens' character, shifts it left two spaces to get it to bit positions 2, 3, 4 and 5 as required by the connections to the output port (Figure 10.6), and adds 00 to it in the bottom two bit positions to identify it for the output decoder. It then outputs it.

The 'units' character of the minutes value is treated similarly except that the code 01 is added to it in bit positions 0 and 1.

Following the output of the two MINS characters, the SECS value is identically treated. The 'tens' value of SECS is output with the code 10 followed by the 'units' value with the code 11.

The binary-to-BCD conversion subroutine

Figure 10.12 shows the binary-to-BCD conversion subroutine which is called BCDCON. Its operation is straightforward. It takes in an

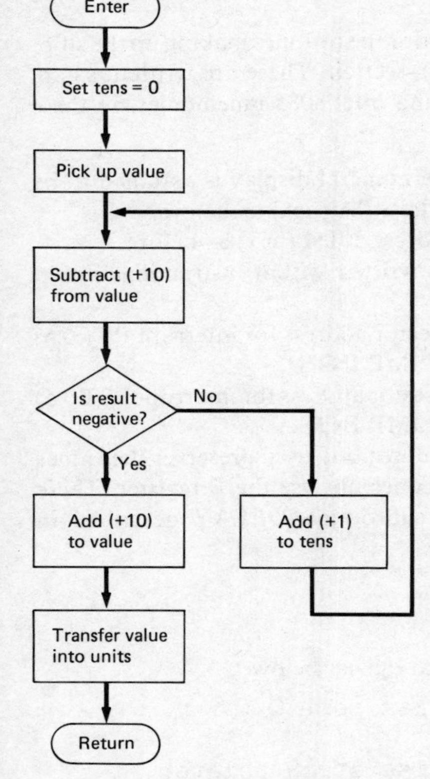

Figure 10.12 Binary to binary-coded decimal conversion subroutine (BCDCON)

input binary number, in the parameter called 'VALUE' in the flowchart, and detects how many 'tens' it contains by cycling in a loop. Each time it passes around the loop 10 (decimal) is subtracted from VALUE and (+1) is added to the variable TENS.

Each time around the loop the result of the subtraction is tested to see if it is negative. If it is not the process continues. If it is, ten has been subtracted once too often. Thus ten is added back to VALUE. The result is the 'units' part of VALUE and is placed in the variable UNITS to be passed back to the calling routine.

Parameter passing

The program contains two interrupt handling routines and three subroutines. Various parameter values must be exchanged with these as set out below:

1 GO is a universal variable used by the main program and altered by the interrupt handling routines.
2 The delay subroutine must be passed a parameter value specifying the length of the required delay.
3 SECS and MINS are universal variables used in the main program and in the S_2 interrupt service routine and the output subroutine.
4 The value of the number to be converted must be passed to subroutine BCDCON. The tens and units values must be passed back from it to the calling program.

As has been explained in previous chapters there are various ways in which these parameters can be held in the microcomputer. For example, a location in memory could be allocated to each of them. They could then be retrieved and rewritten using addresses held in the H,L register pair or using LDA and STA orders (see Appendix 1).

Alternatively the parameters can be held in the processor registers. This is only possible, of course, if the number of parameters is limited. However, as long as this is the case, and as long as care is taken to ensure that parameter values are not corrupted by subroutines using the registers without storing and restoring them, it is the most convenient and the fastest method.

Accordingly it is suggested that the parameters be held as follows:

1 GO is held in the B register.
2 The delay parameter is passed to the delay subroutine in the C register. This is the same method as was used in the example of Chapter 7.
3 SECS is held in the E register and MINS is held in the D register.
4 VALUE is passed to BCDCON using the A register. The values of 'tens' and 'units' are passed back to the calling program in registers H and L.

Program code

Some suggested program listings for the routines making up the stop-watch are given in the following section. These are written, as are other examples in this book, using Intel 8085 mnemonics. In these examples:

1 The output port used for the numeral display is assumed to be port C of a PIC and has address 0A (hex) as before.
2 The stack is initialised to address 10D4 (hex) as before.
3 All constants and addresses written within instructions are in hexadecimal code.
4 Address 0034 (the interrupt vector address for interrupt RST 6.5) must contain the instruction JMP INTS1.
5 Address 002C (the interrupt vector address for interrupt RST 5.5) must contain the instruction JMP INTS2.
6 It is assumed that the delay subroutine used preserves the values in the D and E registers and does not use the B register. These conditions are met by the subroutine DELAY described in Chapter 7.

Main program

The main program instructions are given below:

```
        MVI   A,92    ;Initialise port C
        OUT   0B
        LXI   SP,10D4 ;Initialise stack pointer
        MVI   A,0C    ;Initialise interrupts RST
        SIM           ;5.5 and RST 6.5
        MVI   C,XX    ;Set delay parameter to XX
        MVI   B,00    ;Set (B) - parameter GO -
                      ;to 0
ALOOP:  CALL  OUTPUT  ;Call OUTPUT subroutine
        MOV   A,B     ;Test if GO = 1. Jump to
        DCR   A       ;ALOOP if GO = 0
        JNZ   ALOOP
        CALL  DELAY   ;Call DELAY subroutine
        INR   E       ;Increment SECS
        MVI   A,3C    ;Is SECS = 60? Note 60
        CMP   E       ;(decimal) = 3C (hex)
        JNZ   ALOOP   ;No. Jump to ALOOP
        INR   D       ;Increment MINS
        MVI   E,00    ;Set SECS = 0
        MVI   A,64    ;Is MINS = 100? Note 100
        CMP   D       ;(decimal) = 64 (hex)
        JNZ   ALOOP   ;No. Jump to ALOOP
        MVI   D,00    ;Set MINS = 0
        JMP   ALOOP   ;Jump to ALOOP
```

The delay time must be adjusted, as described previously, to give an exact period of 1 s for the loop. The exact value for this must be used to replace the XX (X represents any hexadecimal character) written above in the sixth instruction down from the top of the listing.

Interrupt service routines

The interrupt service routine for the interrupt from S_1 is called INTS1; that from S_2 is called INTS2. The instructions for INTS1 and INTS2 are as follows:

```
INTS1:  MVI  A,01  ;Test if GO = 1
        CMP  B
        JNZ  CONT  ;No. Go to CONT
        MVI  B,00  ;Yes. Set GO = 0
        JMP  OUT
CONT:   MVI  B,01  ;Set GO = 1
OUT:    EI         ;Enable interrupts
        RET        ;Return

INTS2:  MVI  A,00  ;Test if GO = 0
        CMP  B
        JNZ  GOON  ;No. Go to GOON
        MVI  E,00  ;Yes. Set SECS = 0
        MVI  D,00  ;Set MINS = 0
GOON:   EI         ;Enable interrupts
        RET        ;Return
```

The output subroutine

This is called OUTPUT and the instructions are as follows:

```
OUTPUT: MOV  A,D    ;Put value of MINS into A
        CALL BCDCON ;Call conversion routine
        MOV  A,H    ;Put TENS into A
        RLC         ;Shift left twice
        RLC
        ANI  FC     ;Mask with pattern 11111100
        ADI  00     ;Add 00
        OUT  0A     ;Output to port C
        MOV  A,L    ;Put UNITS into A
        RLC         ;Output UNITS of MINS
        RLC
        ANI  FC
        ADI  01
        OUT  0A
```

(Continued overleaf)

```
MOV   A,E     ;Put value of SECS into A
CALL  BCDCON  ;Call conversion routine
MOV   A,H     ;Output TENS of SECS
RLC
RLC
ANI   FC
ADI   02
OUT   0A
MOV   A,L     ;Output UNITS of SECS
RLC
RLC
ANI   FC
ADI   03
OUT   0A
RET           ;Return
```

The binary-to-BCD conversion subroutine

This is called BCDCON and the instructions are as follows:

```
BCDCON:   MVI  H,00     ;Set TENS to zero
CYCLE:    SUI  0A       ;Subtract (+10) (decimal) from A
          JM   RESTORE  ;If result is (-ve) go to RESTORE
          INR  H        ;Add 1 to H register
          JMP  CYCLE    ;Go to CYCLE
RESTORE:  ADI  0A       ;Add (+10) (decimal) to A
          MOV  L,A      ;Put units into L
          RET           ;Return
```

10.5 Discussion

The digital stopwatch discussed in previous sections contains both an output subroutine, interrupt handling routines and a delay subroutine.

The accuracy of the stopwatch depends on the precision with which the basic timing loop (the loop A to B to A of Figure 10.8) can be set. The loop contains the delay subroutine plus other instructions to output to the display, to convert the output values to BCD form, to increment the seconds count and so on. The time that one cycle of the loop occupies can be found by adding the execution times of all these instructions. Much the largest part of this cycle time must, however, be due to the delay subroutine.

Even if there are, say, 200 other instructions in the loop, outside the delay subroutine, at an average execution time of 2 μs or thereabouts these will only occupy 400 μs. Since the loop must take 1 s altogether the delay subroutine must occupy:

$$(1{,}000{,}000 - 400) = 999{,}600\ \mu s$$

In practice it may be difficult to obtain a delay this long without slightly modifying the subroutine DELAY described earlier. It will be recalled that the time interval taken by this subroutine is controlled by:

1 A constant loaded into the E register which determines how often an inner loop is cycled and
2 A parameter passed to the subroutine in the C register of the processor.

These constants each have a maximum size of eight bits, i.e. of 255 (decimal). Thus the maximum number of cycles of the inner loop in DELAY that are possible is

$$255 \times 255 = 65{,}025$$

If the delay to be produced by the subroutine is to be 999,600 μs as suggested above the inner loop must occupy

$$999{,}600/65{,}025 = 15.4\ \mu s\ \text{(approx.)}$$

To obtain a delay this long it may be necessary to increase the execution time of the inner loop of DELAY. This can be easily achieved in a number of ways. For instance a few more NOP instructions could be added inside this loop.

The accuracy of the one-second loop in the stopwatch main program is also of interest. The maximum time over which the stopwatch can be used is 100 min. Suppose that the watch timing error must be less than one second over this period. In 100 min the timing loop is cycled $100 \times 60 = 6{,}000$ times. It can easily be shown that an error of $\pm 166\ \mu s$ in each cycle can be tolerated. For instance if the error is $+166\ \mu s$, over 6,000 cycles the time taken is

$$\begin{aligned} &6{,}000 \times 1{,}000{,}166\ \mu s \\ &= 6 \times 1{,}000.166 \\ &= 6{,}000.996\ s \end{aligned}$$

an error of less than 1 s in 100 min. There is, therefore, some scope for small variations in the time taken by this loop. The time added to it when, for instance, the stopwatch goes through the extra instructions needed to increment MINS and reset SECS to zero at the end of each elapsed minute is not large enough to cause any significant error.

Another way of implementing a stopwatch like the one just described would, of course, be to use an interval timer to produce 1 s, or even 0.1 s, interrupts and to use these to control the basic time interval. **Q10.4**

Questions

10.1 Describe the steps involved in the design of a microcomputer-based product. What are the differences between this process and the design of a traditional system using hard-wired logic?

10.2 Discuss the steps involved in software development. Outline the aids available to help this process, briefly describing the application of each of them.

10.3 Write and run a program to make a microcomputer system act as a stopwatch as described in this chapter.

10.4 Assuming that an interval timer chip is available, discuss how the stopwatch program can be modified to make use of interrupts from the timer which occur every 0.1 s. Assume that these interrupts appear on the RST 7.5 input to the processor chip.

10.5 Show, by modifying the flowcharts given in this chapter, how the lap time facility described in Section 10.4 could be added to the stopwatch.

10.6 Write the program code for a stopwatch with a lap time facility and run the program.

10.7 Modify the stopwatch flowcharts and output display system to allow the measurement of intervals in minutes, seconds and one-tenths of a second. This will require a total of six digits in the output liquid-crystal display.

10.8 Write the program code for the stopwatch of Question 10.7.

10.9 A digital clock is to be made using a microcomputer. It possesses the following inputs and outputs:

(a) A control input button to alter the clock 'mode'. The three modes available are normal time display, alarm set and time set. Pressing this control button must cause the mode to change cyclically. For instance, if the clock is in normal time display, one press of the button must change it to alarm set. If the clock is in the time set mode, one press must change it to normal time display.

(b) A control button for setting the hours. One press of this button in either the alarm set or time set modes must advance the 'hours' setting of the alarm time or actual time, respectively.

(c) A control button for setting the minutes. This must operate in the same way as the hours button.

(d) Output lines to control a display of the time in hours and minutes.

(e) An output line to activate a bleeper alarm.

Suggest how the inputs and outputs should be connected to the microcomputer, draw flowcharts showing the program modules required and code the program.

Appendix 1 The Intel 8085 instruction set

This appendix summarises the instruction set of the Intel 8085 microprocessor. This information is presented by courtesy of the Intel Corporation.

Instructions are written as:

INSTRUCTION MNEMONIC	SOURCE OR DESTINATION OR BOTH (if appropriate)	HEXADECIMAL CODING

Thus, for example, the instruction

```
MOV   C,H   4C
```

causes the data byte in the H register to be written into the C register (the destination of the data in this type of instruction is specified before the source). The hexadecimal representation of the instruction is 4C.

In these instructions:

A,B,C,D,E,H,L	represent the processor registers
M	represents the memory location whose address is held in the H,L register pair.
byte	represents an 8-bit data quantity or a port address
dble	represents a 16-bit data quantity
adr	represents a 16-bit memory address

When instructions refer to a pair of registers as do, for example, the LXI orders, the pairs are denoted as follows:

PSW — represents the register pair A and F
B — represents the register pair B and C
D — represents the register pair D and E
H — represents the register pair H and L
SP — represents the stack pointer (which is 16 bits)
PC — represents the program counter (which is 16 bits)

The status byte (F) contains flag bits as follows:

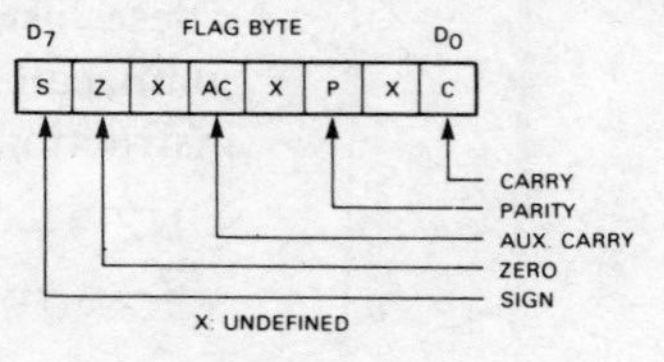

Data transfer instruction group

These instructions (see Figure A1) move data between the processor registers or between memory and a register. They do not alter any flag bits.

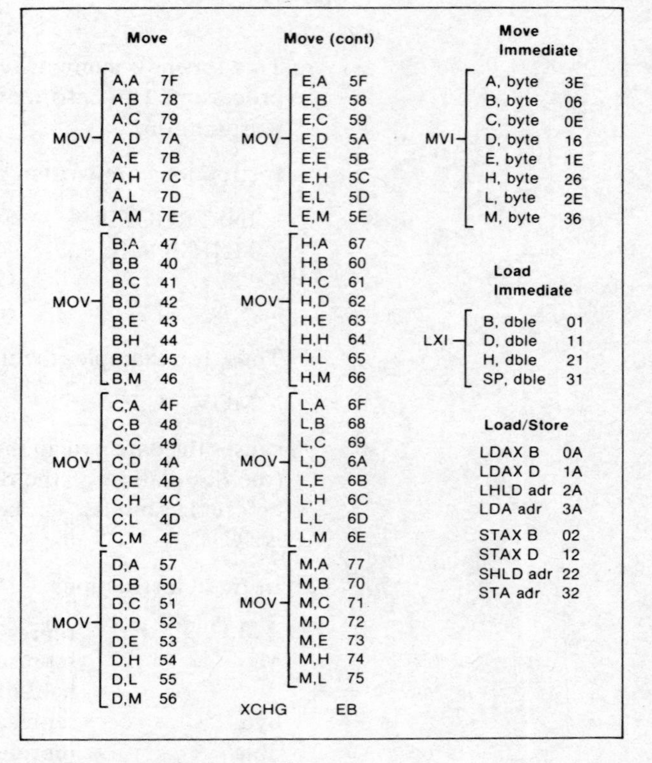

Move

Instruction	Operands	Code
MOV	A,A	7F
MOV	A,B	78
MOV	A,C	79
MOV	A,D	7A
MOV	A,E	7B
MOV	A,H	7C
MOV	A,L	7D
MOV	A,M	7E
MOV	B,A	47
MOV	B,B	40
MOV	B,C	41
MOV	B,D	42
MOV	B,E	43
MOV	B,H	44
MOV	B,L	45
MOV	B,M	46
MOV	C,A	4F
MOV	C,B	48
MOV	C,C	49
MOV	C,D	4A
MOV	C,E	4B
MOV	C,H	4C
MOV	C,L	4D
MOV	C,M	4E
MOV	D,A	57
MOV	D,B	50
MOV	D,C	51
MOV	D,D	52
MOV	D,E	53
MOV	D,H	54
MOV	D,L	55
MOV	D,M	56

Move (cont)

Instruction	Operands	Code
MOV	E,A	5F
MOV	E,B	58
MOV	E,C	59
MOV	E,D	5A
MOV	E,E	5B
MOV	E,H	5C
MOV	E,L	5D
MOV	E,M	5E
MOV	H,A	67
MOV	H,B	60
MOV	H,C	61
MOV	H,D	62
MOV	H,E	63
MOV	H,H	64
MOV	H,L	65
MOV	H,M	66
MOV	L,A	6F
MOV	L,B	68
MOV	L,C	69
MOV	L,D	6A
MOV	L,E	6B
MOV	L,H	6C
MOV	L,L	6D
MOV	L,M	6E
MOV	M,A	77
MOV	M,B	70
MOV	M,C	71
MOV	M,D	72
MOV	M,E	73
MOV	M,H	74
MOV	M,L	75
XCHG		EB

Move Immediate

Instruction	Operands	Code
MVI	A, byte	3E
MVI	B, byte	06
MVI	C, byte	0E
MVI	D, byte	16
MVI	E, byte	1E
MVI	H, byte	26
MVI	L, byte	2E
MVI	M, byte	36

Load Immediate

Instruction	Operands	Code
LXI	B, dble	01
LXI	D, dble	11
LXI	H, dble	21
LXI	SP, dble	31

Load/Store

Instruction	Code
LDAX B	0A
LDAX D	1A
LHLD adr	2A
LDA adr	3A
STAX B	02
STAX D	12
SHLD adr	22
STA adr	32

Figure A1 Data transfer instructions

Arithmetic and logical groups of instructions

These are shown in Figure A2. Note that:

* indicates instructions that affect all flag bits (C, Z, S, P and AC).
** indicates instructions that affect all flags except the carry flag.
† indicates instructions that affect only the carry flag.

Transfer of control group of instructions

These instructions cause the program to jump. They comprise the jump, call and return orders. When a conditional jump, call or return instruction is specified the condition codes used are:

NZ — not zero (flag $Z = 0$)
Z — zero (flag $Z = 1$)

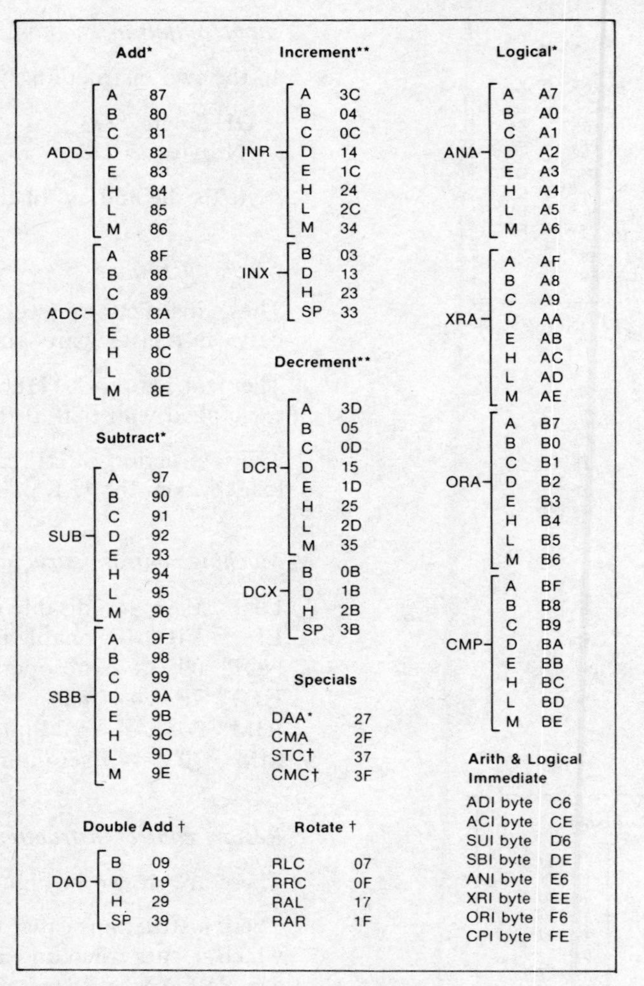

Add*

Instruction	Register	Code
ADD	A	87
	B	80
	C	81
	D	82
	E	83
	H	84
	L	85
	M	86
ADC	A	8F
	B	88
	C	89
	D	8A
	E	8B
	H	8C
	L	8D
	M	8E

Subtract*

Instruction	Register	Code
SUB	A	97
	B	90
	C	91
	D	92
	E	93
	H	94
	L	95
	M	96
SBB	A	9F
	B	98
	C	99
	D	9A
	E	9B
	H	9C
	L	9D
	M	9E

Double Add †

Instruction	Register	Code
DAD	B	09
	D	19
	H	29
	SP	39

Increment**

Instruction	Register	Code
INR	A	3C
	B	04
	C	0C
	D	14
	E	1C
	H	24
	L	2C
	M	34
INX	B	03
	D	13
	H	23
	SP	33

Decrement**

Instruction	Register	Code
DCR	A	3D
	B	05
	C	0D
	D	15
	E	1D
	H	25
	L	2D
	M	35
DCX	B	0B
	D	1B
	H	2B
	SP	3B

Specials

Instruction	Code
DAA*	27
CMA	2F
STC†	37
CMC†	3F

Rotate †

Instruction	Code
RLC	07
RRC	0F
RAL	17
RAR	1F

Logical*

Instruction	Register	Code
ANA	A	A7
	B	A0
	C	A1
	D	A2
	E	A3
	H	A4
	L	A5
	M	A6
XRA	A	AF
	B	A8
	C	A9
	D	AA
	E	AB
	H	AC
	L	AD
	M	AE
ORA	A	B7
	B	B0
	C	B1
	D	B2
	E	B3
	H	B4
	L	B5
	M	B6
CMP	A	BF
	B	B8
	C	B9
	D	BA
	E	BB
	H	BC
	L	BD
	M	BE

Arith & Logical Immediate

Instruction	Code
ADI byte	C6
ACI byte	CE
SUI byte	D6
SBI byte	DE
ANI byte	E6
XRI byte	EE
ORI byte	F6
CPI byte	FE

Figure A2 Arithmetic and logical instructions

Jump

Instruction	Code
JMP adr	C3
JNZ adr	C2
JZ adr	CA
JNC adr	D2
JC adr	DA
JPO adr	E2
JPE adr	EA
JP adr	F2
JM adr	FA
PCHL	E9

Call

Instruction	Code
CALL adr	CD
CNZ adr	C4
CZ adr	CC
CNC adr	D4
CC adr	DC
CPO adr	E4
CPE adr	EC
CP adr	F4
CM adr	FC

Return

Instruction	Code
RET	C9
RNZ	C0
RZ	C8
RNC	D0
RC	D8
RPO	E0
RPE	E8
RP	F0
RM	F8

Figure A3 Transfer of control instructions

NC — no carry (flag C = 0)
C — carry (flag C = 1)
PO — odd parity (flag P = 0)
PE — even parity (flag P = 1)
P — plus (flag S = 0)
M — minus (flag S = 1)

Thus, for example, the instruction

JNC adr

(see Figure A3) causes program execution to jump to the instruction at address (adr) if flag C = 0.

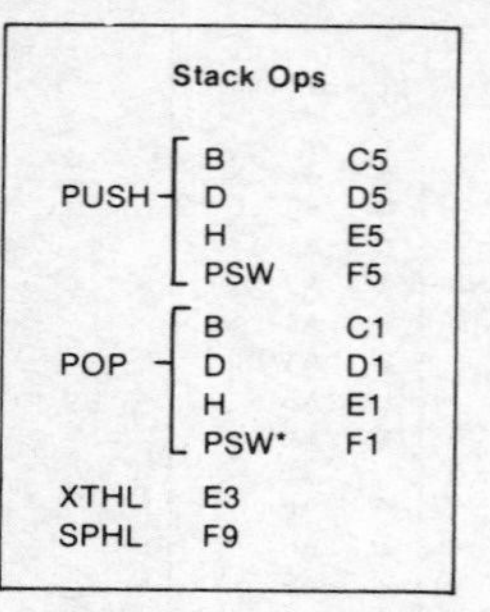

Figure A4 Stack operations

Input/output instructions

In the two instructions:

OUT byte D3
IN byte DB

'byte' is the address of the I/O port through which data is to flow.

Stack operations

These instructions (see Figure A4) cause data to be exchanged between register pairs and the stack.

The instruction XTHL causes the data in the H,L pair to be exchanged with that at the top of the stack.

The instruction SPHL causes the stack pointer register (SP) to be loaded from the H,L pair.

Machine control instructions

DI F3 — disable interrupts
EI FB — enable interrupts
NOP 00 — no operation
HLT 76 — halt
RIM 20 — read interrupt mask
SIM 30 — set interrupt mask

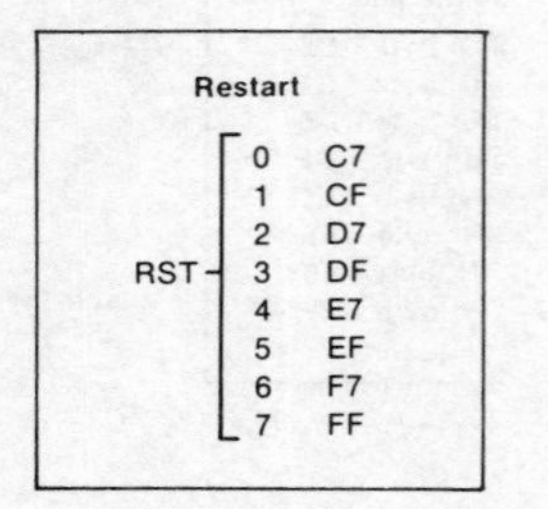

Figure A5 Restart control instructions

Restart control instructions

These are shown in Figure A5.

These instructions cause the processor to take similar action to that which occurs when an external interrupt arrives on one of the RST 5.5, RST 6.5 or RST 7.5 input pins.

The vector addresses for the RST orders are:

RST 0 — address 0000 (hex)
RST 1 — address 0008 (hex)
RST 2 — address 0010 (hex)
RST 3 — address 0018 (hex)
RST 4 — address 0020 (hex)
RST 5 — address 0028 (hex)
RST 6 — address 0030 (hex)
RST 7 — address 0038 (hex)

Appendix 2 Some microprocessor chips

Eight-bit systems

Intel 8085

Technology: NMOS.

Arithmetic: Twos complement binary and binary-coded decimal add and subtract.

Clock frequency: 3 or 5 MHz.

Bus organisation: The 8085 multiplexes the lower 8 address bits on the data bus.

Address range: 16-bit addresses are used, giving an address space of 64 Kbytes.

Processor registers: See Figure A6.

16 bits	
Program counter	
Stack pointer	
H	L
D	E
B	C

Accumulator	Status register
8 bits	8 bits

Figure A6

Zilog Z80

Technology: NMOS.

Arithmetic: 8- and 16-bit twos complement binary and binary-coded decimal add and subtract.

Clock frequency: 2.5 or 4 MHz.

Bus organisation: Separate data (8-bit) and address (16-bit) busses.

Address range: 64 Kbytes.

Processor registers: See Figure A7.

MAIN REGISTER SET

Accumulator (A)	Flags (F)
B	C
D	E
H	L
8 bits	8 bits

ALTERNATE REGISTER SET

A′	F′
B′	C′
D′	E′
H′	L′
8 bits	8 bits

Interrupt vector (I)	Memory refresh (R)
Index IX	
Index IY	
Stack pointer SP	
Program counter PC	
16 bits	

Figure A7

Address modes: Immediate, immediate extended, relative address, extended address, indexed address, register address, implied address, register indirect address, bit address.

Figure A8

Motorola MC 6809

Technology: NMOS.

Arithmetic: Binary twos complement add and subtract plus unsigned 8-bit multiplication. Some 16-bit arithmetic.

Clock frequency: 4 MHz.

Bus organisation: Separate data (8-bit) and address (16-bit) busses.

Address range: 64 Kbytes.

Processor registers: See Figure A8.

Address modes: Direct page (using direct page register), indexed address, autoincrement address, autodecrement address, relative address, immediate.

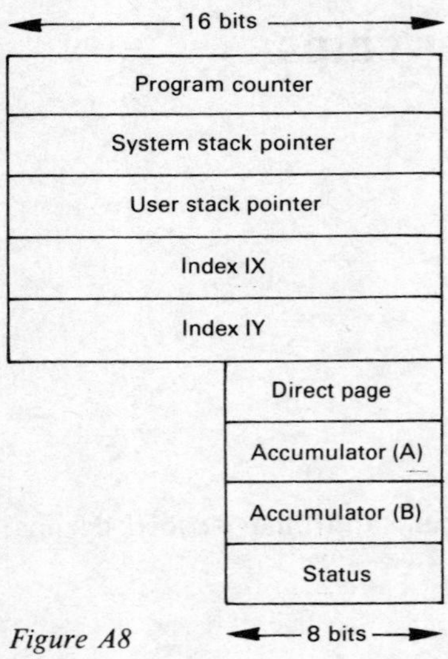

Sixteen-bit systems

Intel 8086

Technology: HMOS.

Arithmetic: 16-bit binary twos complement and BCD arithmetic; 16-bit unsigned binary multiply and divide.

Clock frequency: 5 MHz.

Bus organisation: 16-bit data and the lower 16 bits of the address are multiplexed on to a common bus.

Address range: 20-bit addresses are used giving an address range of 1 Mbytes.

Processor registers: See Figure A9.

Address modes: Direct address, relative address (to base and index registers), register address, indexed address, immediate.

Data types: Bits, bytes, words (16 bits), strings.

Figure A9

Zilog Z8000

Technology: NMOS.

Arithmetic: 16-bit binary and BCD arithmetic. Signed multiply and divide.

Clock frequency: 4 MHz.

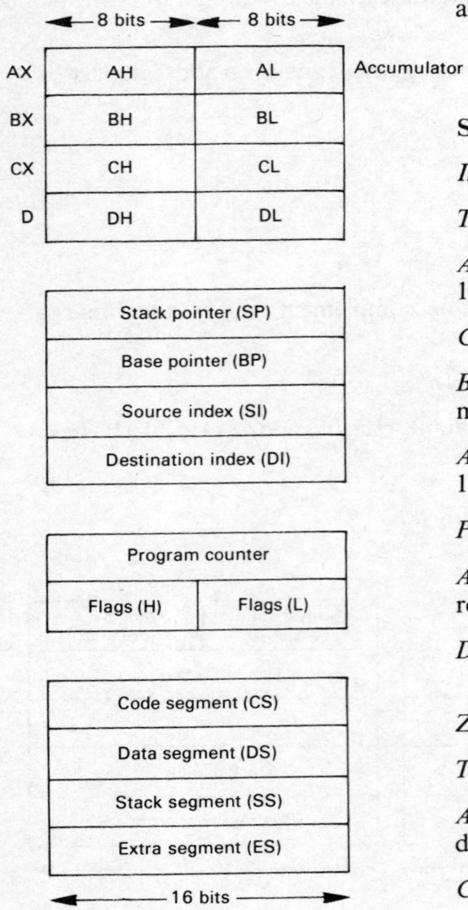

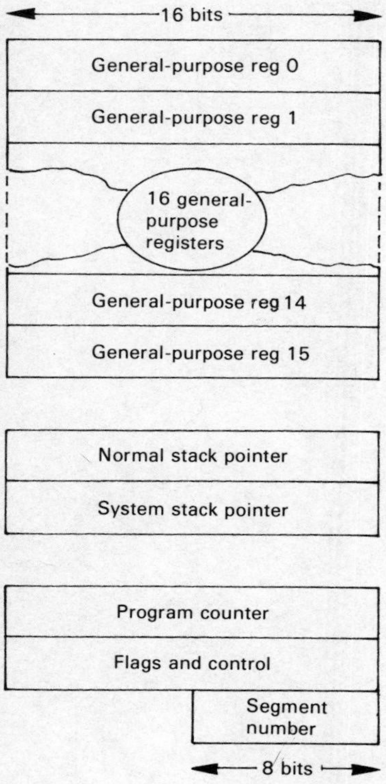

Bus organisation: 16-bit data and the lower 16 bits of the address are multiplexed on to a common bus.

Address range: The Z8002 has an address range of 64 Kbytes, the Z8001 has a range of 8 Mbytes.

Processor registers: See Figure A10. The general-purpose registers may be used as 16 registers of 16 bits, or 8 registers of 32 bits, or 4 registers of 64 bits.

Address modes: register, indirect register, direct, indexed, immediate, relative, base address, base indexed, autoincrement and autodecrement.

Data types: bits, BCD characters, bytes, words (16 bits), long words (32 bits) and byte or word strings.

Figure A10

Motorola MC 68000

Technology: HMOS.

Arithmetic: 8-. 16- or 32-bit binary arithmetic. Signed and unsigned multiply and divide.

Clock frequency: 8 MHz.

Bus organisation: Separate 16-bit data bus and 23-bit address bus. A twenty-fourth address bit is generated externally to the processor chip.

Address range: 24-bit addresses are used giving an address range of 16 Mbytes.

Processor registers: See Figure A11.

Address modes: register, absolute (direct), relative, register indirect (with post-increment or predecrement), immediate, implied.

Data types: bits, BCD characters, bytes, words (16 bits), long words (32 bits).

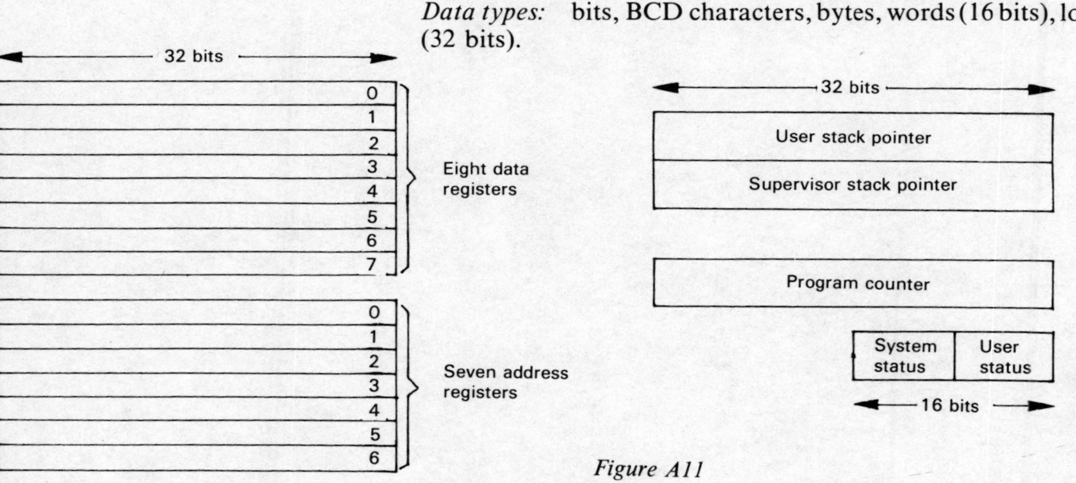

Figure A11

Answers to Questions

1.1 See Section 1.1.

1.2 See Section 1.2.

1.3 See Sections 1.1, 1.2 and 1.3. Further reading is also required to fully answer this question.

1.4 See Sections 1.3, 1.6(e) and 1.7. Further details of memories are given in Section 2.3.

1.5 2^{24} addresses, that is 16,384 Kbytes or 16 Mbytes.

1.6 See Section 1.2. When a JUMP instruction is encountered in a program the following steps occur:

1 The processor tests whether the condition specified in the JUMP (if any) is satisfied.

2 If the condition is satisfied the address in the instruction is loaded into the program counter.

3 If the condition is not satisfied the program counter is incremented to point to the next instruction.

1.7 See Section 1.3.

1.8
(a) MVI C, 92
(b) MVI D, 64
(c) MOV A, C
(d) ADD D
(e) STA 3130

1.9 To produce a musical note the computer must cause a pulse train to be sent to the speaker. The frequency of this train determines the pitch of the note heard. For example if a 100 μs pulse is sent once every 200 μs, the speaker receives a square wave of frequency 5,000 Hz. If a 100 μs pulse is sent every 400 μs the speaker receives a pulse train with a fundamental frequency of 2,500 Hz and so on. A flowchart of the procedure is shown in Figure A. By altering the delay period, the frequency of the note can be varied.

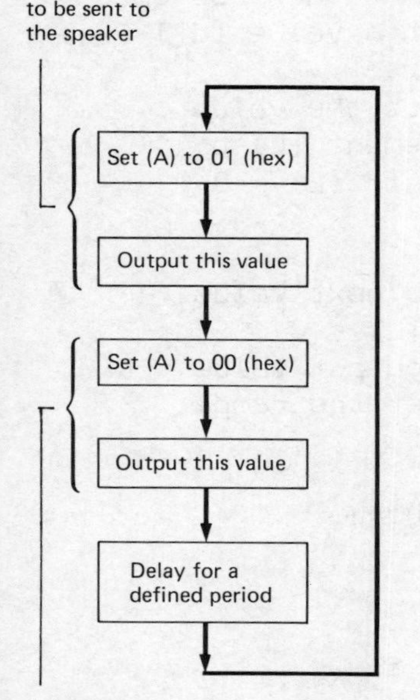

Figure A

1.10

```
START:  MVI  A,01     ;Set output line to 1
        OUT  32
        MVI  A,00     ;Reset output line to 0
        OUT  32
```

```
          MVI  A,14
REPEAT:   NOP            ;Delay loop cycled 20 times
          DCR  A
          JNZ  REPEAT
          JMP  START     ;Go back to START
```

Notes of different frequencies may be obtained by altering the number of times the delay loop is cycled, i.e. by changing the constant in the MVI A, 14 instruction.

1.11 Assume that the values $d_0, d_1, d_2, \ldots, d_9$ are stored in the memory starting at address 0B00:

```
START:    MVI  A,E7
REPEAT:   NOP            ;Delay loop (1.976 ms)
          NOP
          DCR  A
          JNZ  REPEAT
          LXI  H,0B00    ;Set H,L register pair to
                         ;point to address 0B00
          MOV  A,M       ;Fetch a value (d ) from
                                          n
                         ;memory
          OUT  32        ;Output the value
          INR  L         ;Increment (L) by 1
          MVI  A,09      ;Test if (L) = 9
          SUB  L
          JZ   RESET
          JMP  START     ;Go to next value
RESET:    MVI  L,00      ;Set (L) = 0
          MVI  A,00      ;Set output value = 0
          OUT  32        ;(reset the ramp)
          JMP  START
```

The delay loop is cycled 247 (decimal) times.

2.1 See Sections 2.1, 2.3, 2.4 and 2.5.

2.2 See Section 2.1.

2.3 See Section 2.2 and Appendix 2.

2.4 See Section 2.2. Fourth-generation machines are more powerful than their predecessors. They possess instructions for manipulation of a wider range of data types, they are faster, they have more comprehensive arithmetic facilities and they can directly address a larger memory space. These properties make them more suitable than earlier machines for use as the basis of powerful general-purpose computers. This, together with the continuing reduction in cost of large-scale integrated circuits means that large-scale computing power will become available to an ever-increasing section of the population.

Fourth-generation microprocessors also bring sophisticated tasks within the capability of instrument-scale equipment. As an example of this it is currently possible to design a system to aid medical general practitioners in the running of their practice and in diagnosis of some clinical conditions.

2.5 See Section 2.2.

2.6 See Sections 2.2 and 2.3.

2.7 See Section 2.3.

2.8 See Sections 2.4 and 4.8.

2.9 Suppose that:

1 Address line 0 is connected to the least significant 'register select' input to the PPI.
2 Address line 1 is connected to the most significant 'register select' input to the PPI.
3 Address line 3 is connected (through an inverter) to the $\overline{\text{CHIP SELECT}}$ input of the PPI.

Then the addresses used in the PPI are:

Port A	= 08 (hex)
Port B	= 09 (hex)
Port C	= 0A (hex)
Control register	= 0B (hex)

The system is shown in Figure B. To initialise the PPI the instructions needed are:

```
MVI  A,A7
OUT  0B
```

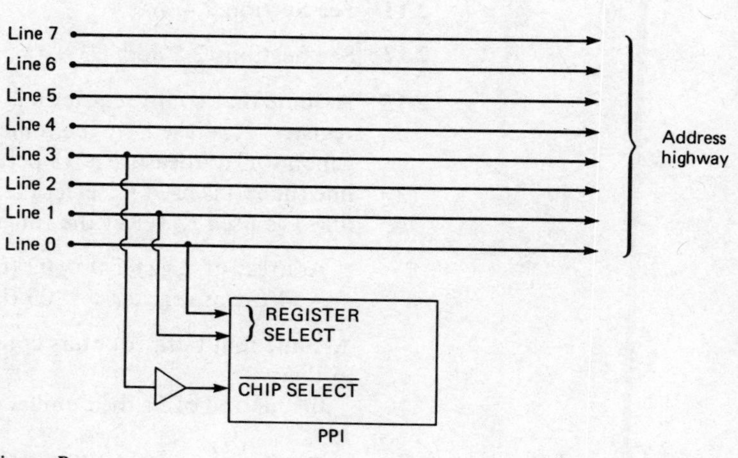

Figure B

2.10 Address allocation could be:

00 to 03	first PPI
04 to 07	second PPI
08 to 0B	third PPI
0C to 0F	fourth PPI
10 to 13	fifth PPI
14 to 17	sixth PPI
18 to 1B	first timer-counter
1B to 1F	second timer-counter

This allows four addresses for each device. The system is shown in Figure C.

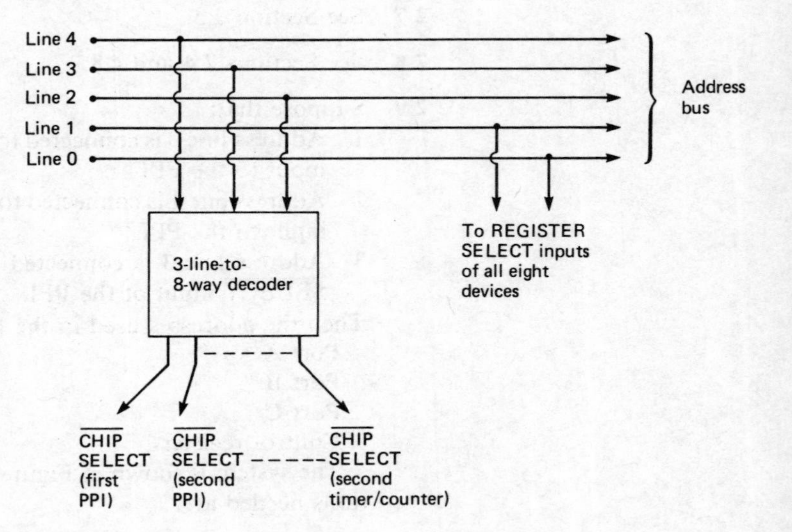

Figure C

2.11 See Section 2.4.

2.12 See Sections 2.5 and 1.3.

2.13 Assume that count register 0 is used to count the 'events' and count register 1 is used, in conjunction with the external clock pulse generator, to measure a 5 s period. The least significant address bus line (line 0) is used to select the required count register. Address bus line 1 is used to select the timer-counter itself. So:

Address of register 0 = 02 (hex)
Address of register 1 = 03 (hex)

Assume that both counters count down from a value initially placed in them.

In a period of 5 s the number of clock generator pulses is $(5 \times 25) = 125$.

The program is as follows:

```
        MVI  A,7D   ;Load +125 into A
        OUT  03     ;Output to count register 1
        MVI  A,78   ;Load +120 into A
        OUT  02     ;Output to count register 0
READ:   IN   03     ;Read register 1
        CPI  00     ;Is the value 0?
        JZ   END    ;If time is up go to END
        JMP  READ   ;If time is not up go to READ
END:    IN   02     ;Read number in register 0
        MOV  B,A    ;Subtract value from 120 to
        MVI  A,78   ;get count of events
        SUB  B
        STA  addr.  ;Store result at address
                    ;'addr'
        HLT         ;Halt
```

2.14 The data input lines to the punch are connected to one port of the PPI, e.g. port B, configured to be an output. The PPI group B is set to operate in mode 1 (handshaking mode). 'Ready' from the punch is connected to $\overline{\text{ACK}}$ on the PPI (port C bit C2). 'Data available' on the punch is driven through an inverter from $\overline{\text{OBF}}$ (bit C1). Assume the PPI addresses are as in Question 2.9. To configure the PPI:

```
MVI  A,04
OUT  0B
```

To output data:

```
MVI  A,(data)
OUT  09
```

or, if the data to be output is held in a register, say the processor B register:

```
MOV  A,B
OUT  09
```

3.1 See Section 3.1.

3.2 See Sections 1.3, 2.1, 2.2, 2.3 and 3.1.

3.3 See Sections 3.2 and 3.6.

3.4 See Sections 3.1 ('States') and 3.4.

3.5 See Sections 1.3 and 3.3.

3.6 See Section 3.7.

3.8 See Sections 3.4 and 3.5 and Figures D, E and F.

3.9 See Sections 3.4 and 3.5.

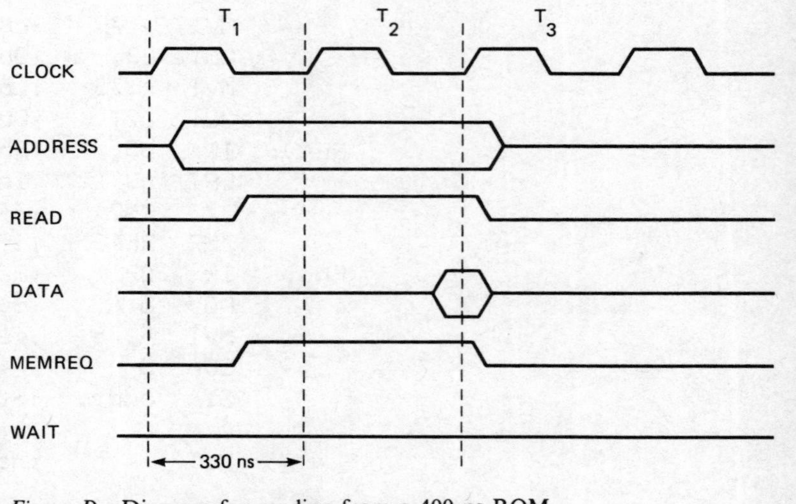

Figure D Diagram for reading from a 400 ns ROM

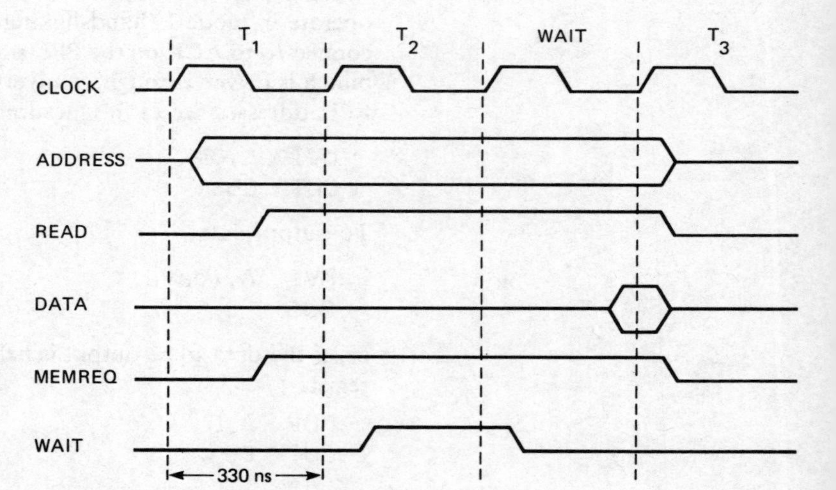

Figure E Diagram for reading from a 550 ns RAM

4.1 See Sections 4.1 and 4.2.

4.2 See Section 4.1.
ROM Start address 0000 End address 2FFF
RAM Start address 6000 End address 7FFF.

4.3 See Section 4.7:
(a) The RAM can be built from eight Intel 3101A RAM chips. The configuration is shown in Figure G. Address bus lines 0–3 inclusive go to all chips. As shown, a two-bit-to-four-line address decoder is required.

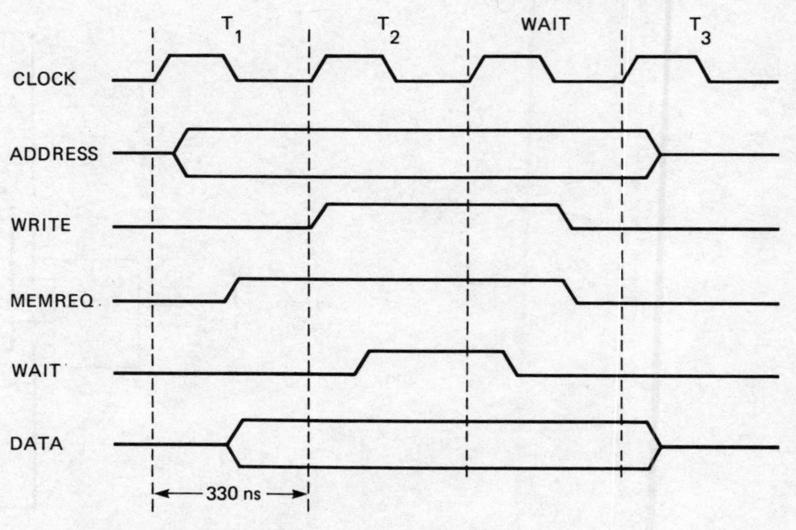

Figure F Diagram for writing to a 550 ns RAM

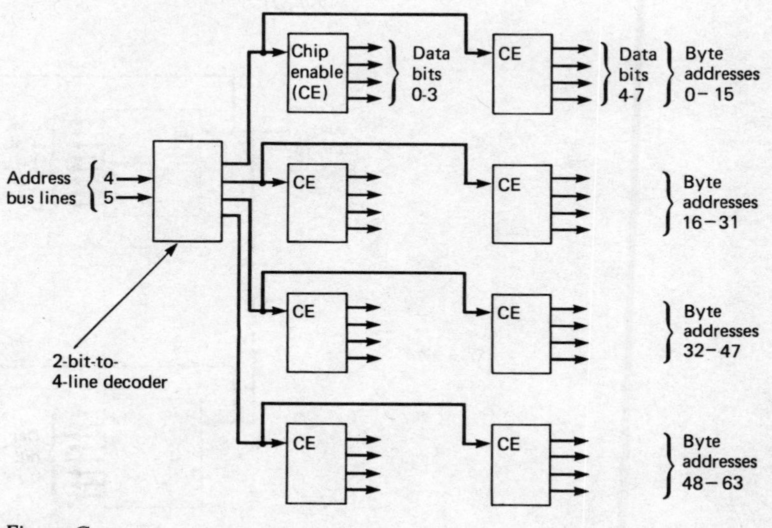

Figure G

(b) The EPROM can be built from four Intel 2732 EPROM chips as shown in Figure H. Each chip contains 4,096 bytes of storage. Address bus lines 0–11 inclusive go to all chips. Again a two-bit-to-four-line decoder is used.

(c) The ROM can be built from Intel 2364A chips. These each contain 8,192 bytes of storage. The configuration is shown in Figure I. Address bus lines 0–12 go to all chips. Address bus line 13 is used to select either addresses 0–8,191 or 8,192–16,383 as shown. No address decoder is needed.

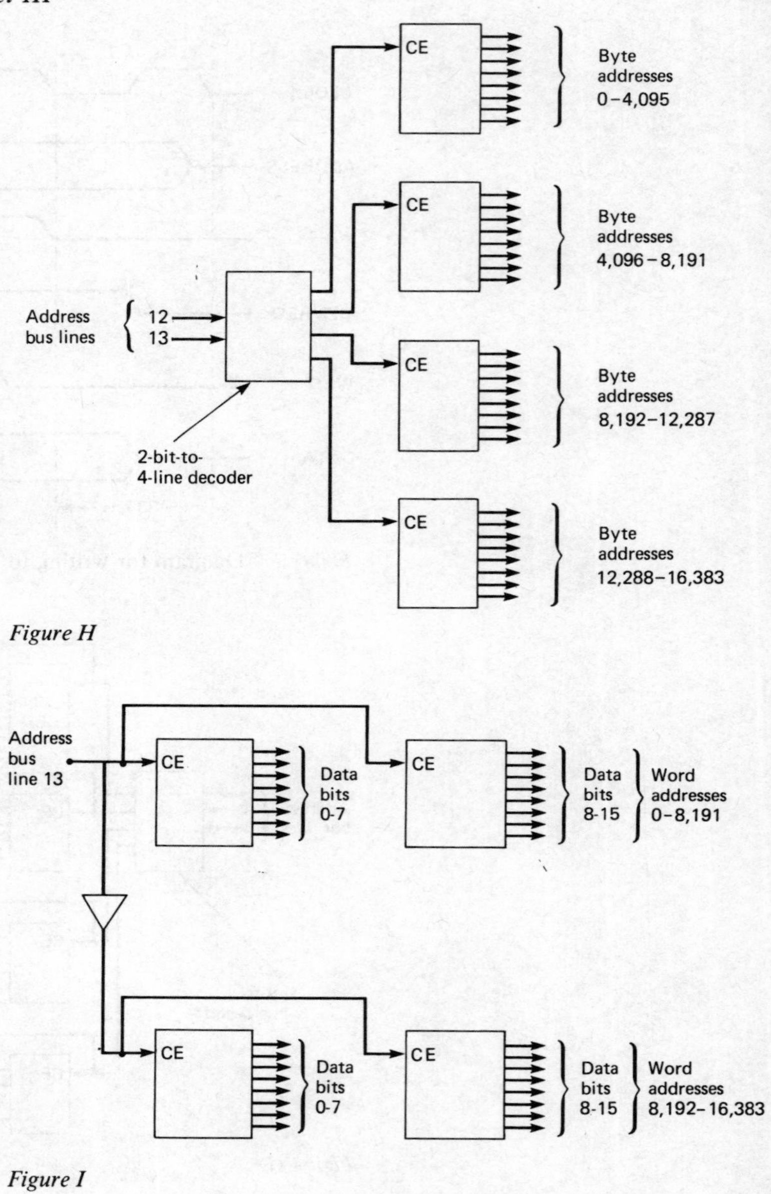

Figure H

Figure I

4.4 The Intel 2114 RAM chip contains 1,024 addresses each of 4 bits. To obtain a memory of 8,192 bytes, therefore, pairs of 2114s are used to give byte addresses as below:

First pair	0 to 1,023
Second pair	1,024 to 2,047
Third pair	2,048 to 3,071
Fourth pair	3,072 to 4,095

Fifth pair	4,096 to 5,119
Sixth pair	5,120 to 6,143
Seventh pair	6,144 to 7,167
Eighth pair	7,168 to 8,191

Address bus lines A_0–A_9 go in parallel to all chips. Address bus lines A_{10}, A_{11} and A_{12} are decoded in a three-bit-to-eight-line decoder. The eight outputs from this are used to select pairs of memory chips as indicated above.

4.5 See Section 4.7. The address bus lines should be buffered to drive the memory inputs. If buffers are placed in lines A_0–A_{12}, and if quad buffers are used, four extra chips will be needed for this. The data bus lines, D_0–D_7, should also be buffered from the memory data inputs. Two chips will be required for this. The total number of chips (including 16 memory chips) is 22.

4.6 See Section 4.2.

4.7 The top six address lines (A_{10}–A_{15} inclusive) must be decoded. When the pattern on these lines is 111110 or 111111, a peripheral device request is being sent. Any other pattern refers to memory. This is a reasonable choice of peripheral addresses, but requires rather a large decoder (6 bits).

4.8 See Section 4.8.

4.9 See Section 4.5.

(a) Sixty-four AND gates, each having six inputs, are required. Each gate detects one of the 64 possible combinations of 6 bits.

(b) Nine three-bit-to-eight-line decoder chips are needed. Eight of these have the three least significant of the six input bits fed directly into their inputs. These eight chips supply the 64 outputs. The ninth chip has, as inputs, the three most significant of the six bits. Its eight outputs are used to enable the expansion inputs of the other chips. See also Figure 4.14.

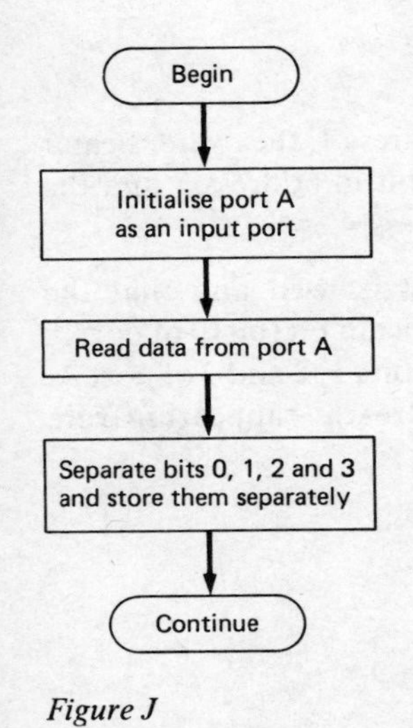

Figure J

4.10 Suppose that the microcomputer contains a peripheral interface circuit as shown in Figure 4.21. The signals from the washing machine can be connected to the bottom four bits (bits 0, 1, 2 and 3) of port A of this device – see flowchart of Figure J. Assume addresses of 08 (hex) for port A and 0B (hex) for the PIC control register. The program code is then as follows:

```
MVI  A,92          ;Initialise PIC so that port
OUT  0B            ;A (and port B incidentally)
                   ;are inputs
IN   08            ;Read data from port A
MOV  B,A           ;Place input data in register B
ANI  01            ;AND with 01 (hex) to separate
                   ;bit 0
```

(Continued)

```
STA  (address 1)  ;Store result in 'address 1'
MOV  A,B          ;Restore input pattern to A
ANI  02           ;AND with 02 (hex) to separate
                  ;bit 1
RRC               ;Shift result to least
                  ;significant position
STA  (address 2)  ;Store result in 'address 2'
MOV  A,B          ;Restore input pattern to A
ANI  04           ;AND with 04 (hex) to separate
                  ;bit 2
RRC               ;Shift result to least
RRC               ;significant position
STA  (address 3)  ;Store result in 'address 3'
MOV  A,B          ;Restore input pattern to A
ANI  08           ;AND with 08 (hex) to separate
                  ;bit 3
RRC               ;Shift result to least
RRC               ;significant position
RRC
STA  (address 4)  ;Store result in 'address 4'
continue
.
.
.
```

This code places the 'wash tub full' bit in address 1, the 'water heater on' bit in address 2, the 'wash tub empty' bit in address 3 and the 'water temperature hot enough' bit in address 4.

4.11 Suppose that a peripheral interface circuit is used and that the 'on–off' switch is connected to the least significant bit (bit 0) of port A and the 'duration' switches are connected to bits 1, 2 and 3 of port A. Port B is used as an output port with the square wave appearing from the bit 0 position – see flowchart of Figure K.

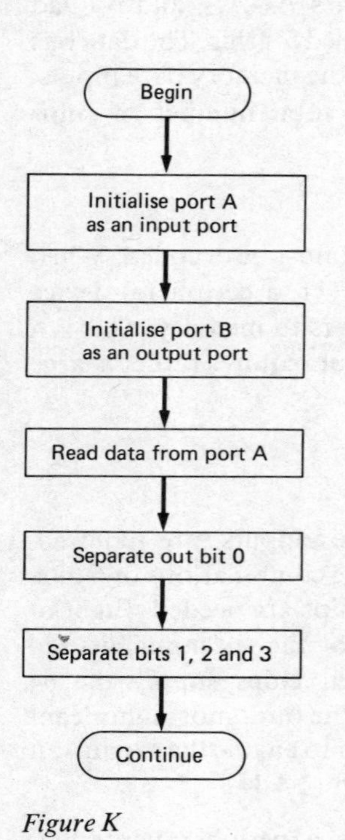

Figure K

5.1 See Sections 5.1 and 5.2.

5.2 See Sections 5.2, 5.3 and 5.4.

5.3 See Section 5.2.

5.4 See Sections 5.2, 5.4, 5.5 and Chapter 6.

5.5 See Section 5.5.

5.6 See Sections 5.4 and 7.8.

5.7 Assume that a multiplication subroutine, MULT, with two input parameters (the operands to be multiplied together) and one output parameter (the product of the multiplication) is to be employed – see flowchart of Figure L.

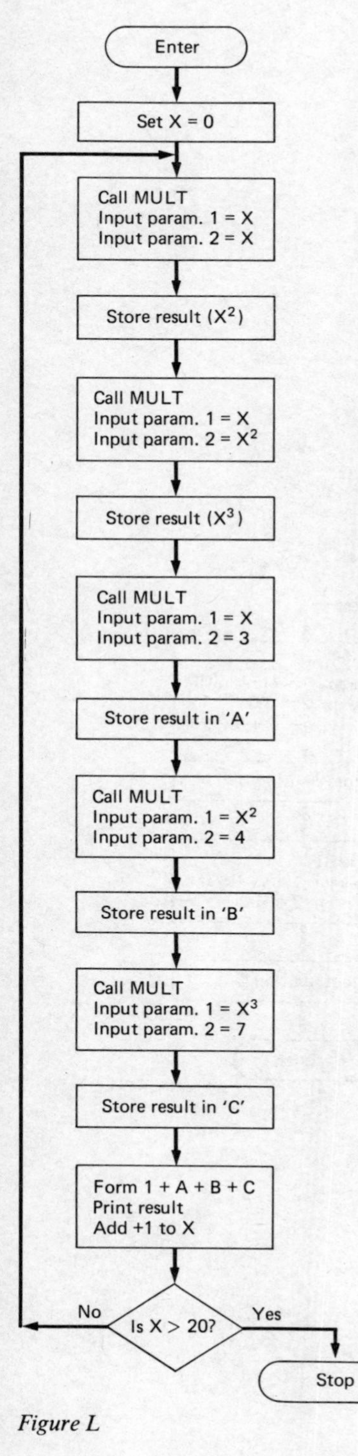

Figure L

5.8 The subroutine must:

(a) Pick up the numbers from memory one by one and add them into an accumulating sum, detecting when 100 have been processed.

(b) Square the numbers and add the squares into a second accumulating sum.

(c) Divide both results by 100 (or multiply them by 0.01).

(d) Pass both results back to the calling program. There are 100 input parameters and two output parameters (the mean and variance). Thus the input parameters are best passed to the subroutine by storing them in RAM, in addresses 0B00 to 0B63 as mentioned, and by passing a pointer to them in H and L.

The output values may be passed back to the calling program using the processor registers.

5.9 To pass the input parameters to the subroutine they are stored in addresses 0B00 to 0B63. The calling program then performs the instruction:

```
LXI  H,0B00
```

to load the pointer to the data into the H,L register pair. The subroutine accesses the input values by repeating the instructions:

```
MOV  A,M
INX  H
```

to scan through them. If the calculated results are formed in the A register then instructions of the type:

```
MOV  B,A
```

will place them into other suitable registers (B, C, D or E) for return to the calling program.

5.10 As can be seen from Figure M two subroutines, MULT and DIVIDE, are needed to overcome the lack of multiplication and division instructions in the 8085 microcomputer.

5.11 The 'update' sections (see Figure N) of the program could be written as subroutines. A number could be passed to them in a register for comparison with the current largest or smallest value.

(Figures M and N appear overleaf)

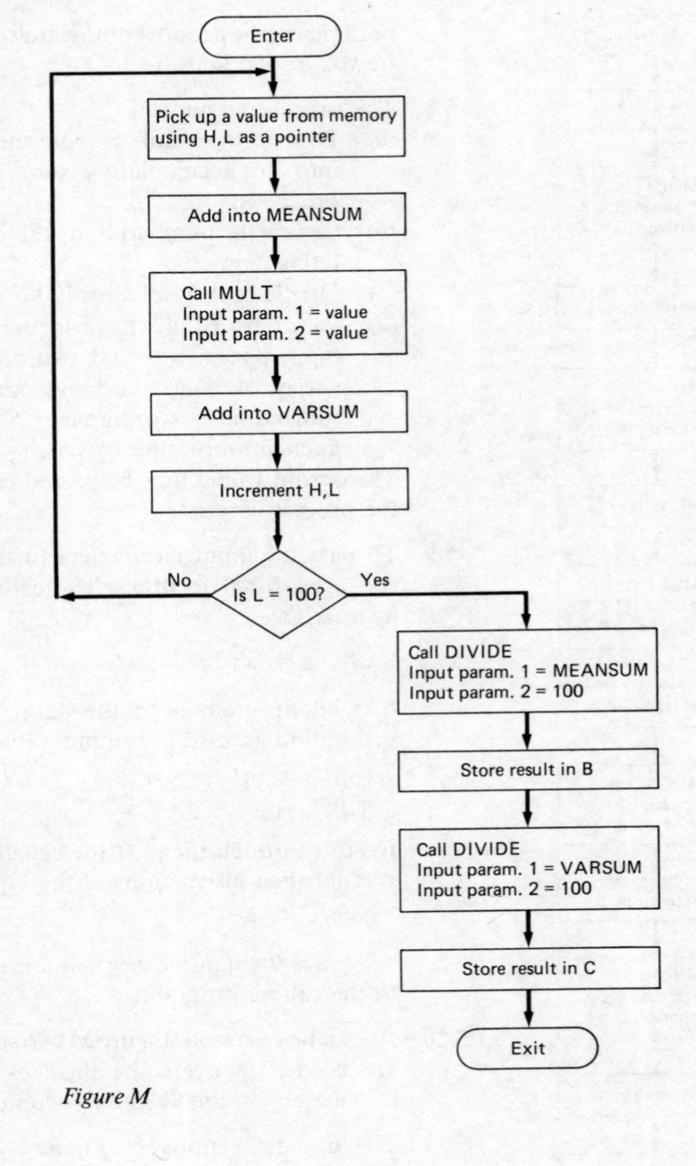
Enter
Pick up a value from memory using H,L as a pointer
Add into MEANSUM
Call MULT
Input param. 1 = value
Input param. 2 = value
Add into VARSUM
Increment H,L
Is L = 100?
No
Yes
Call DIVIDE
Input param. 1 = MEANSUM
Input param. 2 = 100
Store result in B
Call DIVIDE
Input param. 1 = VARSUM
Input param. 2 = 100
Store result in C
Exit

Figure M

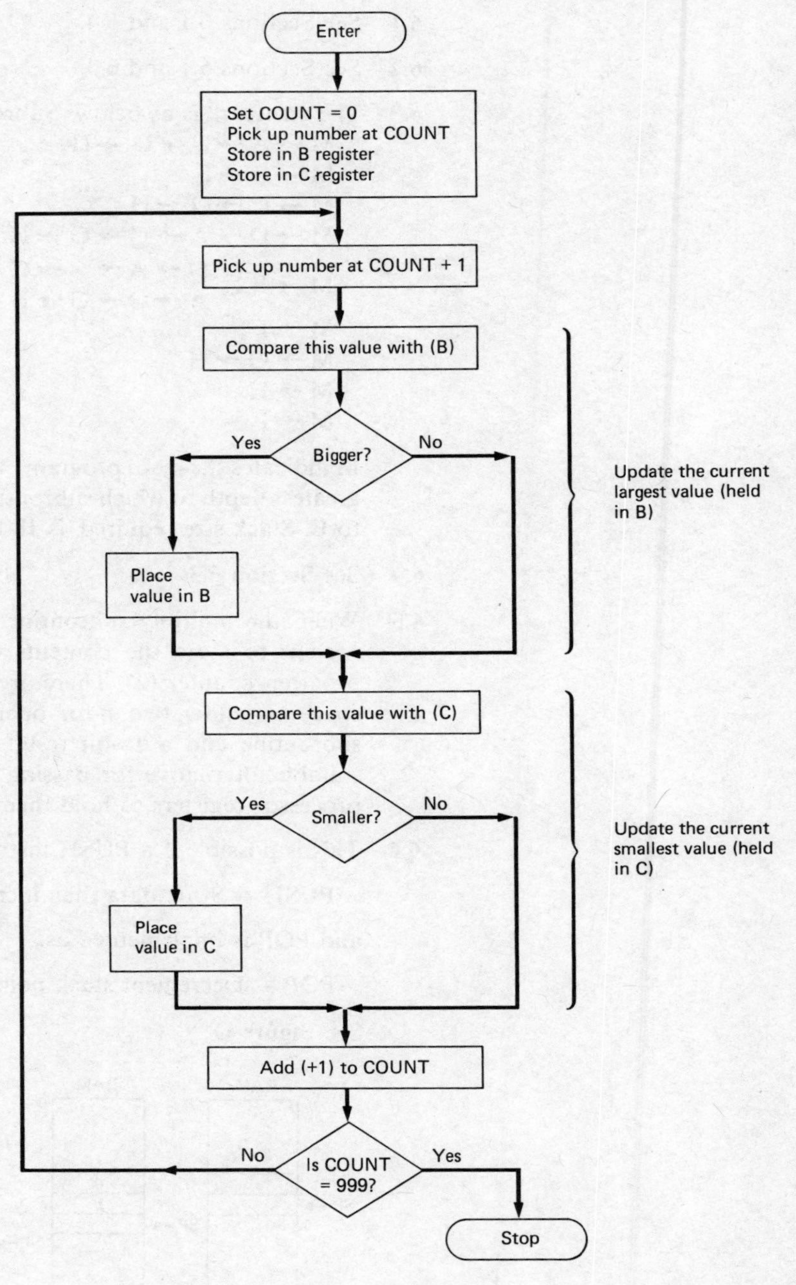
Enter
Set COUNT = 0
Pick up number at COUNT
Store in B register
Store in C register
Pick up number at COUNT + 1
Compare this value with (B)
Bigger?
Yes
No
Place
value in B
Update the current
largest value (held
in B)
Compare this value with (C)
Smaller?
Yes
No
Place
value in C
Update the current
smallest value (held
in C)
Add (+1) to COUNT
Is COUNT
= 999?
No
Yes
Stop

Figure N

6.1 See Sections 6.1 and 6.4.

6.2 See Sections 6.1 and 6.3.

6.3 The structure is as below. Subroutine calls are shown by arrows.

M → A → C → G → H
M → B → F
M → C → G → H
M → D → A → C → G → H
M → E ↗ D → A → C → G → H
       ↘ A → C → G → H
M → F
M → G → H
M → H
M → I

M indicates the main program. The size of stack is determined by the greatest depth to which subroutines are nested. This is six, in the call to E. Stack size required is 18 locations.

6.4 See Section 6.3.

6.5 When the multiply subroutine is called, 5 bytes of the stack are needed to store the contents of the processor registers (3) and program counter (2). There are thus 3 bytes left. This is sufficient space to allow two 8-bit operands to be passed to a multiply subroutine and a 16-bit result to be returned from it. The most suitable alternative for passing the arguments would be to use the processor registers to hold them.

6.6 This is possible if a PUSH instruction is implemented as:

PUSH = Store data then increment stack pointer

and POP is implemented as:

POP = Decrement stack pointer then retrieve data

See Figure O.

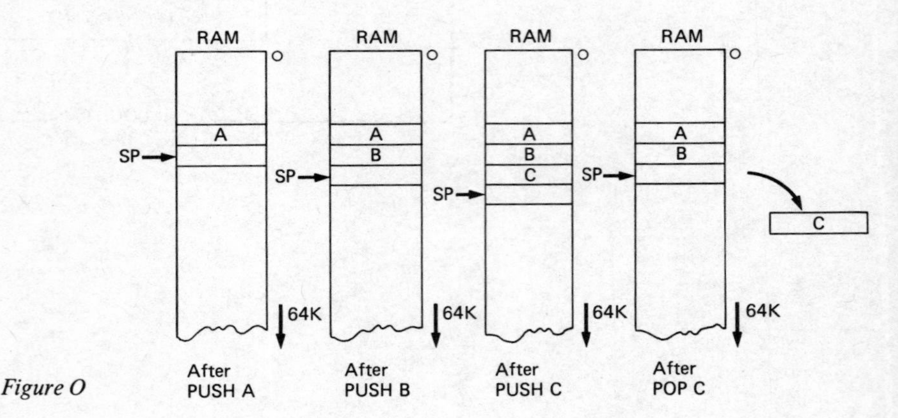

Figure O

6.7 *(a)* Suppose that the arguments are exchanged using the processor registers.

Input arguments B — held in the B register
C — held in the C register
D — held in the D register
E — held in the E register
F — held in the H register

```
MOV  A,B  ;Put B into A register
ADD  C    ;Form (B + C)
MOV  B,A  ;Store (B + C) in B register
MOV  A,D  ;Put D into A register
SUB  E    ;Form (D - E)
MOV  D,A  ;Put (D - E) into D register
MOV  A,B  ;Form (B + C) - (D - E) + F
SUB  D
ADD  H
RET       ;Return
```

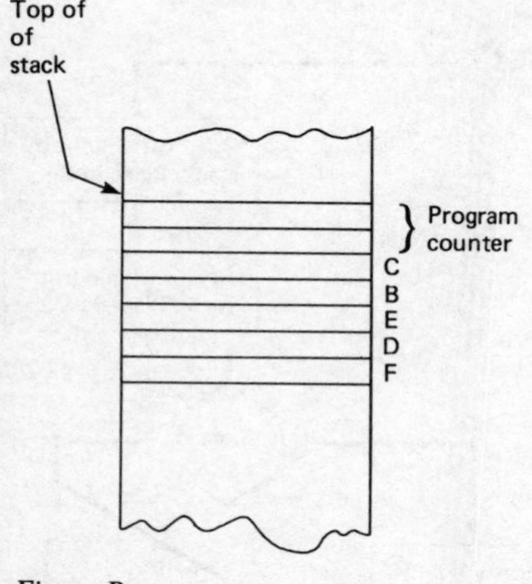

Figure P

(b) Suppose that the arguments are exchanged using the stack. On entry to the subroutine the stack contents are as shown in Figure P.

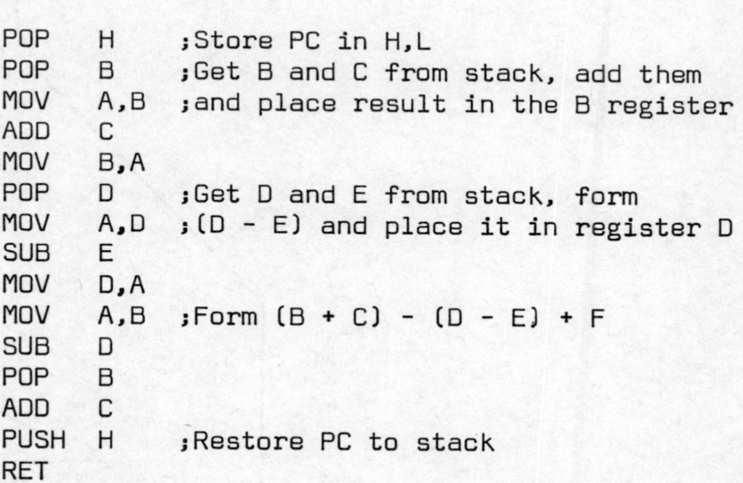

```
POP   H    ;Store PC in H,L
POP   B    ;Get B and C from stack, add them
MOV   A,B  ;and place result in the B register
ADD   C
MOV   B,A
POP   D    ;Get D and E from stack, form
MOV   A,D  ;(D - E) and place it in register D
SUB   E
MOV   D,A
MOV   A,B  ;Form (B + C) - (D - E) + F
SUB   D
POP   B
ADD   C
PUSH  H    ;Restore PC to stack
RET
```

In both subroutines the result is returned to the calling program in the A register.

6.8 Suppose the expressions are stored in RAM starting at address 'ADDRESS'. The flowchart is then as shown in Figure Q overleaf.

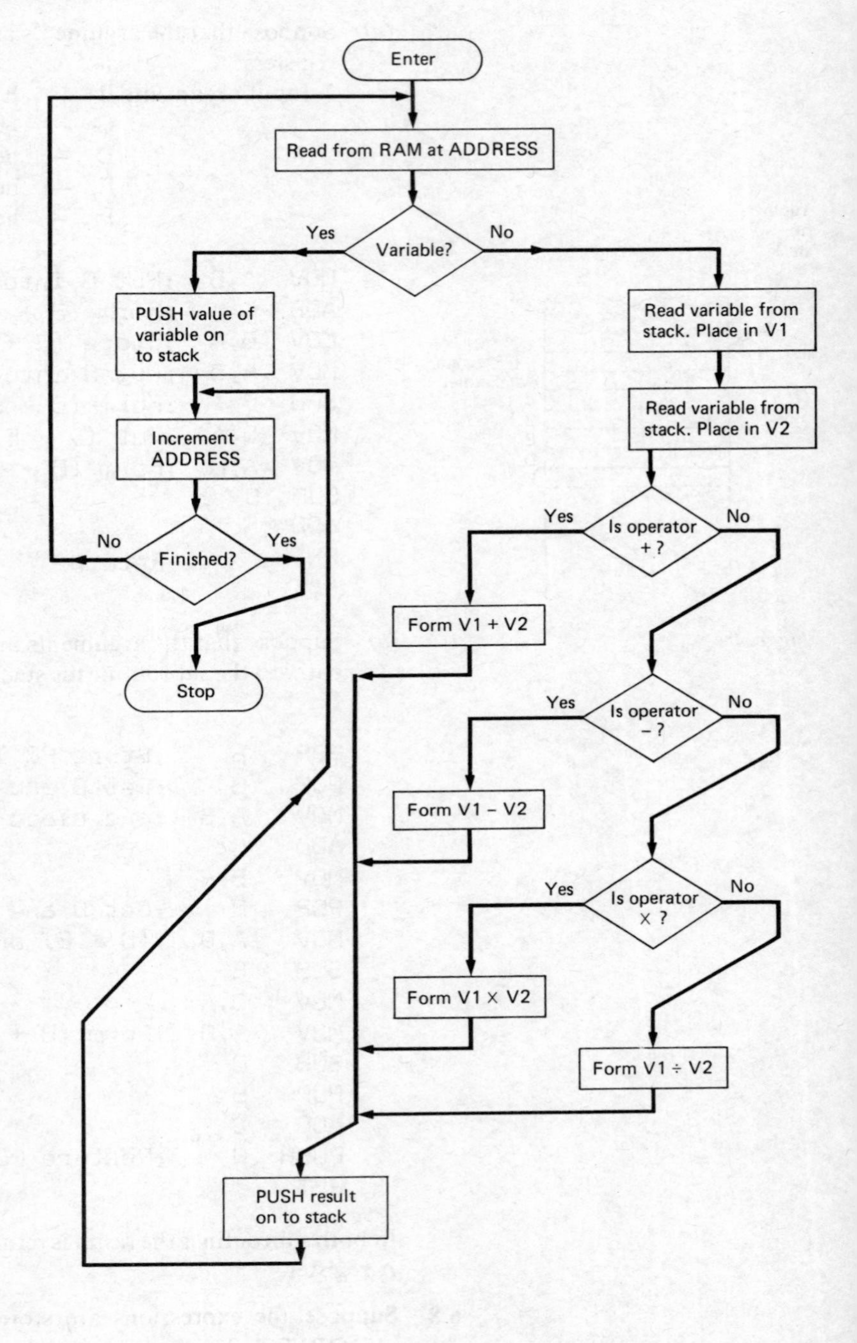
Enter
Read from RAM at ADDRESS
Variable?
Yes
No
PUSH value of variable on to stack
Read variable from stack. Place in V1
Read variable from stack. Place in V2
Increment ADDRESS
Finished?
No
Yes
Stop
Is operator + ?
Yes
No
Form V1 + V2
Is operator – ?
Yes
No
Form V1 – V2
Is operator × ?
Yes
No
Form V1 × V2
Form V1 ÷ V2
PUSH result on to stack

Figure Q

7.1 See Sections 7.2 and 7.3.

7.2 *(a)*

```
Program counter          03A0
Stack pointer            0FFE
        ADDRESS
       0FFE  -  C0
Stack  0FFF  -  00
       1000  -  XX
```

(b)

```
Program counter          03D4
Stack pointer            0FFC
        ADDRESS
       0FFC  -  B8
       0FFD  -  03
Stack  0FFE  -  C0
       0FFF  -  00
       1000  -  XX
```

(c)

```
Program counter          0605
Stack pointer            0FFA
        ADDRESS
       0FFA  -  E3
       0FFB  -  04
       0FFC  -  B8
Stack  0FFD  -  03
       0FFE  -  C0
       0FFF  -  00
       1000  -  XX
```

(d)

```
Program counter          03B8
Stack pointer            0FFE
        ADDRESS
       0FFE  -  C0
Stack  0FFF  -  00
       1000  -  XX
```

7.3 See Section 7.4.

7.4 Suppose that the value of N is passed to the subroutine in the A register, and the result is passed back from the subroutine in the H and L registers:

```
         LXI  H,0000  ;Set (H,L) = 0
         LXI  D,0001  ;Set (D,E) = 1
REPEAT:  CMP  E       ;Is (E)>N (in A)?
         RC           ;If it is, return
         DAD  D       ;Add (D,E) to H,L
         INX  D       ;Increment D,E by (+2)
         INX  D
         JMP  REPEAT
```

This subroutine does not save the machine state. Extra instructions can easily be added to do this, however, if it is required.

7.5 Suppose that the multiply subroutine accepts two operands passed to it as follows:

1 Operand 1 in the B,C register pair (most significant byte in B).
2 Operand 2 in the DE register pair (most significant byte in D).

Suppose also that the result of the multiplication is returned in the B,C register pair.

```
       MOV   E,D    ;Put N into E
       DCR   D      ;Put (N - 1) into C
       MOV   C,D
       MVI   D,00   ;Set (D) = 0
       MVI   B,00   ;Set (B) = 0
NEXT:  CALL  MULT   ;Call multiply
       DCR   E      :Put (N - 2) into D,E
       RZ           ;Return if (E) = 0
       JMP   NEXT
```

The result of this subroutine is held in the B and C registers.

7.6 Suppose that the value of N is passed to the subroutine in the H,L register pair and that the value of M is passed in the B,C register pair:

```
      MVI  A,00  ;Set (A) = 0
REP:  MOV  M,A   ;Set memory address (H,L) = 0
      INX  H     ;Increment (H,L)
      MOV  A,H   ;Put (H) into A
      CMP  B     ;Compare with B
      JNZ  REP   ;If H ≠ B, jump to REP
      MOV  A,L   ;Put (L) into A
      CMP  C     ;Compare with C
      JNZ  REP
      MOV  M,A   ;Clear last address
      RET        ;Return
```

7.7 Suppose that the value of *n* is passed to the subroutine in the H,L register pair and that a subroutine MULT is available. Operands are passed to MULT in the B and C registers and the result is returned in the B,C register pair:

```
MVI   A,0B  ;Find address of xn
ADD   H
MOV   H,A
MOV   A,M   ;Fetch Xn into A
MOV   B,A   ;Put Xn into B and C
MOV   C,A
CALL  MULT  ;Call MULT
MOV   L,A   ;Put Xn into L
MVI   H,00  ;Set (H) = 0
INX   H     ;Form 1 + Xn in H,L
DAD   B     ;Add Xn^2 into H,L
RET         ;Return
```

The result of this subroutine is held in the H,L register pair.

7.8 Let the delay subroutine produce a time delay of T s. Suppose that the pulse train comes from the least significant bit of a port with address 'ADDRESS'. The program flowchart is as shown in Figure R.

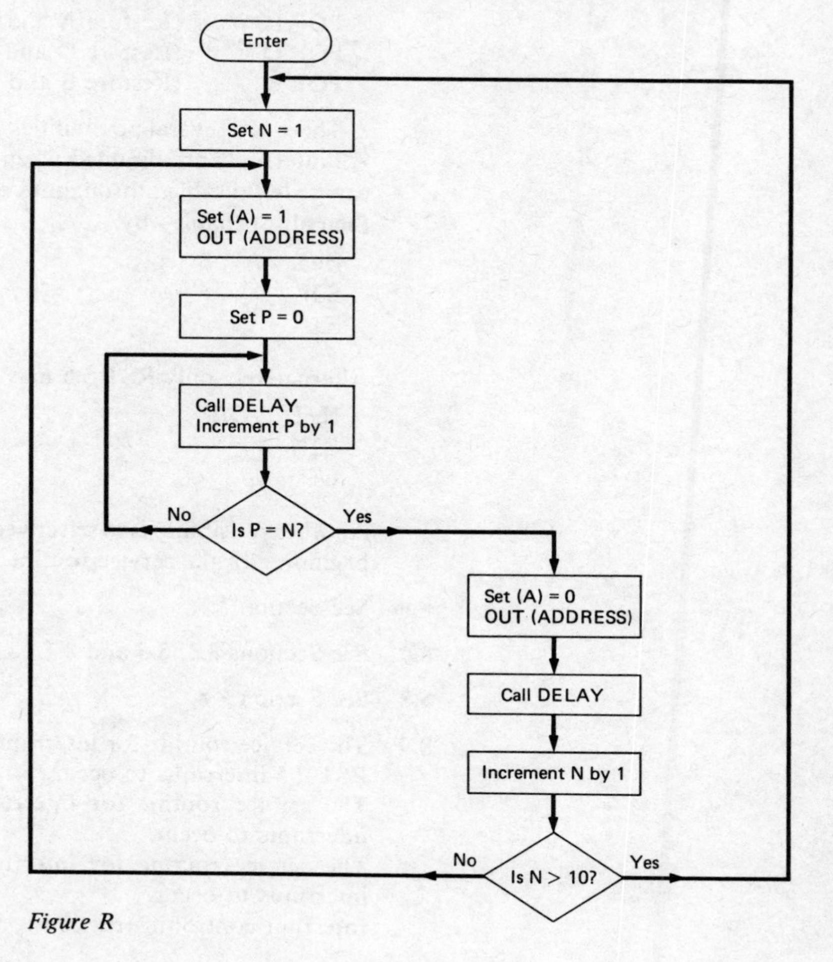

Figure R

8.1 See Sections 8.1, 8.2 and 8.3.

8.2 See Sections 8.1 and 8.2.

8.3 See Section 8.4.

8.4 See Section 8.6.

8.5 See Sections 8.3 and 8.8. An instruction, JMP 00B0, must be placed in the dedicated location for interrupt RST 5.5, i.e. at address 002C. The interrupt service routine must contain orders to save the contents of the processor registers. Thus it should begin with orders such as:

PUSH B [Push (B) and (C) to the stack]
PUSH D [Push (D) and (E) to the stack]
PUSH PSW [Push (A) and (status) to the stack]

At the end of the service routine these values are restored by:

POP PSW (Restore A and status register).
POP D (Restore D and E registers).
POP B (Restore B and C registers).

There are several possibilities for control of the interrupt system. All interrupts are disabled when any one of them is accepted. They can be left disabled throughout execution of the service routine and then all re-enabled by:

```
MVI  A,08
SIM
EI
```

Alternatively only RST 5.5 may be re-enabled by:

```
MVI  A,0E
SIM
EI
```

Another possibility is to selectively re-enable specific interrupts at the beginning of the service routine for RST 5.5.

8.6 See Section 8.7.

8.7 See Sections 8.3, 8.5 and 8.7.

8.8 See Section 8.8.

8.9 The service routine for interrupt RST 5.5 must allow RST 6.5 and RST 7.5 interrupts to occur.
The service routine for interrupt RST 6.5 must allow RST 7.5 interrupts to occur.
The service routine for interrupt RST 7.5 must allow RST 5.5 interrupts to occur.
Interrupt control instructions:

Main program – which resets all mask bits to zero and enables all interrupts:

```
MVI  A,08
SIM
EI
```

RST 5.5 service routine – which enables interrupts RST 6.5 and RST 7.5 and disables interrupt RST 5.5:

```
MVI  A,09
SIM
EI
```

RST 6.5 service routine – which enables RST 7.5 and disables RST 5.5 and RST 6.5:

```
MVI  A,0B
SIM
EI
```

RST 7.5 service routine – which enables RST 5.5 and disables RST 6.5 and RST 7.5:

```
MVI  A,0E
SIM
EI
```

The TRAP interrupt can automatically interrupt any of the service routines. No interrupts are enabled at the start of the TRAP interrupt service routine. All interrupts are enabled at the end of each routine, including TRAP.

8.10 See Section 8.8.

8.11 See Section 8.8.

8.12 The power failure is, perhaps, the most critical interrupt, the timer interrupt the second most critical and the tape reader interrupt least critical. So, arrange for power failure to interrupt using TRAP, the timer to interrupt using RST 7.5 and the reader to interrupt using RST 6.5. Then the main program, which enables interrupts TRAP, RST 7.5 and RST 6.5 is:

```
MVI  A,09
SIM
EI
```

Whenever any interrupt program is run the higher priority interrupts are re-enabled. Thus the service routine for RST 6.5 is

```
MVI  A,0B
SIM
EI
```

the service routine for RST 7.5 is

```
MVI  A,0F
SIM
EI
```

and the service routine for TRAP is

```
MVI  A,0F
SIM
EI
```

9.1 See Sections 9.1, 9.2 and previous chapter.

9.2 See Section 9.2.

9.3 See Section 9.2.

9.4 The light-emitting diodes can be connected to eight bits of a PIC output port, for example to port C, see Figure 9.5. The program to examine store locations 10,000 to 10,255 [2710 (hex) to 280F (hex)] has the flowchart shown in Figure S. This assumes that port C output contains a staticiser.

9.5 It would be possible. The push-button could be connected to the least significant line of port A, configured to be an input (see Figure 9.5). If mode 1 of the PIC is used it can be arranged that a bit in port A is set to '1' when the button is pressed and is reset when the processor reads from the port. The program flowchart is then as shown in Figure T.

9.6 Assume that all ports are in mode 0. The bit pattern placed in the PIC control register can then be 10010010. The bits controlling port C are, in this example, not relevant. The code is:

```
MVI  A,92
OUT  (address, control register)
IN   (address, port A)
MOV  B,A
IN   (address, port B)
MOV  C,A
```

In this example 'address, control register' is the address sent on the bus to:
(a) select the PIC itself and
(b) select the control register within the PIC.
'Address, port A' and 'address, port B' are similar.

9.7 To initialise ports A and B as inputs, and port C as an output, the code placed in the control register must be 10010010. Thus:

```
MVI  A,92
OUT  (address, control register)
IN   (address, port A)
MOV  B,A
IN   (address, port B)
ADD  B
OUT  (address, port C)
```

9.8 Let the light-emitting diode be connected to the least significant bit of port C, configured to be an output. Consider the time-delay subroutine of Chapter 7. The delay produced by one cycle of the inner loop is 8 μs since this loop contains four instructions. Thus if this loop is cycled 125 times the delay is (125×8) μs $= 1$ ms. If this loop is cycled 250 times, and if the outer loop is also cycled 250 times, the

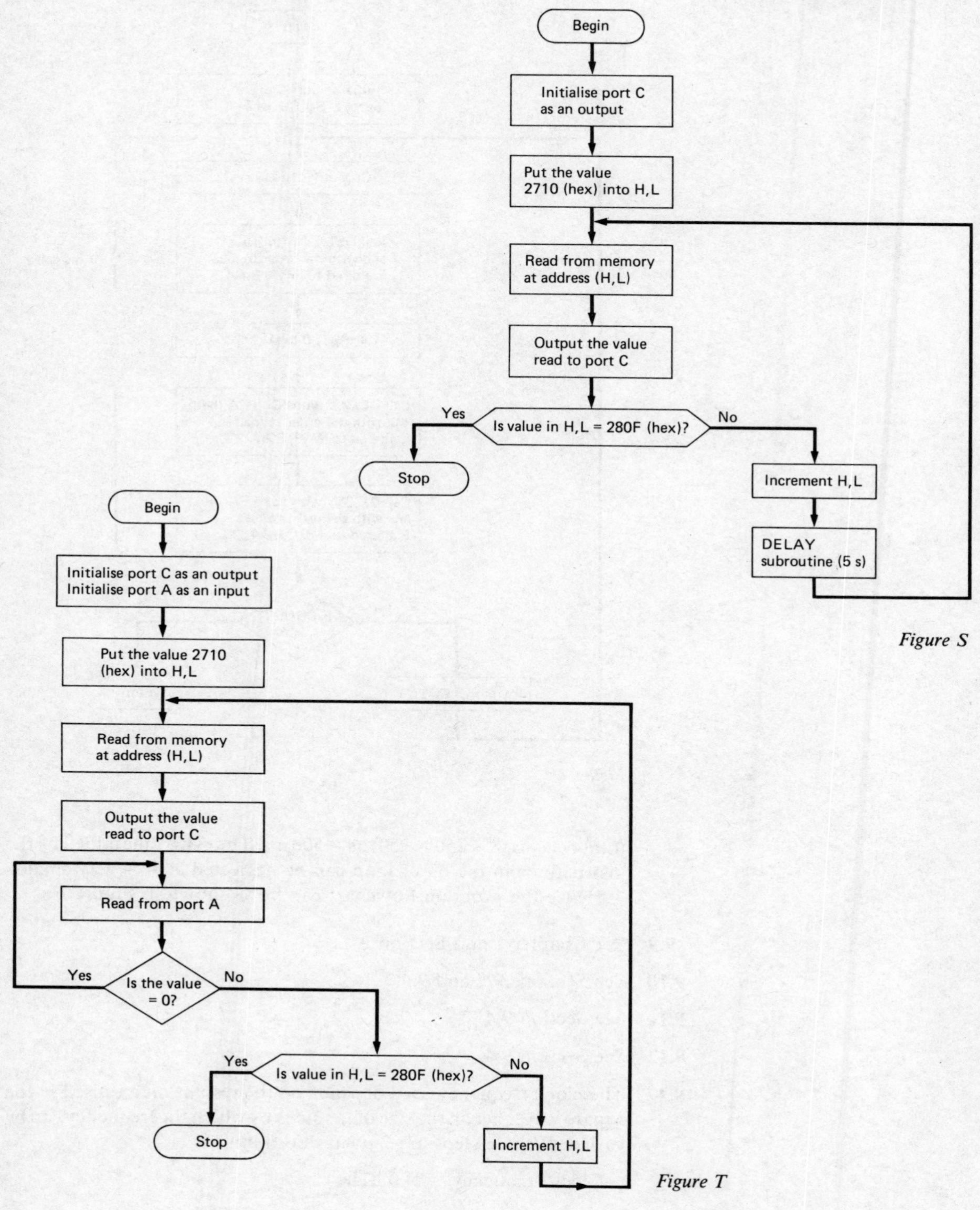

Figure S

Figure T

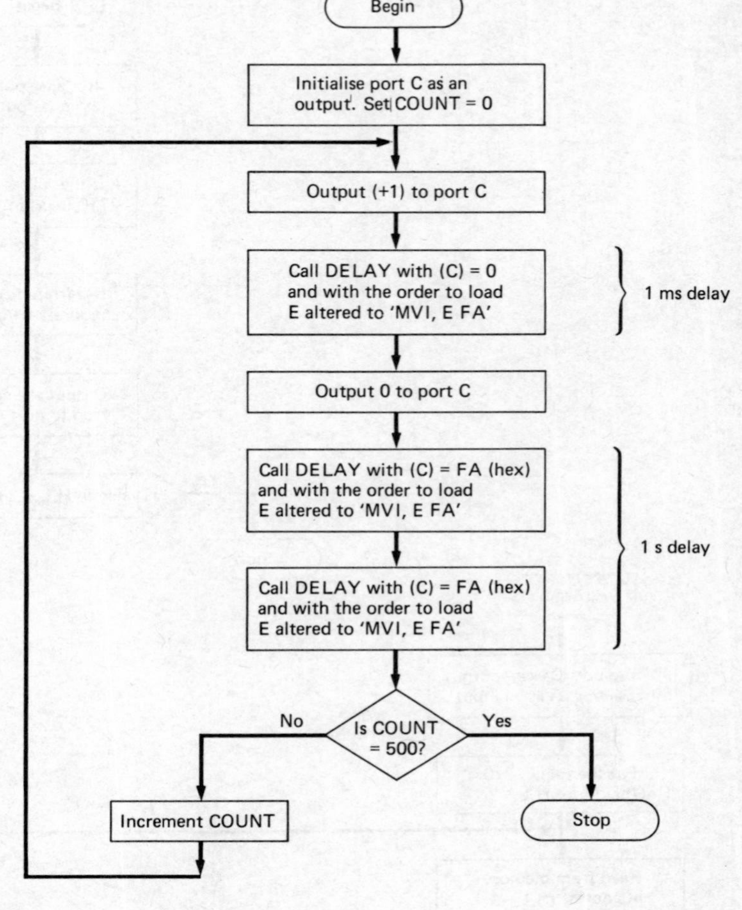

Figure U

total delay is $(8 \times 250 \times 250)$ μs = 500 ms. The extra time added by the instructions in the outer loop can be neglected as it is very small.

Hence the program flowchart can be as shown in Figure U.

9.9 See Chapter 1 and Section 9.4.

9.10 See Sections 9.2 and 9.4.

9.11 See Section 9.4.

9.12 See Section 9.4.

9.13 The clock frequency used depends on the resolution required in the square wave, i.e. on the size of the steps by which the frequency can be varied. If these steps are 2 μs in duration:

Clock frequency = 500 kHz

Counter value for 500 μs = 250
Counter value for 100 ms = 50,000

A resolution of 1 μs is not possible since this would require a counter value greater than 64K for the 100 ms delay.

To set up the counter:

```
MVI  A,30  ;Send control word to counter - see
OUT  13    ;Section 9.5
MVI  A,FA  ;Set counter to 00FA (250)
OUT  10
MVI  A,00
OUT  10
.          ;Further program steps
.
MVI  A,50  ;Set counter value to C350 (50,000)
OUT  10
MVI  A,C3
OUT  10
.
.
```

9.14 Suppose that the switches are connected to the four least significant bits of port A of a PIC and the LEDs to the four least significant bits of port C. The switch positions and LED states are related as shown in Table A (when a switch is down a '1' is entered in the appropriate column and when an LED is on a '1' is entered).

Table A

Switches				*LEDs*				*Address*
A	*B*	*C*	*D*	*L*	*M*	*N*	*O*	*(hex)*
0	0	0	0	0	0	0	0	0B00
0	0	0	1	0	0	0	0	0B01
0	0	1	0	1	0	0	0	0B02
0	0	1	1	1	0	0	0	0B03
0	1	0	0	0	0	0	1	0B04
0	1	0	1	0	0	0	0	0B05
0	1	1	0	1	1	0	0	0B06
0	1	1	1	1	0	0	0	0B07
1	0	0	0	0	0	0	1	0B08
1	0	0	1	0	0	0	0	0B09
1	0	1	0	1	0	0	0	0B0A
1	0	1	1	1	0	0	0	0B0B
1	1	0	0	0	0	0	1	0B0C
1	1	0	1	0	0	0	0	0B0D
1	1	1	0	1	1	1	0	0B0E
1	1	1	1	1	0	0	0	0B0F

A table of the values of L, M, N and O is stored in a suitable place in the memory, e.g. at addresses 0B00 to 0B0F as shown. The program is then:

```
      MVI  H,0B         ;Set address 0B00
      MVI  L,00         ;into H,L register pair
      MVI  A,92         ;Initialise PIC with C as
      OUT  (address     ;output port, A as input
           control      ;port
           register)
REP:  IN   (address,    ;Read switches
           port A)
      ADD  L            ;Add value on switches
                        ;into L
      MOV  L,A
      MOV  A,M          ;Get table entry
      OUT  (address,    ;Output to lights
           port C)
      MVI  L,00         ;Rest (L) for next step
      JMP  REP          ;Repeat
```

10.1 See Section 10.2.

10.2 See Sections 10.2 and 10.3.

10.3–10.8 The next six questions in this chapter are concerned with developing and running programs to illustrate the use of the microcomputer as a stop watch. This subject has been introduced in the text of the chapter in a fairly comprehensive way (Section 10.4) and sample program code in Intel 8085 assembly language for the task set in Question 10.3 has been given.

The actual code produced for these questions will be governed by the type of microcomputer available to run the programs produced. Thus it is suggested that you (the student) should attempt the questions using the explanation of Section 10.4 as a basis for your experiments, but adapting the program code to run on whatever microcomputer can be most readily obtained.

It is most likely that the correctness of the programs developed will be immediately apparent, at least in so far as their main functioning is concerned. In other words, faulty programs will either not run at all or will produce bizzare results from which it will be obvious that a fault exists. However it is important that expert help should be available to you to assist you to find and correct such faults. You are advised, therefore, to make sure that your programs are run under supervision. You should also take care, when your programs do eventually run, to measure the accuracy with which they perform the specified timing operations and to adjust their internal parameters until they are as precise as possible. Hints:

10.4 The interval timer produces an interrupt exactly every 0.1 s. These are used for timing so the delay subroutine can be discarded. The program should increment a count each time that a timer interrupt occurs. Whenever this count reaches ten SECS is incremented by unity. In this method of working the exact time occupied by the program instructions does not matter as long as the instructions can be executed within the period available.

10.5 It is suggested that a new button 'lap time' be added to the stopwatch. Pressing this button should cause entry to an interrupt routine 'INTLAP'. If INTLAP is entered whilst GO is at '1' the stopwatch should continue operating (counting in SECS and MINS) but the displayed time value should be frozen. A new variable 'FREEZE', set and reset by INTLAP, can be used to control this.

10.9 The input control buttons should be connected so as to send interrupts to the microcomputer when they are pressed. The 'mode' button interrupt service routine increments a variable 'MODE' each time that it is activated. If MODE becomes greater than 2 it is reset to zero. Thus:

MODE = 0 means 'normal time display'
MODE = 1 means 'alarm set'
MODE = 2 means 'time set'

Each time that the 'hours' button is pressed the corresponding interrupt service routine tests the value of MODE. If this is 2, the hours setting of the normal time count is advanced by 1. If it is 1 the hours setting of the alarm time count is advanced by 1. If it is 0 no operation is performed.

The 'minutes' button operates similarly. There are thus three interrupt service routines. Lines RST 5.5, RST 6.5 and RST 7.5 can be used to activate these. The output display is similar to that of the stop-watch discussed earlier. A 24-hour display may be used, requiring four digits.

The bleeper alarm may be activated by a single output line. It is suggested that a short section of program code should be developed to cause the bleeper to be switched on and off a preset number of times (say 10) and for preset periods. (Say 1 s on followed by 1 s off).

Index